New American Review

if you
subscribe
to these views...

why not subscribe to New American Review

As a charter subscriber, you will receive the next four issues of NEW AMERICAN REVIEW at the special price of $4.00 (regular price $5.00).

NAR This issue of *New American Review* completes our first year of publication. The very strong support that the first two issues have received leads us to believe that there is a permanent place for NAR among the literary periodicals. To test this belief and to provide for this place we are offering it now on a subscription basis. If the first three issues, then, have won your confidence in NAR's future, we hope that you will act on it by sending back the enclosed subscription card.

The major item in NAR #3 is Philip Roth's 28,000 word story, "Civilization and Its Discontents." Since we published a related story by Mr. Roth, "The Jewish Blues," in the first issue, the objection may be raised that, for all our statements to the contrary, NAR is already showing signs of becoming a coterie magazine. This objection is likely to be aggravated by the feeling that the content of this story, "Jewish" consciousness in extremis, is hardly new these days, that, indeed, it is part of a vogue which already takes up an undue amount of print and attention. But against our own reservations on these scores, there stood the specific quality of "Civilization and Its Discontents": its extraordinary wit, candor, and power; its steady ability to touch bottom, the point at which ethnic singularities take on the universal implications of human life itself. In the end, the desire to publish the best writing we receive won out, a decision which should please all but the most "trendentious" of our readers.

Our other stories tend to provide a representative range of the concerns and talents in current American fiction. There is R. V. Cassill's "The Rationing of Love," a finely wrought tale of a father and son's relationship across the cultural gap that has opened in middle America. There is also Donald Barthelme's experimental study, "Robert Kennedy Saved from Drowning," which reverses the much-noted trend from fiction to journalism by raising the materials of reportage to a more subtle level of imagination. The result is a beguiling portrait: as one of our editors puts it, "Bobby Kennedy in plaster of Paris." Finally, three young writers, M. F. Beal, Leonard Michaels, and John Malone, contribute work that fronts from different directions on the strange realities of our days.

NAR's *coverage of present-day American culture features Albert Goldman's lucid essay on the growing significance of Rock, both the music and the scene. Mr. Goldman manages to chart the protean development of "The Beat" from the days of Little Richard and Elvis Presley to the present sophistication of the Beatles and the Doors and to detect amid the din, flashing lights, and masquerades of the new discotheques the emerging art and life-style of the "youth" generation. Our* Looking at Films *department is occupied by Robert Garis, who focuses on* The Graduate, *with a sidelong look at the career of Mike Nichols and the new fashion of satire. Lionel Abel extends our coverage of the arts to the theater season in New York, where he finds the houses to be filling up while the plays grow more empty. The recent obscenity trial in London over* Last Exit to Brooklyn *is reported on in depth by the English critic Frank Kermode, who served as one of the defense witnesses.* NAR Perspectives *turns this time on the intricate, often institutionally distorted, relations between children and adults that we call learning. George Dennison's essay deals with an experimental school, Paul West's with what one might call an experimental home; but they are of a piece in being written with uncommon sense and feeling that are a far cry from the cant and jargon that usually surround this subject. Finally, we are particularly pleased to publish a new section of Josephine Herbst's remarkable literary memoirs that began appearing some years ago in* The Noble Savage.

The poetry selections in NAR #3 are highlighted by Hayden Carruth's beautiful elegy to his father as well as by groups of poems from John Berryman and Stephen Berg, respectively. There are the established voices of J. V. Cunningham and May Swenson, and the new voices of Al Lee, Bob Dawson, Allan Kaplan, and John Knoepfle. Together they make up a striking display of the richness and relevance of present-day poetry.

T S

NUMBER 3

New American Review

PUBLISHED BY THE NEW AMERICAN LIBRARY
NEW YORK AND TORONTO · THE NEW ENGLISH
LIBRARY LIMITED, LONDON

NEW AMERICAN REVIEW

EDITOR: THEODORE SOLOTAROFF
POETRY EDITOR: STANLEY MOSS
ASSISTANT EDITOR: NANCY HARDIN

EDITORIAL COMMITTEE:

Edward T. Chase, Barbara Collins, Jonathan Dolger,
Robert Gutwillig, Robert Haynie, Rosilyn Heller,
Katharine Kidde, Edward Kuhn, Jr., Thomas McCormick,
Patrick O'Connor, Jean Read, James Trupin, Wendy Weil

Art Director: William Gregory
Editorial Assistant: Linda Scher
Production Associates: Irene Kask, Ruth Randall,
    Sandra Salzman

Cover Photo: Irwin Goldstein

First Printing, April, 1968

Library of Congress Catalog Card Number: 67-27377

The editors invite submissions. Manuscripts will not be returned
unless accompanied by stamped, self-addressed envelope.

CONTENTS

CONTRIBUTORS

Civilization and Its Discontents

DID I MENTION, Doctor, that when I was fifteen I actually took it out of my pants and whacked off on the 107 bus from New York?

I had been treated to a perfect day by my sister and Morty Feibish, her fiancé—a doubleheader at Ebbets Field, followed afterwards by a seafood dinner at Sheepshead Bay. An exquisite day. Hannah and Morty were to stay overnight in Flatbush with Morty's family, and so I was put on a subway to Manhattan about ten o'clock—and there boarded the bus for New Jersey, upon which I took not just my cock in my hands but my whole life, when you think about it. The passengers were mostly drowsing off by the time we had emerged from the Lincoln Tunnel—including the girl in the seat beside me, whose tartan skirt folds I had begun to press up against with the corduroy of my trouser legs—and I had it out and in my fist by the time we were climbing onto the Pulaski Skyway.

You might have thought that given the rich satisfactions of the day, I'd have had my fill of excitement and my dick would have been the last thing on my mind heading home that night. Bruce Edwards, a new catcher up from the minors—and just what we needed (we being Morty, myself, and Burt Shotton, the Dodger manager)—had gone something like six for eight in his first two games in the majors (how sharp my memory of that day! how utterly insane, whipping out my joint like that! imagine, just imagine what would have been had I been caught red-handed! imagine if I had gone ahead and come all over that sleeping *shikse's* golden arm!), and then for dinner Morty had ordered me a lobster, the first of my life.

Now, maybe the lobster is what did it. That taboo so easily and simply broken, confidence may have been given to the whole slimy, suicidal, Dionysian side of my nature;

7

the lesson may have been learned that to break the law, all you have to do is—just go ahead and break it! All you have to do is stop trembling and quaking and finding it unimaginable and beyond you: all you have to do, *is do it!* What else, I ask you, were all those prohibitive dietary rules and regulations all about to begin with, what else but to give us little Jewish children practice in being repressed? Practice, darling, practice, practice, practice. Inhibition doesn't grow on trees, you know—takes patience, takes concentration, takes a dedicated and self-sacrificing parent and a hard-working attentive little child to create in only a few years' time a really constrained and tight-ass human being. Why else the two sets of dishes? Why else the kosher soap and salt? Why else, I ask you, but to remind us three times a day that life is boundaries and restrictions if it's anything, hundreds of thousands of little rules laid down by none other than None Other, rules which either you obey without question, regardless of how groundless and gratuitous they may appear (and thus remain, by obeying, in His good graces), or you transgress, most likely in the name of outraged common sense—which you transgress because even a child doesn't like to go around feeling like an absolute moron and schmuck—yes, you transgress, only with the strong likelihood (my father assures me) that comes next Yom Kippur and the names are written in the big book where He writes the names of those who are going to get to live until the following September (a scene which manages to engrave itself deeply upon my imagination) and lo, your own precious name ain't among them. Now who's the schmuck, huh? And it doesn't make any difference either (this I understand from the outset, about the way this God, Who runs things, reasons) how big or how small the rule is that you break: it's the breaking alone that gets His goat—it's the simple fact of waywardness, and that alone, that He absolutely cannot stand, and which He does not forget either, when He sits angrily down (fuming probably, and surely with a smashing miserable headache, like my father at the height of his constipation) and begins to leave the names out of that book.

When duty, discipline, and obedience give way—ah, here, *here* is the message I take in each Passover with my mother's *matzoh brei*—what follows there is no predicting. Renunciation is all, cries the koshered and bloodless piece of steak my family and I sit down to eat at dinner time. Self-control, sobriety, sanctions—this is the key to a human life, saith all those endless dietary laws. Let the *goyim* sink *their* teeth into whatever lowly or degraded creature crawls and grunts across the face of the dirty earth, we will not contaminate our humanity thus. Let *them* (if you know who I mean) gorge themselves upon anything and everything that moves, no matter how odious and abject the animal, no matter how grotesque or *shmutzig* or dumb the creature in question happens to be. Let them eat eels and frogs and pigs and crabs and lobsters; let them eat vulture, let them eat ape-meat and skunk if they like—a diet of abominable creatures well befits a breed of mankind so hopelessly shallow and empty-headed as to drink, to divorce, and to fight with their fists. All they know, these imbecilic eaters of the execrable, is to swagger, to insult, to sneer, and sooner or later to hit. Oh, also they know how to go out into the woods with a gun, these geniuses, and kill innocent wild deer, deer who themselves *nosh* quietly on berries and grasses and then go on their way, bothering no one. You stupid *goyim!* Reeking of beer and empty of ammunition, home you head, a dead animal (formerly *alive*) strapped to each fender, so that all the motorists along the way can see how strong and manly you are; and then, in your houses, you take these deer—who have done you, who have done nothing in all of nature, not the least bit of harm—you take these deer, cut them up into pieces, and cook them in a pot. There isn't enough to eat in this world, they have to eat up the *deer* as well! They will eat *anything*, anything they can get their big *goy* hands on! And the terrifying corollary, *they will do anything as well.* Deer eat what deer eat, and Jews eat what Jews eat, but not these *goyim.* Crawling animals, wallowing animals, leaping and angelic animals—it makes no difference to them —what they want they take, and to hell with the other thing's feelings (let alone kindness and compassion). Yes, it's all written down in history, what they have done, our illustrious neighbors who own the world and know absolutely nothing of human boundaries and limits.

. . . Thus saith the kosher laws, at least to the child I was, growing up under the tutelage of Sophie and Jack P., and in a school district of Newark where in my entire class there are only two little Christian children, and they live in houses I do not enter, on the far fringes of our neighborhood. . . . Thus saith the kosher laws, and who am I to argue that they are wrong? For look at little Alex himself, the subject of our every sentence—age fifteen, he sucks one night on a lobster's claw and within the hour his cock is out and aimed at a *shikse* on a Public Service bus. And his superior Jewish brain might as well be *made* of *matzoh brei!*

SUCH A CREATURE, needless to say, has never been boiled alive in our house—the lobster I refer to. A *shikse* has never been in our house period, and so it's a matter of conjecture in what condition she might emerge from my mother's kitchen.

Ha ha. A *shikse* has never been in our house because *I* have brought her there, is what I mean to say. I do recall one that my own father brought home with him for dinner one night when I was still a boy: a thin, tense, shy, deferential, soft-spoken, aging cashier from his office named Anne McCaffery.

Doctor, could he have been slipping it to her? I can't believe it! Only it suddenly occurs to me. Could my father have been slipping it to this lady on the side? I can still remember how she sat down beside me on the sofa, and in her nervousness made a lengthy to-do of spelling her first name and pointing out to me how it ended with an E, which wasn't always the case with someone called Anne, and so on and so forth . . . and meanwhile, though her arms were long and white and skinny and freckled (Irish arms, I thought) inside her smooth white blouse, I could see that she had breasts that were nice and substantial—and I kept taking peeks at her legs, too. I was only eight or nine, but she really did have such a terrific pair of legs that I couldn't keep my eyes off them, the kind of legs that every once in a while it surprises you to find some pale spinster with a pinched face walking around on top of . . . With those legs—why, *of course* he was *shtupping* her . . . Was he not?

Why he brought her home, *he* said, was "for a real Jewish meal." For weeks he had been jabbering about the new *goyische* cashier ("a very plain drab person," he said, "who dresses in *shmatas*") who had been pestering him—so went the story he couldn't stop telling us—for a real Jewish meal from the day she had come to work in the Boston and Northeastern office. Finally my mother couldn't take any more. "All right, bring her already—she needs it so bad, so I'll give her one." Was he taken then by surprise, I wonder? Who will ever know? At any rate, a Jewish meal was what she got all right.

I don't think I have ever heard the word "Jewish" spoken so many times in one evening in my life, and let me tell you, I am a person who has heard the word "Jewish" spoken.

"This is your real Jewish chopped liver, Anne. Have you ever had real Jewish chopped liver before? Well, my wife makes the real thing, you can bet your life on that. Here, you eat it with a piece of bread. This is real Jewish rye bread, with seeds. That's it, Anne, you're doing very good, ain't she doing good, Sophie, for her first time? That's it, take a nice piece of real Jewish rye, now take a big fork full of the real Jewish chopped liver"—and on and on, right down to the Jell-O—"that's right, Anne, the Jell-O is kosher too, sure, of course, has to be—oh no, oh no, no cream in your coffee, not after meat, ha ha, hear what Anne wanted, Alex—?"

But babble-babble all you want, Dad dear, a question has just occurred to me, twenty-five years later (not that I have a single shred of evidence, not that until this moment I have ever imagined my father capable of even the slightest infraction of domestic law . . . but since infraction seems suddenly to be all I am able to talk about), a question has arisen in the audience: why *did* you bring a *shikse*, of all things, into our home? Because you couldn't bear that a Gentile woman should go through life without the experience of eating Jewish Jell-O?—Or because you could no longer live your own life without making Jewish confession? Without confronting your wife with your crime, so she might accuse, castigate, humiliate, punish, and thus bleed you forever of your forbidden lusts! Yes, a regular Jewish desperado, my father. I recognize the syndrome perfectly. Come, someone, anyone, find me out and condemn me—I did the most terrible thing you can think of: I took what I am not supposed to have! Chose pleasure for myself over duty to my loved ones! Please, catch me, catch me, before God forbid I get away with it completely—and go out and do again something I actually like!

And did my mother oblige? Did Sophie put together the two tits and two legs and come up with four? Me it seems to have taken a quarter of a century to do such steep calculation. Oh, I must be making this up, really. My father . . . and a *shikse?* Can't be. Was beyond his ken. My own father —fucked *shikses?* I'll admit under duress that he fucked my mother . . . but *shikses?* I can no more imagine him knocking over a gas station.

But then why is she shouting at him so, what is this scene of accusation and denial, of castigation and threat and unending tears . . . what is this all about except that he has indeed done something that is very bad and maybe even unforgivable? The scene itself is like some piece of heavy furniture that sits in my mind and simply will not be budged—which leads me to believe that, yes, it actually did happen. My sister, I see, is hiding behind my mother: Hannah is clutching her around the middle and whimpering, while my mother's own tears are tremendous and fall from her face all the way to the linoleum floor. Simultaneous with the tears she is screaming so loud at him that her veins stand out—and screaming at me, too, because, looking further into this thing, I find that while Hannah hides behind my mother, *I take refuge behind the culprit himself.* Oh, this is pure fantasy, this is right out of the casebook, is it not? No, no, that is nobody else's father but my own who now brings his fist down on the kitchen table and shouts back at her, "I did no such thing! That is a lie and wrong!" Only wait a minute—it's *me* who is screaming "I didn't do it!" *The culprit is me!* And why my mother weeps so is because my father refuses to potch my behind, which she promised would be potched, "and good," when he found out the terrible thing that *I* had done.

When I am bad and rotten in small ways she can manage it herself: she has only to put me in my coat and galoshes— nice touch, Mom, those galoshes!—lock me out of the house, and announce through the door that she is never going to let me in again, so I might as well be off and into my new life. She has only to take that simple and swift course of action to get instantaneously a confession, a self-scorification, and, if she should want it, a signed warranty that I will be 100 percent pure and good for the rest of my life—all this if only I am allowed back inside that door, where they happen to have my bed and my clothes and *the refrigerator*. But when I am really wicked, so evil that she can only raise her arms to God Almighty to ask Him what she has done to deserve such a child, at such times my father is called in to mete out justice; my mother is herself too sensitive, too fine a creature, it turns out, to administer corporal punishment: "It hurts me," I hear her explain to my Aunt Clara, "more than it hurts him. That's the kind of person I am. I can't do it, and that's that." Oh, poor mother . . .

But look, what is going on here after all? Surely, Doctor, we can figure this thing out, two smart Jewish boys like ourselves. . . . A terrible act has been committed, and it has been committed by either my father or me. The wrongdoer, in other words, is one of the two members of the family who owns a penis. Okay. So far so good. Now: did he fuck between those luscious legs the Gentile cashier from the office, or have I eaten my sister's chocolate pudding? You see, she *didn't* want it at dinner, the little whiner, but apparently *did* want it saved so she could have it before she went to bed. Well, good Christ, how was I supposed to know all that, Hannah? Who looks into the fine points when he's hungry? I'm eight years old and chocolate pudding happens to get me hot. All I have to do is see that deep shimmering chocolatey surface gleaming out at me from the refrigerator, and my life isn't my own. Furthermore, I *thought* it was *left over!* And that's the truth! Jesus Christ, is that what this screaming and *shrying* is all about, that I ate the little bitch's chocolate pudding? Look, even if I did, I didn't mean it! I thought it was something else! I swear, I swear, I didn't mean to do it! . . . But is that me— or is that my father hollering out his defense before the jury? Sure, that's him—he did it, okay, okay, Sophie, leave me alone, already, I did it, *but I didn't mean it!* Shit, the next thing he'll tell her is why he should be forgiven is because he didn't *like* it either. What do you mean, you

didn't *mean* it, schmuck—you stuck it in there, didn't you?
Then stick up for yourself now, like a man! Tell her, tell
her: "That's right, Sophie, I slept with the *shikse*, and what
you think and don't think on the subject don't mean shit to
me. Because the way it works, in case you ain't heard, is
that I am the man around here, *and I call the shots!*" And
slug her if you have to! Deck her, Jake! Surely that's what
a *goy* would do, would he not? Do you think one of those
big-shot deer hunters with a gun collapses in a chair when
he gets caught committing the seventh and starts weeping
and begging his wife to be *forgiven?*—forgiven for *what?*
What after all does it consist of? You put your dick some
place and moved it back and forth and stuff came out the
front. So, Jake, what's the big deal? How long did the
whole thing last that you should suffer such damnation from
her mouth—such guilt, such recrimination and self-loathing!
Poppa, why do we have to have such guilty deference to
women, you and me—when we don't! We mustn't! Who
should run the show, Poppa, is *us!* "Daddy has done a terrible terrible thing," cries my mother—or is that my imagination? Isn't what she is saying more like, "Oh, Alex has
done a terrible terrible thing again, Daddy—" Whatever,
she lifts Hannah (of all people, Hannah!) who until that
moment I had never really taken seriously as a genuine
object of anybody's love, takes her up into her arms and
starts kissing her all over her sad, sallow unloved face, and
saying that her little girl is the only one in the whole wide
world she can really trust . . . But if I am eight, Hannah is
twelve, and nobody is picking her up, I assure you, because
the poor kid's problem is that she is overweight, "and how,"
my mother says. She's not even supposed to *eat* chocolate
pudding. Yeah, *that's* why I took it! Tough shit, Hannah,
it's what the *doctor* ordered, not me. I can't help it if
you're fat and "sluggish" and I'm skinny and brilliant. I
can't help it that I'm so beautiful they stop mother when
she is wheeling me in my carriage so as to get a look at my
gorgeous *punim*—you hear her tell that story, it's something
I myself had nothing to do with, it's a simple fact of nature,
that I was born beautiful and you were born, if not ugly,
certainly not something people wanted to take special looks
at. And is that my fault, too? How you were born, four

whole years before I even entered the world? Apparently this is the way God wants it to be, Hannah! In the big book!

But the fact of the matter is, she doesn't seem to hold me responsible for anything: she just goes on being good to her darling little baby brother, and never once strikes me or calls me a dirty name. I take her chocolate pudding, and she takes my shit, and never says a word in protest. Just kisses me before I go to bed, and carefully crosses me going to school, and then stands back and obligingly allows herself to be swallowed up by the wall (I guess that's where she is) when I am imitating for my beaming parents all the voices on "Allen's Alley," or being heralded to relatives from one end of North Jersey to the other for my perfect report card. Because when I am not being punished, Doctor, I am being carried around that house like the Pope through the streets of Rome . . .

You know, I can really come up with no more than a dozen memories involving my sister from those early years of childhood. Mostly, until she emerges in my adolescence as the only sane person in that lunatic asylum whom I can talk to, it is as though she is someone we see maybe once or twice a year—for a night or two she visits with us, eating at our table, sleeping in one of our beds, and then, poor fat thing, she just blessedly disappears.

EVEN IN THE Chinese restaurant, where the Lord has lifted the ban on pork dishes for the obedient children of Israel, the eating of lobster Cantonese is considered by God (Whose mouthpiece on earth, in matters pertaining to food, is my Mom) to be totally out of the question. Why we can eat pig on Pell Street and not at home is because . . . frankly I still can't figure the whole thing out, but at the time I believe it has largely to do with the fact that the elderly man who owns the place, and whom amongst ourselves we call "*Schmendrick*," isn't somebody whose opinion of us we have cause to worry about. Yes, the only people in the world whom it seems to me the Jews are not afraid of are the Chinese. Because, one, the way they speak English makes my father sound like Lord Chesterfield; two, the insides of their heads are just so much fried rice anyway;

and three, to them we are not Jews but *white*—and maybe even Anglo-Saxon. Imagine! No wonder the waiters can't intimidate us. To them we're just some big-nosed variety of WASP! Boy, do we eat! Suddenly even the pig is no threat —though to be sure it comes to us so chopped and shredded, and is then set afloat on our plates in such oceans of soy sauce, as to bear no resemblance at all to a pork chop, or a hambone, or, most disgusting of all, a *sausage* (ucchh!) . . . But why then can't we eat a lobster, too, disguised as something else? Allow my mother a logical explanation. The syllogism, Doctor, as used by Sophie Portnoy. Ready? Why we can't eat lobster. "Because it can kill you! Because I ate it once, and I nearly died!"

Yes, she too has committed her transgressions, and has been duly punished. In her wild youth (which all took place before I got to know her), she had allowed herself to be bamboozled (or flattered and shamed as I see it) into eating lobster Newburg by a mischievous and attractive insurance agent who worked with my father for Boston and Northeastern, a lush named (could it be better?) Doyle.

It was at a convention held by the company in Atlantic City, at a noisy farewell banquet, that Doyle led my mother to believe that even though that wasn't what it smelled like, the plate the waiter had shoved in front of her corsage contained nothing but chicken à la king. To be sure, she sensed that something was up even then, suspected even as the handsome drunken Doyle tried to feed her with her own fork that tragedy, as she calls it, was lurking in the wings. But high herself on the fruit of two whiskey sours, she rashly turned up her long Jewish nose to a very genuine premonition of foul play, and—oh, hotheaded bitch! wanton hussy! improvident adventuress!—surrendered utterly to the spirit of reckless abandon that apparently had taken possession of this hall full of insurance agents and their wives. Not until the sherbet arrived did Doyle—who my mother also describes as "in looks a second Errol Flynn, and not just in looks"—did Doyle reveal to her what it was she had actually ingested.

Subsequently she was over the toilet all night throwing up. "My *kishkas* came out from that thing! Some practical joker! That's why to this day I tell you, Alex, never to commit a practical joke—because the consequences can be tragic! I was so sick, Alex," she used to love to remind herself and me, and my father too, five, ten, fifteen years after the cataclysm itself, "that your father, Mr. Brave One here, had to call the hotel doctor out of a sound sleep to come to the room. See how I'm holding my fingers? I was throwing up so hard, they got stiff just like this, like I was *paralyzed*, and *ask* your father—Jack, tell him, tell him what you thought when you saw what happened to my fingers from the lobster Newburg." "What lobster Newburg?" "That your friend Doyle forced down my throat." "Doyle? What Doyle?" "Doyle, The *Shicker Goy* Who They Had To Transfer To The Wilds Of South Jersey He Was Such A Run-Around. Doyle! Who Looked Like Errol Flynn! Tell Alex what happened to my fingers, that you *thought* happened—" "Look, I don't even know what you're talking about," which is probably the case: not everybody quite senses my mother's life to be the high drama she herself experiences—also, there is always a possibility that this story has more to do with imagination than reality (more to do, needless to say, with the dangerous Doyle than the forbidden lobster). And then of course my father is a man who has a certain amount of worrying to do each day, and sometimes he just has to forgo listening to the conversations going on around him in order to fulfill his anxiety requirement. It can well be that he hasn't really heard a word she's been saying.

But on it goes, nonetheless, my mother's monologue. As other children hear the story of Scrooge every year, or are read to nightly from some favorite book, I am continually *shtupped* full of the suspense-filled chapters of her perilous life. This in fact is the literature of my childhood, these stories of my mother's—the only bound books in the house, outside of school books, are those that have been given as presents to my parents when one or the other was recuperating in the hospital. One-third of our library consists of *Dragon Seed* by Pearl S. Buck (my mother's hysterectomy) and the other two-thirds are *Argentine Diary* by William L. Shirer and *The Autobiography of Casanova* (my father's appendectomy). Otherwise our books are written by Sophie Portnoy, each an addition to that famous series of hers entitled, *You Know Me, I'll Try Anything Once*. For the idea that seems to generate and inform her works is that she is in actuality some sort of daredevil who goes exuberantly out into life in search of the new and the thrilling, only to be slapped down for her inquiring, impassioned spirit. She actually seems to think of herself as a woman at the very frontiers of experience, some doomed dazzling combination of Marie Curie, Anna Karenina, and Amelia Earhart. At any rate, that is the sort of romantic image of her which this little boy goes to bed with, after she has buttoned him into his pajamas and tucked him between the sheets with the story of how she learned to drive a car when she was pregnant with my sister, and the very first day that she had her license—"the very first *hour*, Alex"—"some maniac" slammed into her rear bumper, and consequently she has never driven a car from that moment on. Or the story of how she was searching for the goldfish in a pond at Saratoga Springs, New York, where she had been taken at the age of ten to visit her old sick Aunt Yetta, and accidentally fell in, right to the bottom of the filthy pool, and has not gone into the water since, not even down the shore, when it's low tide and a lifeguard is on duty. And then there is the lobster, which even in her drunkenness she knew wasn't chicken à la king, but only "to shut up the mouth on that Doyle" had forced down her throat, and subsequently the near-tragedy happened, and she has not of course eaten anything even faintly resembling lobster since. And does not want me to either. Ever. Not, she says, if I know what is good for me. "There are plenty of good things to eat in the world, Alex, without eating a thing like a lobster and running the risk of having paralyzed hands for the rest of your life."

Whew! Have I got grievances! Do I harbor hatreds I didn't even know were there! Is it the process, Doctor, or is it what we call "the material"? All I do is complain, the repugnance seems bottomless, and I'm beginning to wonder if maybe enough isn't enough. I hear myself indulging in exactly the kind of ritualized bellyaching that gives psychoanalytic patients such a bad name with the general public. Could I really have detested this childhood and resented

these poor parents of mine to the same degree then as
I seem to now, looking backwards upon what I was from
the vantage point of what I am—and am not? Is this truth
I'm delivering up, or is it just plain *kvetching*? Or is *kvetching* for people like me a *form* of truth? Regardless, my conscience wishes to make it known, before the beefing begins
anew, that *at the time* my life was not this thing I feel so
estranged from and so resentful of now. Vast as my confusion was, deep as my inner turmoil must seem in retro-
spect, I don't remember that I was one of those kids who
went around wishing he lived in another house with other
people, whatever my unconscious yearnings may have been
in that direction. After all, where else would I find an
audience like those two for my imitations? I used to leave
them in the aisles at mealtime—my mother once actually wet
her pants, Doctor, and had to go running in hysterical
laughter to the bathroom from my impression of Mister
Kitzel on "The Jack Benny Show." What else? Walks, walks
with my father in Weequahic Park on Sundays that I still
haven't forgotten. You know, I can't go off to the country
and find an acorn on the ground without thinking of him
and those walks. And that's not nothing, nearly thirty
years later.

And have I mentioned, vis-à-vis my mother, the running
conversation we two had in those years before I was even
old enough to go off by myself to a school? During those
five years when we had each other alone all day long, I do
believe we covered just about every subject known to man.
"Talking to Alex," she used to tell my father when he
came home exhausted at night, "I can do a whole afternoon of ironing, and never even notice the time go by."
And mind you, I am only *four*.

And as for the hollering, the cowering, the crying, even
that had vividness and excitement to recommend it; moreover, that nothing was never simply nothing but always
SOMETHING, that the most ordinary kind of occurrence
could explode without warning into A TERRIBLE CRISIS,
this was to me *the way life is*. The novelist, what's his name,
Markfield, has written in a story somewhere that until he
was fourteen he believed "aggravation" to be a Jewish
word. Well, this was what I thought about "tumult" and

"bedlam," two favorite nouns of my mother's. Also "spatula." I was already the darling of the first grade, and in every schoolroom competition expected to win hands down, when I was asked by the teacher one day to identify a picture of what I knew perfectly well my mother referred to as "a spatula." But for the life of me I could not think of the word in English. Stammering and flushing, I sank defeated into my seat, not nearly so stunned as my teacher but pretty badly shaken up just the same . . . and that's how far back my fate goes, how early in the game it was "normal" for me to be in a state resembling torment—in this particular instance over something as monumental as a kitchen utensil. Oh, all that conflict over a spatula, Momma. Imagine how I feel about you! !

I AM REMINDED at this joyous little juncture of when we lived in Jersey City, back when I was still very much my mother's papoose, still very much a sniffer of her body perfumes and a total slave to her *kugel* and *grieben* and *ruggelech*—there was a suicide in our building. A fourteen- or fifteen-year-old boy named Ronald Ninberg, who had been crowned by the women in the building "José Iturbi the Second," hung himself from the shower head in his bathroom. "With those golden hands!" the women wailed, referring of course to his piano playing—"With that talent!" Immediately followed by, "You couldn't look for a boy more in love with his mother than Ronald!"

I swear to you, this is not bullshit or a screen memory, these are the very words these women use. The great dark operatic themes of human suffering and passion come rolling out of those mouths like the prices of Oxydol and Del Monte canned corn! My own mother, let me remind you, when I returned this past summer from my month in Europe, greets me over the phone with the following salutation: "Well, how's my lover?" Her *lover* she calls me, while her husband is listening on the other extension! And it never occurs to her, if I'm her lover, who is he, the *shmegeggy* she lives with? No, you don't have to go digging where these people are concerned—they wear the old unconscious on their *sleeves!*

Mrs. Ninberg, weeping in our kitchen: "Why? Why?

Why did he do this to us?" Hear? Not what might *we* have done to *him*, oh no, never that—why did he do this *to us*? To us! Who would have given our arms and legs to make him happy and a famous concert pianist into the bargain! Really, can they be this blind? Can people be so abysmally stupid and live? Do you *believe* it? Can they actually be equipped with all the machinery, a brain, a spinal cord, and the four apertures for the ears and the eyes—equipment, Mrs. Ninberg, nearly as impressive as color TV—and still go through life without a single clue about the feelings and yearnings of anyone other than themselves? Mrs. Ninberg, you shit, I remember you, I was only six, but I remember you, and what killed your Ronald, the concert-pianist-to-be is obvious: YOUR FUCKING SELFISHNESS AND STU-PIDITY! "All the lessons we gave him," weeps Mrs. Nin-berg . . . Oh, look, look, why do I carry on like this? Maybe she means well, surely she must—at a time of grief, what can I expect of such simple people? It's only because in her misery she doesn't know what else to say that she says that God-awful thing about all the lessons they gave to some-body who is now a corpse. What are they, after all, these Jewish women who raised us up as children? In Calabria you see their suffering counterparts sitting like stones in the churches, swallowing all that hideous Catholic bullshit; in Calcutta they beg in the streets, or if they are lucky, are off somewhere in a dusty field hitched up to a plow . . . Only in America, Rabbi Golden, do these peasants, our mothers, get their hair dyed orange at the age of sixty, and walk up and down Collins Avenue in Florida in pedal-pushers and mink stoles—and with opinions on every sub-ject under the sun. It isn't their fault they were given a gift like speech—look, if cows could talk, they would say things just as idiotic. Yes, yes, maybe that's the solution then: think of them as cows, who have been given the twin miracles of speech and mah-jongg. Why not be charitable in one's thinking, right, Doctor?

My favorite detail from the Ronald Ninberg suicide: even as he is swinging from the shower head, there is a note pinned to the dead young pianist's short-sleeved shirt— which is what I remember most about Ronald, by the way: this tall emaciated teen-age catatonic, swimming around all by himself in those oversized short-sleeved sport shirts, and with the lapels starched and ironed back so fiercely they looked to have been bullet-proofed . . . And Ronald himself, every limb strung so tight to his backbone that it looked as though if you touched him he'd begin to hum . . . and those fingers, of course, those long white grotesqueries, seven knuckles at least before you got down to the nicely gnawed nail, those Bela Lugosi hands that my mother would tell me—and tell me—and tell me—because nothing ever once!—*nothing!*—were "the hands of a born pianist."

Pianist! Oh, that's one of the words they just love, almost as much as *doctor,* Doctor. And *residency.* And best of all, *his own office. He opened his own office in Livingston.* "Do you remember Seymour Schmuck, Alex?" she asks me, or Aaron Putz or Howard Schlong, or some yo-yo I went to grade school with twenty-five years ago. "Well, I met his mother on the street today, and she told me that Seymour is now the biggest brain surgeon in the entire Western Hemisphere. He owns six different split-level ranch-type houses made all of fieldstone in Livingston, and belongs to the boards of eleven synagogues, all brand-new and designed by Marc Kugel, and last year with his wife and his two little daughters, who are so beautiful they are already under contract to Metro, and so brilliant that they should be in college—he took them all to Europe for an eighty-million-dollar tour of seven thousand countries, some of them you never even heard of, that they made them just to honor Seymour, and on top of that, he's so important, your friend Seymour, that in every single city in Europe that they visited he was asked by the mayor himself to stop and do an impossible operation in hospitals that they also built for him right on the spot, and—listen to this—where they pumped into the operating room during the operation the theme song from *Exodus* so everybody should know what religion he is—and that's how big Seymour is today! *And how happy he makes his parents!*"

And you, the implication is, you, when are *you* going to get married already? In Newark and the surrounding suburbs this apparently is the question on everybody's lips: WHEN IS ALEXANDER PORTNOY GOING TO STOP BEING SELFISH AND GIVE HIS PARENTS, WHO

ARE SUCH WONDERFUL PEOPLE, GRANDCHIL-
DREN? "Well," says my father, the tears brimming up in
his eyes, "well," he asks, *every single time I see him*, "is
there a serious girl in the picture, Big Shot? Excuse me for
asking, I'm only your father, but since I'm not going to be
alive forever, I wonder if maybe you could let me in on the
secret."

Yes, shame, shame, on Alex P., the only member of his
graduating class who hasn't made grandparents of his
Mommy and his Daddy. While everybody else has been
marrying nice Jewish girls, and having children, and buying houses, and (my father's phrase) *putting down roots*,
what he has been doing is—chasing cunt. And *shikse* cunt,
to boot! Chasing it, sniffing it, touching it, licking it, *shtupping* it, but above all, *thinking about it*. Day and night, at
work and on the street—thirty-four years old and still he is
roaming the streets with his eyes popping. A wonder he
hasn't been ground to mush by a taxicab, given how he
makes his way across the major arteries of Manhattan during the lunch hour. Thirty-four, and still ogling and day-
dreaming about every girl who crosses her legs opposite
him in the subway! Still cursing himself for speaking not a
word to the succulent pair of tits that rode twenty-five
floors alone with him in an elevator! Then cursing himself
for the opposite as well! For he has been known to walk
up to thoroughly respectable-looking girls in the street, and
despite the fact that since his appearance on Sunday morning TV his face is not entirely unknown to an enlightened
segment of the public—despite the fact that he may be on
his way to his current mistress' apartment for dinner—he has
been known on one or two occasions to mutter, "Look,
would you like to come home with me?" *Of course* she is
going to say "No." Of course she is going to scream, "Get
out of here, you!" or answer curtly, "I have a nice home of
my own, thank you, with a husband in it." What is he doing
to himself, this fool! this idiot! this furtive *boy*! This sex
maniac! He simply cannot—*will* not—control the fires in his
putz, the fevers in his brain, the desire continually burning
away within for the new, the wild, the unthought-of and, if
you can imagine such a thing, *the undreamt-of*. Where cunt
is concerned he lives in a condition that has neither dimin-

ished nor in any significant way been refined from what it was when he was fifteen years old and could not get up from his seat in the classroom without hiding a hard-on beneath his three-ring notebook. Every girl he sees turns out (hold your hats) to be carrying around between her legs—a real cunt. Amazing! Astonishing! Still can't get over this fantastic idea that when you are looking at a girl, you are looking at somebody who is guaranteed to have on her— a cunt! *They all have cunts!* Right there under their dresses! Cunts—for fucking! And, Doctor, Your Honor, whatever your name is—it seems to make no difference how much the poor bastard actually gets—for he is dreaming about tomorrow's pussy even while pumping away at today's!

Do I exaggerate? Am I doing myself in only as a clever way of showing off? Of boasting? Do I really experience this restlessness, this horniness, as an affliction—or as an accomplishment? Both? Could be. Or is it only a means of evasion? Look, at least I don't find myself in my middle thirties locked into a marriage with some nice person whose body has ceased to be of any genuine interest to me—at least I don't have to get into bed every night with somebody who by and large I fuck out of obligation instead of lust. I mean, the nightmarish depression some people must suffer at bedtime . . . On the other hand, even I must admit that there is maybe, from a certain perspective, something a little depressing about my situation too. Of course you can't have everything, or so I understand—but the question I am willing to face is: have I anything? How much longer do I go on sticking this thing into the holes that come available to it—first this hole, then when I tire of this hole, that hole over there . . . and so on. When will it end? Only *why* should it end, God damn it! To please a father and mother? To conform to the norm? Why on earth should I be so defensive about being what was honorably called some years ago, a bachelor? After all, that's all this is, you know— bachelorhood. So what's the crime? Sexual freedom? In this day and age? Why should I bend to the bourgeoisie? Do I ask them to bend to me? Maybe I've been touched by the tarbrush of Bohemia a little—is that so awful? Who am I harming with my lusts? I don't blackjack women, I don't twist arms to get them into bed with me. I am, if I say so

myself, a kind and gentle man; as men go, I am probably
. . . But why must I explain myself! *Excuse* myself! Why
must I justify with my gentleness and kindness my desires!
So I have desires—only they're endless. Endless! Endless!
And that, that may not be such a blessing, taking for the
moment a psychoanalytic point of view . . . But then all
the unconscious can do anyway, Freud tells us, is *want.*
And want! And WANT! Oh, Freud, do I know! This one
has a nice ass, but she talks too much. On the other
hand, this one here doesn't talk at all, at least not so that
she makes any sense—but, boy, can she suck! What cock
know-how! While here is a honey of a girl, with the softest,
pinkest, most touching nipples I have ever drawn between
my lips, only she won't go down on me. Isn't that odd? And
yet—go understand people—it is her pleasure while being
boffed to have one or the other of my forefingers snugly
lodged up her anus. What a mysterious business it all is!
The endless fascination of these apertures and openings!
You see, I just can't stop! Or tie myself to any *one.* I have
affairs that last as long as a year, a year and a half, months
and months of love, both tender and voluptuous, but in the
end—it is as inevitable as death—time marches on and lust
peters out. In the end, I just cannot take that step into
marriage. But why should I? *Why?* Is there a law saying
Alex Portnoy has to be somebody's husband and father?
Doctor, they can stand on the window ledge and threaten
to splatter themselves on the pavement below, they can
pile the Seconal to the ceiling—I may have to live for
weeks and weeks on end in terror of these young and
healthy marriage-bent girls throwing themselves beneath
the subway train, but I simply cannot, I simply *will* not,
enter into a contract to sleep with just one woman for the
rest of my days. Imagine it: suppose I were to go ahead
and marry A, with her sweet tits and so on, what will happen when B appears, whose are even sweeter—or, at any
rate, newer? Or C, who knows how to move her ass in some
special way I have never experienced; or D, or E, or F. I'm
trying to be honest, Doctor—because with sex the human
imagination runs to Z, and then beyond! Tits and cunts and
legs and lips and mouths and tongues and assholes! How
can I give up what I have never even had, for a girl, who

delicious and provocative as once she may have been, will inevitably grow as familiar to me as a loaf of bread? For love? What love? Is that what binds all these couples we know together—the ones who even bother to let themselves be bound? Isn't it something more like weakness? Isn't it rather convenience and apathy and guilt? Isn't it rather fear and exhaustion and inertia, gutlessness, far far more than that "love" that the marriage counselors and the songwriters and the psychotherapists are forever dreaming about? Please, let us not bullshit one another about "love" and its duration. Which is why I ask: how can I be expected to marry someone whom I "love" knowing full well that five, six, or seven years hence I am going to be out on the streets hunting down the fresh new pussy—all the while my devoted wife, who has made me such a lovely home et cetera, silently suffers her loneliness and rejection? How could I face her terrible tears? I couldn't. How could I face my adoring children? And then the divorce, right? The *child* support. The *alimony*. The *visitation* rights. Wonderful prospect, just wonderful. And as for anybody who kills herself because I prefer not to be blind to the future, well, she is her own worry—she has to be! There is surely no need or justification for anybody to threaten suicide just because I am wise enough to see what frustrations and recriminations lie ahead . . . Baby, please, don't howl like that please—somebody is going to think you're being strangled to death. Oh, baby (I hear myself saying last year, this year, the year before), you're going to be all right, really you are; you're going to be just fine and dandy and much better off, really, so please, you bitch, come in off that window ledge *and let me go!* "You! You and your filthy cock!" cries the most recently disappointed (and self-appointed) bride-to-be, my strange, lanky, and very batty friend, who used to earn as much in an hour posing for fashion photographers as her illiterate father would earn in a week in the coal mines of West Virginia: "I thought you were supposed to be a superior person, you muff-diving mother-fucking son of a bitch!" This beautiful girl, who has got me all wrong, is called The Monkey, a nickname that derives from a little perversion she once engaged in shortly before meeting me and going on to bigger things. Doctor, I had never had anybody like her in my life, she was the fulfillment of my most lascivious adolescent dreams—but marry her, can she be serious? You see, for all her preening and perfumes, she has a very low opinion of herself, and simultaneously—and here is the source of much of our trouble—a ridiculously high opinion of me. And simultaneously, a very *low* opinion of me! She is one confused Monkey, and I'm afraid, not too very bright. "An intellectual!" she screams. "An educated, spiritual person! You mean, miserable hard-on you, you care more about the niggers in Harlem that you don't even know, than you do about me, who's been sucking you off for a solid year!" Confused, heartbroken, and also out of her mind. For all this comes to me from the ledge of our hotel room in Athens, as I stand in the doorway of the room, suitcases in hand, begging her to *please* come back inside so that I can catch a plane out of that place. Then the angry little manager, all olive oil, moustache, and outraged respectability, is running up the stairway waving his arms in the air—and so, taking a deep breath, I say, "Look, you want to jump, jump!" and out I go—and the last words I hear have to do with the fact that it was only out of love of me (*"Love!"* she screams) that she allowed herself to do the degrading things I forced quote unquote upon her.

Which is not the case, Doctor. Which is not the case! Which is an attempt on this sly bitch's part to break me on the rack of guilt—and thus get herself a husband. Because at twenty-nine that's what she wants, you see—but that does not mean, you see, that I have to oblige. "In September, you son of a bitch, I am going to be thirty years old!" Correct, Monkey, correct! Which is precisely why it is you and not me who is responsible for your expectations and your dreams! Is that clear? *You!* "I'll tell the world about you, you cold-hearted prick! I'll tell them what a filthy pervert you are, and the dirty things you made me do!"

The cunt! I'm lucky really that I came out of that affair *alive*.

BUT BACK TO my parents, if indeed we have left them, and how it seems that by remaining in my single state I bring these people nothing but grief. That I happen,

Mommy and Daddy, just happen to be the Assistant Human Rights Commissioner for the City of New York apparently doesn't mean shit to you in terms of accomplishment and stature—though that's not exactly so, I know, since whenever my name appears in a news story in the *Times*, they bombard every living relative with a copy of the clipping. Half my father's retirement pay goes down the drain in postage, and my mother is on the phone for days at a stretch and has to be fed intravenously, her mouth is going at such a rate about her Alex. In fact, it is exactly as it always has been: they can't get over what a success and a genius I am, my name in the paper, an associate of the glamorous Mayor, on the side of Truth and Justice, enemy of slumlords and Nazis and rats . . . but still, if you know what I mean, still somehow not entirely perfect.

Now, can you beat that for a serpent's tooth? All they have sacrificed for me and done for me and how they boast about me and are the best public relations firm (they tell me) any child could have, and it turns out that I still won't be perfect. Did you ever hear of such a thing in your life? I just refuse to be perfect. What a pricky kid.

They come to visit: "Where did you get a rug like this?" my father asks, making a face. "Did you get this thing in a junk shop or did somebody give it to you?"

"I like this rug."

"What are you talking," my father says, "it's a worn-out rug."

Light-hearted. "It's worn, but not out. Okay? Enough?"

"Alex, please," my mother says, "it is a very worn rug."

"You'll trip on that thing," my father says, "and throw your knee out of whack, and then you'll really be in trouble."

"And with your knee," says my mother meaningfully, "that wouldn't be a picnic."

At this rate they are going to roll the thing up any minute now, the two of them, and push it out the window.

"The rug is fine. My *knee* is fine."

"It wasn't so fine," my mother is quick to remind me, "when you had the cast on, darling, up to your hip. How he schlepped that thing around! How miserable he was!"

"I was fourteen years old then, Mother."

"Yeah, and you came out of that thing," my father says, "you couldn't bend your leg, I thought you were going to be a cripple for the rest of your life. I told him, 'Bend it! Bend it!' I practically begged him morning, noon, and night, 'Do you want to be a cripple forever? Bend that leg!' "

"You scared the *daylights* out of us with that knee."

"But that was in nineteen hundred and forty-seven!"

My mother's reply? "You'll see, 1947, 1987, someday you'll be a parent, and you'll know what it's like. And then maybe you won't sneer at your family any more."

The legend engraved on the face of the Jewish nickel—on the body of every Jewish child—not IN GOD WE TRUST, but SOMEDAY YOU'LL BE A PARENT AND YOU'LL KNOW WHAT IT'S LIKE.

"You think," my father the ironist asks, "it'll be in our lifetime, Alex? You think it'll happen before I go down into the grave? No—he'd rather take chances with a worn-out rug!" The ironist—and logician! "—And crack his head open! And let me ask you something else, my independent son—who would even know you were here if you were lying bleeding to death on the floor? Half the time you don't answer the phone, I see you lying here with God only knows what's wrong—and who is there to take care of you? Who is there even to bring you a bowl of soup, if God forbid something terrible should happen?"

"I can take care of myself! I don't go around like some people—" boy, still pretty tough with the old man, eh, Al?—"some people I know in continual anticipation of total catastrophe!"

"You'll see," he says, nodding miserably, "you'll get sick—" and suddenly a squeal of anger, a whine out of nowhere of absolute hatred *of me!—"you'll get old, and you won't be such an independent big shot then!"*

"Alex, Alex," begins my mother, as my father walks to my window to recover himself, and, in passing, to comment contemptuously about "the neighborhood he lives in."

"Mother, I'm thirty-four! I am the Assistant Human Rights Commissioner of the City of New York! I graduated first in my law school class! Remember? At twenty-five I was already special counsel to a House Subcommittee—of the United States Congress, Mother! Of America! If I wanted Wall Street, Mother, I could be on Wall Street! I am a highly respected man in my profession, that should be *obvious*! Look, *I* helped solve the television quiz scandal, do you *remember*—?" Oh, why go on? Why go on in my strangled high-pitched adolescent voice? Good Christ, a Jewish man with parents alive is a fifteen-year-old boy, and will remain a fifteen-year-old boy till *they die!*

Anyway, Sophie has by this time taken my hand, and with hooded eyes, waits until I sputter out the last accomplishment I can think of, then speaks: "But to us, to us you're still a baby, darling." And next comes the whisper, Sophie's famous whisper that everybody in the room can hear without even straining, she's so considerate: "Tell him you're sorry. Give him a kiss. A kiss from you would change the world."

Doctor! Doctor! Did I say fifteen? Excuse me, I meant ten! I meant five! I meant zero! A Jewish man with his parents alive is half the time a helpless *infant!* Listen, come to my aid—free me from living my life in the middle of a Jewish joke! Because those jokes are not just jokes, Doctor—it also *hoits*, there is *pain* involved—and that's the part Sam Levenson leaves *out!* They sit in the casino at the Concord, the women in their minks and the men in their phosphorescent suits, and boy, do they laugh, laugh and laugh and laugh—"Help, help, my son the doctor is drowning!"—ha ha *ha*, ha ha *ha*, only what about the *pain*, Myron Cohen! What about the guy who is actually drowning! Actually sinking beneath an ocean of parental relentlessness! What about him—who happens, Myron Cohen, to be *me!* Doctor, Doctor, *please.* I can't live any more in a world given all its meaning and dimension by some vulgar nightclub clown. By some—some *black humorist!* Because that's who the black humorists are—of course!—the Henny Youngmans breaking them up down there in the Fontainebleau, and with what? Stories of murder and mutilation! "Help, help," cries the woman running along the sand at Miami Beach, "my son the doctor is drowning!" Ha ha ha— only it is *my son the patient*, lady! And is he drowning! Doctor, get these people off my ass, will you please? The macabre is very funny on the stage—but not to live it,

thank you! So just tell me how, and I'll do it! Just tell me
what, and I'll say it right to their faces! Scat, Sophie!
Fuck off, Jack! Go *away* from me already!

I mean here's a joke for you, for instance. Three Jews
are walking down the street, my mother, my father, and
me. It's this past summer, just before I am to leave on my
vacation. We have had our dinner ("You got a piece of
fish?" my father asks the waiter in the fancy French restaurant I take them to, *to show I am grown-up—"Oui, mon-
sieur,* we have—" "All right, give me a piece of fish," says
my father, *"and make sure it's hot."*), we have had our
dinner, and afterwards, chewing on my Titralac (for relief
of gastric hyperacidity) I walk a ways with them before
putting them in a taxi for the Port Authority Bus Terminal.
Immediately my father starts in about how I haven't come
to visit in five weeks (ground I thought we two had already
covered in the restaurant, while my mother was whispering to the waiter to make sure her "big boy's" piece of fish
was well done), and now I am going away for a whole
month, and all in all when do they ever see their own son?
"Look," I cry in my strangulated way, "you're seeing me
now! You're with me *right this minute!*" But he is off and
running, and now that he hasn't fishbones to worry about
choking on, there is no reining him in—Mr. and Mrs.
Schmuck have Seymour and his beautiful wife and their
two starlet daughters who come to them *every single Friday night*—"Look, I am a very busy person! I have important things to do—!" "Come on," he replies, "you gotta eat,
you can come for a meal once a week, because you gotta
eat anyway comes six o'clock—well, don't you?" Whereupon
who pipes up but Sophie, informing him that when she
was a little girl her family was always telling her to do
this and to do that, and how unhappy and resentful it
sometimes would cause her to feel, and how my father
shouldn't insist with me because, she concludes, "Alexander
is a big boy, Jack, he has a right to make his own decisions,
that's something I always told him." You always *what?
What* did she say?

Oh, why go on? Why be so obsessed like this? Why be
so petty? Why not be a sport like Sam Levenson and laugh
it all off—right?

Only let me just finish. So they get into the taxi. "Kiss

him," my mother whispers, "you're going all the way to Europe."

Of course my father overhears—that's why she lowers her voice, so we'll all listen—and panic sweeps over him. Every year, from September on, he is perpetually asking me what my plans are for the following August—now he realizes that this time I have outfoxed him: bad enough I am leaving on a midnight plane for another continent, but worse, he hasn't the slightest idea of my itinerary. *I did it! I made it!*

"—But where in Europe? Europe is half the whole globe—" he cries, as I begin to close the taxi door from the outside.

"I told you, I don't know."

"What do you mean? You *gotta* know! How will you get there yourself, if you 'don't know'—"

"Sorry, sorry—"

Desperately now his body comes lurching across my mother's—just as I slam shut the door—*oi*, not on his fingers, please! Jesus, this father! Whom I have had forever! Whom I used to find in the morning fast asleep on the toilet bowl, his pajamas around his knees and his chin hanging onto his chest. Up at quarter to six in the morning, so as to give himself a full uninterrupted hour on the can, in the fervent hope that if he is so kind and thoughtful as this to his bowels, they will relent, they will give in, they will say finally, "Okay, Jack, you win," and make a present to the poor bastard of five or six measly lumps of shit. I tell you, there are mornings when that man would pay twenty-five dollars apiece for a bowl full of turds such as most people drop into the bucket two or three times a day without a second thought. "Jesus Christ!" he groans, when I awaken him so as to wash up for school, and he realizes that it is nearly seven-thirty and down in the bowl over which he has been sleeping for an hour, there is, if he's lucky, one brown angry little pellet such as you expect from the rectum of a rabbit maybe—but not from the rear-end of a man who now has to go out all clogged up to put in a twelve-hour day. "Seven-*thirty*? Why didn't you say something!" Zoom, he's dressed, and in his hat and coat, and with his big black collection book in one hand he bolts his stewed prunes and his bran flakes standing up, fills a pocket with a handful of dried fruits that would bring on in an ordinary human being something resembling dysentery—"I ought to stick a hand grenade up my ass, if you want the truth," he whispers privately to me, while my mother occupies the bathroom and my sister dresses for school in her "room," the sun parlor—"I got enough All-Bran in me to launch a battleship. It's backed up to my throat, for Christ sake." Here, because he has got me snickering, and is amusing himself too in his own mordant way, he opens his mouth and points downward inside himself with a thumb. "Take a look. See where it starts to get dark? That ain't just dark—that's all those prunes rising up where my tonsils used to be. Thank God I had those things out, otherwise there wouldn't be room."

"Very nice talk," my mother calls from the bathroom. "Very nice talk to a child."

"Talk?" he cries. "It's the *truth*," and in the very next instant is thomping angrily around the house hollering, "My hat, I'm late, where's my hat? who saw my hat?" and my mother comes into the kitchen and gives me her patient, eternal, all-knowing sphinx-look . . . and waits . . . and soon he is back in the hallway, apoplectic and moaning, practically in grief, "Where is my hat? Where is that hat!" and softly, from the depths of her omniscient soul, she answers him: "Dummy, it's on your head." Momentarily his eyes seem to empty of all signs of human experience and understanding; he stands there, a blank, a thing, a body full of shit and no more. Then consciousness returns—yes, he will have to go out into the world after all, for his hat has been found, on his head of all places. "Oh yeah," he says, reaching up in wonderment—and then out of the house and into the Kaiser, and Superman is gone until dark.

The Kaiser, time for my story about the Kaiser: how he proudly took me with him when he went after the war to trade in the '39 Dodge for a new automobile, new make, new model, new everything—what a perfect way for an American dad to impress his American son!—and how the fast-talking salesman acted as though he just couldn't believe his ears, was simply incredulous, each time my father said "no" to one after another of the thousand little accessories the cock-sucker wanted to sell us to hang on the car. "Well, I'll tell you my opinion for whatever it's worth," says that worthless son of a bitch, "she'd look two hundred percent better with the whitewalls—don't you think so, young man? Wouldn't you like your dad to get the whitewalls, at least?" Ah, you slimy prick, you! Turning to me like that, to stick it into my old man—you miserable lowlife thieving son of a bitch! Just who the fuck are you, I wonder, to lord it over us—a God damn Kaiser-Fraser salesman! Where are you *now*, you intimidating bastard? "No, no whitewalls," mumbles my humbled father, and I simply shrug my shoulders in embarrassment over his inability to provide me and my family with the beautiful things in life.

Anyway, anyway—off to work in the radio-less whitewall-less Kaiser, there to be let into the office by the cleaning lady. Now, I ask you, why must he be the one to raise the shades in that office in the morning? Why must he work the longest day of any insurance agent in history? For whom? *Me?* Oh, if so, if so, if that is his reason, then it is all really too fucking tragic to bear. The misunderstanding is too great! For *me?* Do me a favor *and don't do it for me!* Don't please look around for a reason for your life being what it is and come up with Alex! Because I am not the be-all and end-all of everybody's existence! I refuse to schlep *those* bags around for the rest of my life! Do you hear me? I refuse! Stop finding it incomprehensible that I should be flying to Europe, thousands and thousands of miles away, just when you have turned sixty-five and are all ready to keel over at any minute, like you read about first thing every morning in the *Times*. Men his age and younger, *they die*—one minute they're alive, and the next dead, and apparently what he thinks is that if I am only across the Hudson instead of the Atlantic . . . What *does* he think? That with me here it won't happen? That I'll race to his side, take hold of his hand, and restore him to life? Does he actually believe that I somehow have the power to stop death? That I am the resurrection and the life? My dad, a real Christer! And doesn't even know it!

His death. His death. The truth is I am hardly less pre-occupied than he is. I never get a telegram, never get a phone call after midnight, that I do not feel my stomach empty out like a washbasin and say aloud, "He's dead." Because apparently I believe it too, believe that I can somehow save him from destruction—can, and must! But where did all of us get this ridiculous and absurd idea that I am so—so powerful, so precious, so necessary to everybody's survival! What was it with these Jewish parents—because I am not in this boat alone, oh no, I am on the biggest troop ship afloat . . . only look in through the portholes and see us there, stacked to the bulkheads in our bunks, moaning and groaning with such pity for ourselves, the sad and watery-eyed sons of Jewish parents, sick to the gills from rolling through these heavy seas of guilt—so I sometimes envision us, me and my fellow wailers, melancholics, and wise guys, still in steerage, like our forebears—and oh sick, sick as dogs, we cry out intermittently, one of us or another, "Poppa, how could you?" "Momma, why did you?" and the stories we tell, as the big ship pitches and rolls, the vying we do—who had the most castrating mother, who the most benighted father, I can match you, you bastard, humiliation for humiliation, shame for shame . . . the retching in the toilets after meals, the hysterical deathbed laughter from the bunks, and the tears—here a puddle wept in contrition, here a puddle from indignation—in the blinking of an eye, the body of a man (with the brain of a boy) rises in impotent rage to flail at the mattress above, only to fall instantly back, lashing itself with reproaches. Oh, my Jewish men friends! My dirty-mouthed guilt-ridden brethren! My sweethearts! My mates! Will this fucking ship ever stop pitching? When? Oh, when, so that we can leave off complaining how sick we are—and go out in the air, and live!

Doctor Spielvogel, it alleviates nothing fixing the blame—blaming is still ailing, of course, of course—but nonetheless, God damn it, just what the fuck *was* it with these Jewish parents, *what*, that they were able to make us little Jewish boys believe ourselves to be princes on the one hand, unique as unicorns on the one hand, geniuses and brilliant like nobody has ever been brilliant and beautiful before in the history of childhood—saviours and sheer perfection on the one hand, and such bumbling, incompetent, thoughtless, helpless, selfish, evil little shits, little *ingrates*, on the other!

"But in Europe where—?" he calls after me, as the taxi pulls away from the curb.

"I don't *know* where," I call after him, gleefully waving farewell. I am thirty-four and free at last of my mother and father! For a month.

"But how will we know your address?"

Joy! Sheer joy! "You won't!"

"But what if in the meantime—?"

"What if what?" I laugh. "What if what are you worried about now?"

"What if—?" And my God, does he really actually shout it out the taxi window? Is his fear, his greed, his maddened need and belief in me so great that he actually shouts these words out into the streets of New York? "*What if I die?*"

Because that is what I hear, Doctor. The last words I hear before flying off to Europe—and with The Monkey, somebody whom I have kept a total secret from them— "What if I die?" and then off I go for my orgiastic holiday abroad.

. . . Now, whether the words I hear are the words spoken is something else again. And whether what I hear I hear out of compassion for him, out of my agony over the inevitability of this horrific occurrence, his death, or out of my eager anticipation of that event, is also something else again. But this of course you understand, this of course is your bread and your butter.

I WAS SAYING that the detail of Ronald Ninberg's suicide that most appeals to me is the note to his mother found pinned to that roomy straitjacket, his nice stiffly laundered sports shirt. Know what it said? Guess. The last message from Ronald to his Momma? Guess.

> *Mrs. Blumenthal called. Please bring your mah-jongg rules to the game tonight.*
>
>   *Ronald*

Now, how's *that* for good to the last drop? How's that for a good boy, a thoughtful boy, a kind and courteous and well-behaved boy, a nice Jewish boy such as no one will

ever have cause to be ashamed of? Say thank you, darling.
Say you're welcome, darling. Say you're sorry, Alex. Say
you're sorry! *Apologize!* Yeah, for what? What have I done
now? Hey, I'm hiding under my bed, my back to the wall,
refusing to say I'm sorry, refusing too to come out and take
the consequences. *Refusing!* And she is after me with a
broom, trying to sweep my rotten carcass into the open.
Why, shades of Gregor Samsa! Hello Alex, good-bye Franz!
"You better tell me you're sorry, you, or else! And I don't
mean maybe either!" I am five, maybe six, and she is or-
elsing me and not-meaning-maybe as though the firing
squad is already outside lining the street with newspaper
preparatory to my execution.

And now comes the father: after a pleasant day of trying to sell life insurance to black people who aren't even
exactly sure they're alive, home to an hysterical wife and a
metamorphosed child—because what did I do, me, the soul
of goodness? Incredible, beyond belief, but either I kicked
her in the shins, or I bit her. I don't want to sound like I'm
boasting but I do believe it was *both*.

"Why?" she demands to know, kneeling on the floor to
shine a flashlight in my eyes, "why do you *do* such a thing?"
Oh, simple, why did Ronald Ninberg give up his ghost
and the piano? BECAUSE WE CAN'T TAKE ANY
MORE! BECAUSE YOU FUCKING JEWISH MOTHERS
ARE JUST TOO FUCKING MUCH TO BEAR! I have
read Freud on Leonardo, Doctor, and pardon the hubris,
but my fantasies exactly: this big smothering bird beating
frantic wings about my face and mouth *so that I cannot
even get my breath*. What do we want, me and Ronald and
Leonardo? *To be left alone!* If only for half an hour at a
time! Stop already hocking us to be *good!* hocking us to be
nice! Just leave us alone. God damn it, to pull our little
dongs in peace and think our little selfish thoughts—stop
stop stop with the respectabilizing of our hands and our
tushies and our mouths! Fuck the vitamins! Fuck the cod
liver oil! Just give us each day our daily flesh! And forgive
us our trespasses—which aren't even trespasses to begin
with!

"—a little boy you want to be who kicks his own mother
in the shins—?" My father speaking . . . and look at his

arms, will you? I have never really noticed before the size of the forearms the man has got on him. He may not have whitewall tires or a high school education, but he has arms on him that are no joke. And, Jesus, is he angry. But why? In part, you *schmuck*, I kicked her for *you!*

"—a human bite is worse than a dog bite, do you know that, you? Get out from under that bed! Do you hear me, what you did to your mother is worse than a dog could do!" and so loud is his roar, and so convincing, that my normally placid sister runs to the kitchen, great gruntfuls of fear erupting from her mouth, and in what we now call the fetal position crouches down between the refrigerator and the wall. Or so I seem to remember it—though it would make sense, I think, to ask how I know what is going on in the kitchen if I am still hiding beneath my bed.

"The bite I can live with, the shins I can live with—" her broom still relentlessly trying to poke me out from my cave—"but what am I going to do with a child who won't even say he's sorry? Who won't tell his own mother that he's sorry and will never never do such a thing again, *ever!* Daddy, what are we going to do, Daddy, with such a little boy in our house!"

Is she *kidding*? Is she *serious*? Why doesn't she call the cops and get me shipped off to child's prison, if this is how incorrigible I really am? "Alexander Portnoy, age five, you are hereby sentenced to hang by your neck until you are dead for refusing to say you are sorry to your mother." You'd think the child lapping up their milk and taking baths with his duck and his boats in their tub was the most wanted criminal in America. When actually what we are playing in that house is some farce version of *King Lear*, with me in the role of Cordelia! On the phone she is perpetually telling whosoever isn't listening on the other end that her biggest fault is that she's too good. Because *surely* they're not really listening—*surely* they're not sitting there nodding and taking down on their telephone pads this kind of transparent, self-serving, insane horseshit that even a pre-school-age child can see through. "You know what my biggest fault is, Rose? I hate to say it about myself, but I'm too good." These are actual words, Doctor, tape-recorded

these many years in my brain. And killing me still! These
are the actual messages that these Roses and Sophies and
Goldies and Pearls transmit to one another *daily!* "I give
my everything to other people," she admits, sighing, "and
I get kicked in the teeth in return—and my fault is that as
many times as I get slapped in the face, I can't stop being
good."

Shit, Sophie, just *try*, why don't you? Why don't we *all*
try! Because to be *bad*, Mother, that is the real struggle: to
be bad—and to enjoy it! That is what makes men of us boys,
Mother. But what my conscience, so-called, has done to my
sexuality, my spontaneity, my courage! Never mind some
of the things I try so hard to get away with—because the
fact remains, *I don't*. I am marked like a road map from
head to toe with my repressions. You can travel the length
and breadth of my body over superhighways of shame and
inhibition and fear. See, I am too good too, Mother, I too
am moral to the bursting point—just like you! Did you ever
see me try to smoke a cigarette? I look like Bette Davis.
Today boys and girls not even old enough to be *bar-
mitzvahed* are sucking on marijuana like it's peppermint
candy, and I'm still all thumbs with a Lucky Strike. Yes,
that's how good *I* am, Momma. Can't smoke, hardly drink,
no drugs, don't borrow money or play cards, can't tell a lie
without beginning to sweat as though I am passing over
the Equator. Oh, I say *fuck* a lot, but, I assure you, that's
about the sum of my success with transgressing. Look what
I have done with The Monkey—given her up, run from her
in fear, the girl whose cunt I have been dreaming about
lapping all my life. Why is a little turbulence so beyond
my means? Why must the least deviation from respectable
conventions cause me such inner hell? When I *hate* those
fucking conventions! When I know *better* than the taboos!
Doctor, my doctor, what do you say, LET'S PUT THE ID
BACK IN YID! Liberate this nice Jewish boy's libido, will
you please? Raise the prices if you have to—I'll pay anything! Only enough cowering in the face of the deep, dark
pleasures! Ma, Ma, what was it you wanted to turn me into
anyway, a walking zombie like Ronald Ninberg? Where did
you get the idea that the most wonderful thing I could be
in life was *obedient*? A little *gentleman*? Of all the aspira-

tions for a creature of lusts and desires! "Alex," you say, as
we leave the Weequahic Diner—and don't get me wrong,
I eat it up: praise is praise, and I take it however it comes—
"Alex," you say to me all dressed up in my clip-on tie and
my two-tone "loafer" jacket—"the way you cut your meat!
the way you ate that baked potato without spilling! I could
kiss you, I never *saw* such a little gentleman with his little
napkin in his lap like that!" *Fruitcake,* Mother. Little *fruitcake* is what you saw—and exactly what the training pro-
gram was designed to produce. Of course! Of course! The
mystery really is not that I'm not dead like Ronald Ninberg,
but that I'm not like all the nice young men I see strolling
hand in hand in Bloomingdale's on Saturday mornings.
Mother, the beach at Fire Island is strewn with the bodies
of nice Jewish boys, in bikinis and Bain de Soleil, also little
gentlemen in restaurants, I'm sure, also who helped Mom-
mies set up the mah-jongg tiles when the ladies came on
Tuesday night to play. Christ Almighty! After all those
years of setting up those tiles—one bam! two crack! mah-
jongg!—how I made it into the world of pussy at all, *that's*
the mystery. I close my eyes, and it's not so awfully hard—
I see myself sharing a house at Ocean Beach with somebody
in eye makeup named Sheldon. "Oh, fuck you, Shelly,
they're *your* friends, *you* make the garlic bread." Mother,
your little gentlemen are all grown up now, and there on
lavender beach towels they lie, in all their furious narcis-
sism. And *oi gut*, one is calling out—to me! "Alex? Alexander the King? Baby, did you see where I put my tarragon?"
There he is, Ma, your little gentleman, kissing someone
named Sheldon on the lips! Because of his herb dressing!
"Do you know what I read in *Cosmopolitan?*" says my
mother to my father. "That there are women who are homosexual persons." "Come on," grumbles Poppa Bear, "what
kind of garbage is that, what kind of crap is that—?" "Jack,
please, I'm not making it up. I *read* it in *Cosmo!* I'll *show*
you the article!" "Come on, they print that stuff for the cir-
culation—" Momma! Poppa! There is worse even than that
—there are people who fuck chickens! There are men who
screw stiffs! You simply cannot imagine how some people
will respond to having served fifteen- and twenty-year sentences at some crazy bastard's idea of "good"! So if I kicked

you in the shins, if I sank my teeth in your wrist clear
through the bone, *count your blessings*. For had I kept it *all*
inside me, believe me, you too could have arrived home to
find a pimply adolescent corpse swinging over the bathtub
by his father's belt. Worse yet, this last summer, instead
of sitting *shiva* over a son running off to Europe, you might
have found yourself dining out on my "deck" on Fire Island
—the two of you, me, and Sheldon. And if you remember
what that *goyische* lobster did to your *kishkas*, imagine
what it would have been like trying to keep down Shelly's
sauce *béarnaise?*

So *there.*

WHAT A pantomime I had to put on to get my zylon
jacket off my back and into my lap so as to cover my joint
that night I bared it to the elements. All for the benefit of
the driver, within whose Polack power it lay merely to flip
on the overhead lights and thus destroy in a single moment
fifteen years of neat notebooks and good grades and teeth
cleaning twice a day and never eating a piece of fruit without thoroughly washing it beforehand . . . Is it hot in here!
Whew, is it hot! Boy oh boy, I guess I just better get this
jacket off and put it right down here in a neat little pile in
my lap . . . Only what am I *doing?* A Polack's day, my
father has suggested to me, isn't complete until he has
dragged his big dumb feet across the bones of a Jew. Why
am I taking this chance in front of my worst enemy? What
will become of me if I am caught!

Half the length of the tunnel it takes me to unzip my
zipper silently—and there it is again, up it pops again, as
always swollen, bursting with demands, like some idiot
macrocephalic making his parents' life a misery with his
simpleton's insatiable needs.

"Jerk me off," I am told by the silky monster. "*Here?
Now?*" "Of course here and now. When would you expect
an opportunity like this to present itself a second time?
Don't you know what that girl is who is asleep beside you?
Just look at that nose." "What nose?" "That's the point—
it's hardly even there. Look at that hair, like off a spinning
wheel. Remember 'flax' that you studied in school? That's
human flax! Schmuck, this is the real McCoy. A *shikse!*

And asleep! Or maybe she's just faking it is a strong possibility too. Faking it, but saying under her breath, 'C'mon,
Big Boy, do all the different dirty things to me you ever
wanted to do.'" "Could that be *so*?" "Darling," croons my
cock, "let me just begin to list the many different dirty
things she would like you to start to do: she wants you to
take her hard little *shikse* titties in your hands for one."
"She does?" "She wants you to finger-fuck her *shikse* cunt
till she faints." "Oh, God. Till she faints!" "This is an opportunity such as may never occur again. So long as you live."
"Ah, but that's the point, how long is that likely to be?
The driver's name is all X's and Y's—if my father is right,
these people are direct descendants from the ox!"

But who wins an argument with a hard-on? *Ven der
putz shteht, ligt der sechel in d'rerd.* Know that famous
proverb? When the prick stands up, the brains get buried in
the ground! When the prick stands up, the brains are as
good as dead! And 'tis so! Up it jumps, a dog through a
hoop, right into the bracelet of middle finger, index finger,
and thumb that I have provided. A three-finger hand-job
with staccato half-inch strokes up from the base—this will be
best for a bus, this will (hopefully) cause my zylon jacket
to do a minimal amount of hopping and jumping around.
To be sure, such a technique means forgoing the sensitive tip, but that much of life is sacrifice and self-control is a fact that even a sex fiend cannot afford to be
blind to.

The three-finger hand-job is what I have devised for
jerking off in public places—already I have employed it at
the Empire Burlesque house in downtown Newark. One
Sunday morning—following the example of Smolka, my
Tom Sawyer—I leave the house for the schoolyard,
whistling and carrying a baseball glove, and when no
one is looking (obviously a state of affairs I hardly believe
in) I jump aboard an empty 14 bus, and crouch in my seat
the length of the journey. You can just imagine the crowd
outside the burlesque house on a Sunday morning. Downtown Newark is as empty of life and movement as the
Sahara, except for those outside the Empire, who look like
the crew off a ship stricken with scurvy. Am I crazy to be
going in there? God only knows what kind of disease I am

going to pick up off those seats! "Go in anyway, fuck the disease," says the maniac who speaks into the microphone of my jockey shorts, "don't you understand what you're going to see inside there? A woman's snatch." "A *snatch?*" "The whole thing, right, all hot and dripping and ready to go." "But I'll come down with the syph from just touching the ticket. I'll pick it up on the bottom of my sneakers and track it into my own house. Some nut will go berserk and stab me to death for the Trojan in my wallet. What if the cops come? Waving pistols—and somebody runs—and they shoot me by mistake! Because I'm underage. What if I get killed—or even worse, arrested! What about my parents!" "Look, do you want to see a cunt or don't you want to see a cunt?" "I want to! I want to!" "They have a whore in there, kid, who fucks the curtain with her bare twat." "Okay—I'll risk the syph! I'll risk having my brain curdle and spending the rest of my days in an insane asylum playing handball with my own shit—only what about my picture in the *Newark Evening News!* When the cops throw on the lights and cry, 'Okay, freaks, this is a raid!'—what if the flashbulbs go off! And get me—*me*, already President of the International Relations Club in my second year of high school! Me, who skipped two grades of grammar school! Why, in 1946, because they wouldn't let Marian Anderson sing in Convention Hall, I led my entire eighth-grade class in refusing to participate in the annual patriotic essay contest sponsored by the DAR. I was and still am the twelve-year-old boy who, in honor of this courageous stand against bigotry and hatred, was invited to the Essex House in Newark to attend the convention of the C.I.O. Political Action Committee—to mount the platform and to shake the hand of Dr. Frank Kingdon, the renowned columnist whom I read every day in *P.M.* How can I be contemplating going into a burlesque house with all these degenerates to see some sixty-year-old lady pretend to make love to a hunk of asbestos, when on the stage of the Essex House ballroom, Dr. Frank Kingdon himself took my hand, and while the whole PAC rose to applaud my opposition to the DAR, Dr. Kingdon said, "Young man, you are going to see democracy in action here this morning." And with my brother-in-law-to-be, Morty Feibish, I have already attended meetings of the American Veterans Committee, I have helped Morty, who is Membership chairman, set up the bridge chairs for a chapter meeting. I have read *Citizen Tom Paine* by Howard Fast, I have read Bellamy's *Looking Backward* and *Finley Wren* by Philip Wylie. With my sister and Morty I have listened to the record of marching songs by the gallant Red Army Chorus. Rankin and Bilbo and Martin Dies, Gerald L. K. Smith and Father Coughlin, all those Fascist sons of bitches are my mortal enemies. So what in God's name am I doing in a side seat at the burlesque house jerking off into the pocket of my fielder's glove? What if there's violence! What if there's germs!

Yes, only what if later, after the show, that one there with the enormous boobies, *what if* . . . In sixty seconds I have imagined a full and wonderful life of utter degradation that we lead together on a chenille spread in a shabby hotel room, me (the enemy of America First) and Thereal McCoy, which is the name I attach to the sluttiest-looking slut in the chorus line. And what a life it is too, under our bare bulb (HOTEL flashing just outside our window). She pushes Drake's Daredevil Cupcakes (chocolate with a white creamy center) down over my cock and then eats them off of me, flake by flake. She pours maple syrup out of the Log Cabin can and then licks it from my tender balls until they're clean again as a little baby boy's. Her favorite line of English prose is a masterpiece: "Fuck my pussy, Fuckface, till I faint." When I fart in the bathtub she kneels down naked on the tile floor, leans all the way over, and kisses the bubbles. She sits on my cock while I take a shit, plunging into my mouth a nipple the size of a tollhouse cookie, and all the while whispering every filthy word she knows viciously in my ear. She puts ice-cubes in her mouth until her tongue and lips are freezing, then sucks me off—then switches to hot tea! Everything, everything I have ever thought of, she has thought of too, *and will do*. The biggest whore (rhymes, in Newark, with *poor*) there ever was. And she's mine! "Oh, Thereal, I'm coming, I'm coming, you fucking whore," and so become the only person ever to ejaculate into the pocket of a baseball mitt at the Empire burlesque house in Newark.

The big thing at the Empire is hats. Down the aisle from

me a fellow-addict fifty years my senior is dropping his load in his hat. His *hat*, Doctor! *Oi*, I'm sick. I want to cry. Not into your hat, you *shvantz*, you got to put that thing on your head! You've got to put it on now and go back outside and walk around downtown Newark dripping gissum down your forehead. How will you eat your lunch in that hat!

What misery descends upon me as the last drop dribbles into my mitt. The depression is overwhelming; even my cock is ashamed and doesn't give me a single word of back talk as I start from the burlesque house, chastizing myself ruthlessly, moaning aloud, "Oh, no, *no*," not unlike a man who has just felt his sole skid through a pile of dog turds— sole of his shoe, but take the pun, who cares, who cares . . . Ach! Disgusting! Into his hat, for Christ's sake. *Ven der putz shteht! Ven der putz shteht!* Into the hat that he wears on his *head!*

I SUDDENLY remember how my mother taught me to piss standing up! Listen, this may be the piece of information we've been waiting for, the key to what determined my character, what causes me to be living in this predicament, torn by desires that are repugnant to my conscience, and a conscience repugnant to my desires. Here is how I learned to pee into the bowl like a big man. Just listen to this!

I stand over the circle of water, my baby's weeny jutting cutely forth, while my momma sits beside the toilet on the rim of the bathtub, one hand controlling the tap of the tub (from which a trickle runs that I am supposed to imitate) and her other hand tickling the underside of my prick. I repeat: *tickling my prickling!* I guess she thinks that's how to get stuff to come out of the front of that thing, and let me tell you, the lady is right. "Make a nice sis, *bubala*, make a nice little sissy for Mommy," sings Mommy to me, while in actuality what I am standing there making with her hand on my prong is in all probability my future! Yes, a man's character is being decided, a destiny is being shaped . . . oh, maybe not . . . At any rate, for what the information is worth, in the presence of another man I simply cannot draw water. To this very day. My bladder may be distended to the proportions of a watermelon, but interrupted by another presence before the stream has begun (you want to hear everything, okay, I'm telling everything) which is that in Rome, Doctor, The Monkey and I picked up a common whore in the street and took her back to bed with us. Well, now that's out.

The bus, the bus, what intervened on the bus to prevent me from coming all over the sleeping *shikse's* arm—*I* don't know. Common sense, you think? Common decency? My right mind, as they say, coming to the fore? Well, where is this right mind on that afternoon I came home from school to find my mother out of the house, and our refrigerator stocked with a big purplish slice of raw liver? I believe that I have already confessed to the piece of liver that I bought in a butcher shop and banged behind the billboard on the way to a *bar mitzvah* lesson. Well, I wish to make a clean breast of it, Your Holiness. That—she—it—wasn't my first piece. My first piece I had in the privacy of my own home, rolled round my cock in the bathroom at three-thirty —and then had again, on the end of a fork, at five-thirty, along with the other members of that poor innocent family of mine.

So. Now you know the worst thing I have ever done. I fucked my own family's dinner.

UNLESS YOU SHARE with The Monkey her contention that the most heinous crime of my career was abandoning her in Greece. Second most heinous: leading her into that triumvirate in Rome. In *her* estimation—some estimation, that!—I am solely responsible for making that *ménage,* because mine is the stronger and more moral nature. "You the Great Humanitarian!" she cries. "The one whose *job* it is to protect the poor poor people against their landlords! You, who gave me *Winesburg, Ohio* to read! And *Crime and Punishment!* *You're* why I'm enrolling in college at night! *You're* why I've decided to be something more than just somebody's dumb and stupid piece of ass! And now you want to treat me like I'm nothing but just some hump, to *use*—use for every dirty weirdo thing you want to do—and like *you're* supposed to be the superior intellectual!"

You see, in this Monkey's estimation it was my mission to pull her up from those very abysses of frivolity and waste, of perversity and wildness and lust, into which I myself have been so vainly trying all my life successfully to sink. I am supposed to rescue her from those very temptations I have been struggling all these years to *yield* to! And it is of no consequence to her whatsoever that in bed she herself has been fantasying about this arrangement no less fever- ishly than I have. Doctor, I ask you, who was it that made the suggestion in the first place? Since the night we met, just who has been tempting whom with the prospect of yet another woman in our bed? Believe me, I am not trying to slither out of my own slime—I am trying to slither *into* it!— but it must be made absolutely clear, to you and me if not to her, that this hopelessly neurotic girl, this pathetic screwy cunt, is hardly what could be called *my* victim. I simply will not bend to that *victim* shit! Now she's thirty, wants to be married and a mother, wants to be respectable and live in a house with a husband (particularly as the high-paying years of her merry career appear to be about over), but it does not follow that just because she imagines herself vic- timized and deprived and exploited (and may be, taking a long view of her life) that I am the one upon whom they are going to pin the rap. *I* didn't make her thirty years old and single. *I* didn't take her from the coal fields of West Virginia—and I didn't put her in bed with that whore either! The fact is that it was The Monkey herself, speaking her high-fashion Italian, who leaned out of our rented car and explained to the whore what it was we wanted and how much we were willing to pay. I simply sat there behind the wheel, one foot on the gas pedal, like the getaway driver... And, believe me, when that whore got into the back seat, I thought no; and at the Hotel de la Ville, where we managed to send her up alone to our room, by way of the bar, I thought no again . . . No! No! No!

She wasn't bad-looking, this whore, sort of round and dumpy, but in her early twenties and with a big pleasant open face—and just stupendous tits. That was what we'd picked her out for, after driving slowly up and down the Via Veneto examining carefully the merchandise on parade. The whore, whose name was Lina, took her dress off in the middle of the room. She was wearing underneath it a "merry widow" corset, from which the breasts bubbled up at one end, and her more than ample thighs rippled out at the other. I was astonished by the garment—but then I was astonished by everything, above all that we had gone ahead after all these months of talking and finally done it.

The Monkey came out of the bathroom in her short chemise (ordinarily a sight that made me very hot, that cream-colored silk chemise with a beautiful Monkey in it) and I meanwhile took off all my clothes and sat naked at the foot of the bed. That Lina spoke not a word of English only intensified what was decidedly the feeling that began to ebb and flow between The Monkey and myself, a kind of restrained sadism. We could speak to one another, exchange secrets and plans without the whore's understanding—as she and The Monkey could whisper in Italian without my knowledge of what they might be saying, or plotting . . . Lina spoke first, and The Monkey turned to translate. "She says you have a big one." "I'll bet she says that to all the boys." Then they just stood there in their underwear looking my way—*waiting*. But so was I waiting too. And was my heart pounding! It had come to pass, two women and me . . . so now what happens? Still, you see, I'm saying to myself *No!*

"She wants to know," said The Monkey, after Lina had spoken a second time, "where the *signore* would like her to begin." "The *signore*," said I, "wishes her to begin at the beginning . . ." Oh, very witty that reply, very nonchalant indeed, only we continue to sit there motionless, me and my hard-on, all undressed and no place to go. Finally it is The Monkey who sets our lust in motion. She moves across to Lina, above whom she towers (oh God, isn't she enough? isn't she really sufficient for my needs? how many cocks have I got?) and puts her hand between the whore's legs. We had imagined it beforehand in all its possibilities, dreamed it all out loud for many many months now, and yet I am simply dumbstruck at the sight of The Monkey's middle finger suddenly disappearing up into Lina's cunt.

I can best describe the state I subsequently entered as one of unrelieved *busy-ness*. Boy, was I busy! I mean there was just so much to do. You go here and I'll go there—okay, now you go here and *I'll* go there—all right, now she goes down that way, while I head up this way, and you sort of half turn around on this . . . and so it went, Doctor, until I came my third and final time—The Monkey was by then the one with her back on the bed and I the one with my ass to the chandelier (and the cameras, I fleetingly thought)—and in the middle, feeding her tits into my Monkey's mouth, was our whore. Into whose hole, into what *sort* of hole I deposited my final load is simply a matter of conjecture. I don't think we will know the truth in our lifetime. It could even be that in the end I wound up fucking some dank, odoriferous combination of sopping Italian pubic hair, greasy American buttock, and absolutely rank Hotel de la Ville bedsheet. Then I got up, went into the bathroom, and, you'll all be happy to know, regurgitated my dinner. My *kishkas*, Mother, threw them right up into the toilet bowl. Isn't that a good boy?

When I came out of the bathroom, The Monkey and Lina were lying asleep in one another's arms.

The Monkey's pathetic weeping, the recriminations and the accusations, began immediately after Lina had dressed and departed. I had delivered her into evil. "*Me? You're* the one who stuck your fingers up her snatch and got the ball rolling! *You* kissed her on the fucking lips—" "Because," she screamed, "if I'm going to do something then like I *do* it! But that doesn't mean I *want* to!" And then, Doctor, she began to berate me about Lina's tits, how I hadn't *played* with them enough. "All you ever talk about and think about is tits! Tits! Tits! Tits! Mine are so small and everybody else's in the world you see are so *huge*—so you finally get a pair that are *tremendous*, and what do you do? *Nothing!*" "Nothing is an exaggeration, Monkey—the fact of the matter is that I couldn't always fight my way *past* you—" "I am not a lesbian! Don't you dare call me a lesbian! Because if I am, *you made me one!*" "Oh, Jesus, no—!" "I did it for you—and now you hate me for it!" "Then we won't do it again, all right? Never again if this is the fucking ridiculous result!"

Except the next night we got each other very steamed up at dinner—as in the early days of our courtship, The Monkey retired at one point to the ladies' room at Ranieri's and returned with a finger redolent of pussy, which I held beneath my nose to sniff and kiss at till the main dish arrived—and after a couple of brandies at Doney's, accosted

Lina once again at her station and returned with her to the hotel for round two. Only this time I relieved Lina of her undergarments myself, and mounted her even before The Monkey had come back into the bedroom from the john. If I'm going to do it, I thought, I'm going to do it! All the way! Everything! And no vomiting, either! You're not in Weequahic High School any more!

When The Monkey stepped out of the bathroom and saw what was going on, she wasn't entirely pleased. Silently she sat down on the side of the bed, her little features smaller than I had ever seen them, and, declining an invitation to participate, silently watched until I had had my orgasm and Lina had finished faking hers obligingly then—sweetly, really—Lina made for between The Monkey's legs, but The Monkey pushed her away and went off to sit and sulk in a chair by the window. So Lina—not a person particularly sensitive to interpersonal struggle—lay back on the pillow beside me and began to tell us all about herself. The bane of her existence were the abortions. She was the mother of one child, a boy, with whom she lived on Monte Mario ("in a beautiful new building," The Monkey translated). Unfortunately in her situation she could manage no more than one—"though she loves children"—and so was always in and out of the abortionist's office. Her only precautionary device seemed to be a spermicidal douche of no great reliability.

I couldn't believe that she had never heard of either the diaphragm or the birth control pill. I told The Monkey to explain to her about modern means of contraception that she could surely avail herself of, probably with only a little ingenuity. I got from my mistress a very wry look. The whore listened but was skeptical. It distressed me no end that she should be so ignorant about a matter pertaining to her own well-being (there on the bed with her fingers wandering around in my pubic hair). That fucking Catholic church, I thought . . .

So, when she left us that night, she had not only fifteen thousand of my lire in her handbag, but a month's supply of The Monkey's Enovid—that I had given to her.

"Oh, you are some saviour!" The Monkey shouted at me after Lina had left.

"What do you want her to do—get knocked up every other week?"

"What do I care what happens to *her!*" said The Monkey, her voice turning rural and mean. "She's a *whore!* A whore —and all you really wanted to do was fuck *her!* You couldn't even wait until I was out of the john to do it! And then on top you gave her *my* Enovid!"

"And what's all that mean, huh? What are you trying to say? You know, one of the things you don't always display, Monkey, is the gift of reason. The gift of frankness, yes— the gift of reason, no!"

"Then leave me! You've got what you wanted! Leave me!"

"Maybe I will!"

"To you I'm just another *her*, anyway! You, with all your big words and big shit holy ideals and all I am in your eyes is just a cunt—and a lesbian!—and a whore!"

Skip the fight. It's boring. Sunday: we emerge from the elevator, and who should be coming through the front door of the hotel but our Lina—and with her a child of about seven or eight, a fat little boy made out of alabaster, dressed all in ruffles and velvet and patent leather. Lina's hair is down and her dark eyes, fresh from church, have a familiarly Italian mournful expression. A nice-looking person really. A sweet person (I can't get over this!). And she has come to show off her *bambino!* Or so it looks.

Pointing to the little boy, she whispers to The Monkey, "*Molto elegante, no?*" But then she follows us out to our car, and while the child is preoccupied with the doorman's uniform, suggests that maybe we would like to come to her apartment on Monte Mario this afternoon and all of us do it with another man. She has a friend, she says—mind you, I get this all through my translator—she has a friend who she is sure, she says, would like to fuck the *signorina*. I can see the tears sliding out from beneath The Monkey's dark glasses, even as she says to me, "Well, what do I tell her, yes or no?" "No, of course. Positively not." The Monkey exchanges some words with Lina and then turns to me once again: "She says it wouldn't be for money, it would just be for—"

"No! No!"

All the way to the Villa Adriana she weeps: "I want a child too! And a home! And a husband! I am not a lesbian! I am not a whore!"

Then in Athens she threatens to jump from the window unless I marry her. So I leave.

SHIKSES! In winter, when the polio germs are hibernating and I can bank upon surviving outside of an iron lung until the end of the school year, I ice-skate on the lake in Irvington Park. In the last light of the weekday afternoons, then all day long on crisply shining Saturdays and Sundays, I skate round and round in circles behind the *shikses* who live in Irvington, the town across the city line from the streets and houses of my safe and friendly Jewish quarter. I know where the *shikses* live from the kinds of curtains their mothers hang in the windows. Also the *goyim* hang a little white cloth with a star in the front window, in honor of themselves and their boys away in the service—a blue star if the son is living, a gold star if he is dead. "A Gold Star Mom," says Ralph Edwards solemnly introducing a contestant on "Truth or Consequences" who in just two minutes is going to get a bottle of seltzer squirted at her snatch, followed by a brand-new refrigerator for her kitchen . . . A Gold Star Mom is what my Aunt Clara upstairs is too, except here is the difference—she has no gold star in her window, for a dead son doesn't leave her feeling proud or noble, or feeling anything for that matter. It seems instead to have turned her, in my father's words, into "a nervous case" for life. Not a day has passed since Heshie was killed in the Normandy invasion that Aunt Clara has not spent most of it in bed, and sobbing so badly that a doctor has sometimes to come and give her a shot to calm her hysteria down . . . But the curtains—the curtains are embroidered with lace, or "fancy" in some other way that my mother describes derisively as "*goyische* taste." At Christmastime, when I have no school and can go off to ice-skate at night under the lights, I see the trees blinking on and off behind these Gentile curtains. Not on our block— God forbid!—or on Leslie Street, or Schley Street, or even Fabian Place, but as I approach the Irvington line, here is a *goy*, and there is a *goy*, and there still another—and then

I am into Irvington and it is simply awful: not only is there a tree conspicuously ablaze in every parlor, but the houses themselves are all outlined with colored bulbs advertising Christianity, and phonographs are pumping "Silent Night" out into the street as though—as though?—it were the national anthem, and on the snowy lawns are set up little cutout models of the scene in the manger—really, it's enough to make you sick. How can they possibly *believe* this shit? Not just children but grown-ups too stand around on the snowy lawns smiling down at pieces of wood six inches high that are called Mary and Joseph and little Jesus—and the little cut-out cows and horses are smiling too! God! The idiocy of the Jews all year long, and then the idiocy of the *goyim* on these holidays. What a country! Honestly, how did any of us wind up sane?

But the *shikses*, ah the *shikses* are something else again. Between the smell of the damp sawdust and the wet wool in the overheated boathouse, and the sight of their fresh cold blond hair spilling out of their kerchiefs and hats, I am ecstatic. Amidst these flushed and giggling girls, I lace up my skates with weak, trembling fingers, and then out into the cold and after them I move, down the wooden gangplank on my toes and off onto the ice behind a fluttering covey of them—a nosegay of *shikses*, a garland of Gentile girls! I am so utterly awed that I am in a state of desire *beyond a hard-on*. My circumcised little dong is simply shriveled up with veneration. Maybe it's dread. How do they get so gorgeous, so healthful, so *blond*? My contempt for what they believe in is more than neutralized by my adoration of the way they look, the way they move and laugh and speak—the lives they must lead behind those *goyische* curtains! Maybe a pride of *shikses* is more like it—or is it a pride of *shkutzim*? For these are the girls whose older brothers are the engaging, good-natured, confident, clean, swift, and powerful halfbacks for the college football teams called *Northwestern* and *Texas Christian* and *UCLA*. Their fathers are men with white hair and deep voices who never use double negatives, and their mothers the ladies with the kindly smiles and the wonderful manners who say things like, "I do believe, Mary, that we sold thirty-five cakes at the Bake Sale." "Don't be too late,

dear," they sing out sweetly to their little tulips as they go
bouncing off in their bouffant taffeta dresses to the Junior
Prom with boys whose names are right out of the grade-
school reader, not Aaron and Arnold and Marvin, but
Johnny and Billy and Jimmy and Tod. Not Portnoy or
Pincus or Putz-Vetig, but Smith and Jones and Brown!
These people are the *Americans*, Doctor—like Henry Aldrich and Homer, like The Great Gildersleeve and his
nephew LeRoy, like Corliss and Veronica, like "Oogie
Pringle" who gets to sing beneath Jane Powell's window
in *A Date With Judy*—these are the people for whom Nat
"King" Cole sings every Christmastime, "Chestnuts roasting
on an open fire, Jack Frost nipping at your nose . . ." An
open fire, in *my* house? No, no, theirs are the noses whereof
he speaks. Not his flat black one or my long bumpy one,
but those tiny bridgeless wonders whose nostrils point
northward automatically at birth. And stay that way for
life! These are the children from the coloring books come
to life, the children they mean on the signs we pass in
Union, New Jersey, that say CHILDREN AT PLAY and
DRIVE CAREFULLY, WE LOVE OUR CHILDREN—
these are the girls and the boys who live "next door," the
kids who are always asking for "the jalopy" and getting into
"jams" and then out of them again in time for the final
commercial—the kids whose neighbors aren't the Silver-
steins and the Landaus, but Fibber McGee and Molly, and
Ozzie and Harriet, and Ethel and Albert, and Lorenzo Jones
and his wife Belle, and Jack Armstrong! Jack Armstrong,
the All-American *Goy!*—and Jack as in John, not Jack as in
Jake, like my father . . . Look, we ate our meals with that
radio blaring away right through to the dessert, the glow of
the yellow station band is the last light I see each night before sleep—so don't tell me we're just as good as anybody
else, don't tell me we're Americans just like they are. No,
no, these blond-haired Christians are the legitimate resi-
dents and owners of this place, and they can pump any song
they want into the streets and no one is going to stop them
either. O America, America—it may have been gold in the
streets to my grandparents, and a chicken in every pot to
my father and mother, but to me, a child whose very earliest movie memories are of Ann Rutherford and Alice Faye,

America is a *shikse* nestling under your arm whispering love love love love love!

So: dusk on the frozen lake of a city park skating behind the puffy red earmuffs and the fluttering yellow ringlets of a strange *shikse* teaches me the meaning of the word *longing*. It is almost more than an angry thirteen-year-old little Jewish Momma's boy can bear. Forgive the luxuriating, but these are probably the most poignant hours of my life I'm talking about—I learn the meaning of the word longing, I learn the meaning of the word *pang*. There go the darling things, dashing up the embankment, clattering along the shoveled walk between the evergreens—and so here I go too (if I dare!). The sun is almost all the way down, and everything is purple (including my prose) as I follow unobtrusively at a safe distance until they cross the street on their skates, and go giggling into the little park-side candy store. By the time I get up the nerve to come through the door—every eye will surely be upon me—they have already loosened their mufflers and unzipped their jackets, and are raising cups of hot chocolate between their smooth and burning cheeks—and those noses, mystery of mysteries! each disappears entirely into a cup full of chocolate and marshmallows and comes out at the other end unblemished by liquid! Jesus, look how guiltlessly they eat between meals! What girls! Crazily, impetuously, I order a cup of chocolate myself—and proceed to ruin my appetite for dinner, served promptly by my jumping-jack mother at five-thirty, when my father walks into the house "starved." Then I follow them back to the lake. Then I follow them around the lake. Then at last my ecstasy is over—they go home to the grammatical fathers and the composed mothers and the self-assured brothers who all live with them in harmony and bliss behind their *goyische* curtains, and I start back to Newark, to my palpitating life with my family, lived now behind the aluminum "Venetians" for which my mother has been saving out of her table-money for years.

What a rise in social class we have made with those blinds! Headlong, my mother seems to feel, we have been catapulted into high society. A good part of her life is now given over to the dusting and polishing of the slats of the blinds; she is behind them wiping them during the day, and at dusk, looks out from between her clean slats at the snow, where it has begun to fall through the light of the street lamp—and begins pumping up the worry-machine. It is usually only a matter of minutes before she is appropriately frantic. "Where *is* he already?" she moans, each time a pair of headlights come sweeping up the street and are not his. Where, oh where, our Odysseus! Upstairs Uncle Hymie is home, across the street Landau is home, next door Silverstein is home—everybody is home by five forty-five except my father, and the radio says that a blizzard is already halfway down to Newark from the North Pole. Well, there is just no doubt about it, we might as well call Tuckerman and Farber about the funeral arrangements, and start inviting the guests. Yes, it needs only for the roads to begin to glisten with ice for the assumption to be made that my father, fifteen minutes late for dinner, is crunched up against a telegraph pole somewhere lying dead in a pool of his own blood. My mother comes into the kitchen, her face by now a face out of El Greco. "My two starving Armenians," she says in a breaking voice, "eat, go ahead, darlings—start, there's no sense waiting—" And who wouldn't be grief-struck? Just think of the years to come—her two babies without a father, herself without a husband and provider, all because out of nowhere, just as that poor man was starting home, it had to begin to snow.

Meanwhile I wonder if with my father dead I will have to get a job after school and Saturdays, and consequently give up skating at Irvington Park—give up skating with my *shikses* before I have even spoken a single word to a one of them. I am afraid to open my mouth for fear that if I do no words will come out—or the *wrong* words. "Portnoy, yes, it's an old French name, a corruption of *porte noir*, meaning black door or gate. Apparently in the Middle Ages in France the door to our family manor house was painted . . ." et cetera and so forth. No, no, they will hear the *oi* at the end, and the jig will be up. Al Port then, Al Parsons! "How do you do, Miss McCoy, mind if I skate alongside, my name is Al Parsons—" but isn't Alan as Jewish and foreign as Alexander? I know there's Alan Ladd, but there's also my friend Alan Rubin, the shortstop for our softball team. And wait'll she hears I'm from Weequahic. Oh, what's the difference anyway, I can lie about my name, I can lie about my school, but how am I going to lie about this fucking nose? "You seem like a very nice person, Mr. Porte-Noir, but why do you go around covering the middle of your face like that?" Because suddenly it has taken off, the middle of my face! Because gone is the button of my childhood years, that pretty little thing the people used to look at in my carriage, and lo and behold, the middle of my face has begun to reach out toward God! Porte-Noir and Parsons my ass, kid, you have got J-E-W written right across the middle of that face—look at the shnoz on him, for God's sakes! That ain't a nose, it's a hose! Screw off, Jewboy! Get off the ice and leave these girls alone!

And it's true. I lower my head to the kitchen table and on a piece of my father's office stationery outline my profile with a pencil. And it's *terrible*. How has this happened to me who was so gorgeous in that carriage, Mother! At the top it has begun to aim toward the heavens, while simultaneously, where the cartilage ends halfway down the slope, it is beginning to bend back toward my mouth. A couple of years and I won't even be able to eat, this thing will be directly in the path of the *food!* No! No! It can't be! I go into the bathroom and stand before the mirror, I press the nostrils upwards with two fingers. From the side it's not too bad either, but from the front I look like a pig, and where my upper lip was there is now just teeth and gum. Some *goy*. I look like Bugs Bunny! I cut pieces from the cardboard that comes back in the shirts from the laundry and Scotch-tape them to either side of my nose, thus restoring in profile the nice upward curve that I sported all through my childhood . . . but which is now gone. It actually seems that this sprouting of my beak dates exactly from the time that I discovered the *shikses* skating in Irvington Park—as though my own nose bone has taken it upon itself to act as my parents' agent! Skating with *shikses?* Just you try it, wise guy. Remember Pinocchio? Well, that is nothing compared with what is going to happen to you. They'll laugh and laugh, howl and hoot— and worse, calling you Goldberg in the bargain, send you on your way roasting with fury and resentment. Who do you think they're always giggling about as it is? You!

The skinny Yid and his shnoz following them around the ice every single afternoon—and can't talk! "Please, will you stop playing with your nose," my mother says, "I'm not interested, Alex, in what's growing up inside there, not at dinner." "But it's too *big*." "What? What's too big?" says my father. "My *nose!*" I scream. "Please, it gives you character," my mother says, "so leave it alone!"

But who wants character? I want Thereal McCoy! In her blue parka and her red earmuffs and her big white mittens—Miss America, on blades! With her mistletoe and her plum pudding (whatever that may be), and her one-family house with a bannister and a staircase, and parents who are tranquil and patient and *dignified*, and also a brother Billy who knows how to take motors apart and says "much obliged," and isn't afraid of anything physical, and oh the way she'll cuddle next to me on the sofa in her Angora sweater with her legs pulled back up beneath her tartan skirt, and the way she'll turn at the doorway and say to me, "And thank you ever so much for a wonderful wonderful evening," and then this amazing creature—to whom no one has ever said "Shah!" or "I only hope your children will do the same to you some day!"—this perfect, perfect stranger, who is as smooth and shiny and cool as custard, will kiss me—raising up one shapely calf behind her—and my nose and my name will have become as nothing.

Look, I'm not asking for the world—I just don't see why I should get any less out of life than some schmuck like Oogie Pringle or Henry Aldrich. I want Jane Powell too, God damn it! And Corliss and Veronica. I too want to be the boyfriend of Debbie Reynolds—it's the Eddie Fisher in me coming out, that's all, the longing in all us swarthy Jewboys for those bland blond exotics called *shikses* . . . Only what I don't know yet in these feverish years is that for every Eddie yearning for a Debbie, there is a Debbie yearning for an Eddie—a Marilyn Monroe yearning for her Arthur Miller—even an Alice Faye yearning for Phil Harris. Even Jayne Mansfield was about to marry one, remember, when she was suddenly killed in a car crash? Who knew, you see, who knew back when we were watching *National Velvet*, that this stupendous purple-eyed girl who had the supreme *goyische* gift of all, the courage and know-how to get up and ride around on a horse (as opposed to having one pull your wagon, like the rag-seller for whom I am named)—who would have believed that this girl on the horse with the riding breeches and the perfect enunciation was lusting for our kind no less than we for hers? Because you know what Mike Todd was—a cheap facsimile of my Uncle Hymie upstairs! And who in his right mind would ever have believed that Elizabeth Taylor had the secret hots for Uncle Hymie? Who knew that the secret to a *shikse's* heart (and box) was not to pretend to be some hook-nosed variety of *goy*, as boring and vacuous as her own brother, but to be what one's uncle was, to be what one's father was, to be whatever one was oneself, instead of doing some pathetic little Jewish imitation of one of those half-dead, ice-cold *shagitz* pricks, Jimmy or Johnny or Tod, who look, who think, who feel, who talk like fighter-bomber pilots!

LOOK AT The Monkey, my old pal and partner in crime. Doctor; just saying her name, just bringing her to mind, gives me a hard-on on the spot. But I know I shouldn't call her or see her ever again. Because the bitch is crazy. The sex-crazed bitch is out of her mind!

But—but what was I supposed to be to her but *her* Jewish saviour? The Knight on the Big White Steed, the fellow in the Shining Armor the little girls used to dream would come to rescue them from those castles in which they were always imagining themselves to be imprisoned, well, as far as a certain school of *shikse* is concerned (of whom The Monkey is a gorgeous example), this knight turns out to be none other than a brainy, balding, beaky Jew, with a strong social conscience and black hair on his balls, who neither drinks nor gambles nor keeps showgirls on the side; a man guaranteed to give them kiddies to rear and Kafka to read —a regular domestic Messiah! Sure, he may as a kind of tribute to his rebellious adolescence say *shit* and *fuck* a lot around the house—in front of the children even—but the indisputable and heartwarming fact is that *he is always around the house*. No bars, no brothels, no racetracks, no backgammon all night long at the Racquet Club (about which she knows from her glamorous past) or beer till all

hours down at the American Legion (which she can remember from her mean and squalid youth). No, no indeed
—what we have before us, ladies and gentlemen, direct
from a long record-breaking engagement with his own
family, is a Jewish boy just dying in his every cell to be
Good, Responsible, and Dutiful to a family of his own. The
same people who brought you Harry Golden's *For 2¢ Plain*
bring you now—The Alexander Portnoy Show! If you liked
Arthur Miller as a saviour of *shikses*, you'll just love Alex!
You see, my background was in every way that was crucial
to The Monkey the very opposite of what she had had to
endure eighteen miles south of Wheeling, in a coal town
called Moundsville—while I was drowning in schmaltz (lan-
guishing in Jewish "warmth" as The Monkey would have
it), she was down in West Virginia virtually freezing
to death, nothing but chattel really to a father who was, as
she describes him, little more than first cousin to a mule,
and some kind of incomprehensible bundle of needs to a
mother who was as well-meaning as it was possible to be
if you were a hillbilly one generation removed from the
Alleghenies, a woman who could neither read nor write
nor count all that high, and to top things off, hadn't a single
molar in your head.

A story of The Monkey's which made a deep impression
on me (not that all her stories didn't impress me deeply,
stories always of cruelty, ignorance, and exploitation): Once
when she was eleven, and against her father's will had
sneaked off on a Saturday to a ballet class given by the
local "artiste" (called Mr. Maurice), her father came after
her with a belt, beat her with it around the ankles all the
way home, and then locked her in the closet for the rest
of the day—and with her feet tied together for good measure: "Ketch you down by that queer again, you, and won't
just tie 'em up, I'll break 'em for you in ten different
places!"

When she first arrived in New York, she was eighteen
and hadn't really any back teeth to speak of, either. As
an adolescent (for a reason she still can't fathom) they had
all been pulled by the local practitioner, as gifted a dentist
as she remembers Mr. Maurice to have been a dancer.
When we two met, nearly two years ago now, The Monkey

had already been through her marriage and her divorce. Her husband had been a fifty-year-old Frenchman, who had courted and married her one week in Florence, where she was modeling in a show at the Pitti Palace. Subsequent to the marriage, his sex life consisted of getting into bed with his young and beautiful bride and jerking off into the centerfold of a copy of *Playboy* while she looked on. The Monkey has at her disposal a kind of dumb, mean, rural twang which she sometimes likes to use, and would invariably drop down into it when describing the excesses to which she was expected to be a witness as the tycoon's wife. She could be very funny about the fourteen months she had spent with him, despite the fact that it was probably a grim if not terrifying experience. But he had flown her to London after the marriage for six thousand dollars' worth of dental work, and then back in Paris hung around her neck several hundred thousand dollars more in jewelry, and for the longest while, says The Monkey, this caused her to feel loyal to him. As she put it (before I forbade her ever again to say *like*, and *man*, and *swinger*, and *crazy*, and *a groove*): "It was, like ethics."

What caused her finally to run for her life were the orgies he began to hold after jerking off into his magazines became a bore to both of them. A woman, preferably black, would be engaged for a very high sum to squat naked upon a glass coffee table and take a crap while the tycoon lay flat on his back, directly beneath the table, and masturbated to beat the band. And as the shit splattered on the glass six inches above her husband's nose, The Monkey, our poor Monkey, was expected to sit on the red damask sofa, fully clothed, sipping cognac and watching.

It was a couple of years after her return to New York— I suppose she's about twenty-four or twenty-five by this time—that The Monkey tried to kill herself a little by making a pass at her wrists with a razor, all on account of the way she had been treated at Le Club, or El Morocco, or L'Interdit, by her current boyfriend, one or another of the hundred best-dressed men in the world. Thus she found her way to the illustrious Dr. Morris Frankel, henceforth to be known in these confessions as Harpo. Off and on during these past five years The Monkey has thrashed around on

Harpo's couch, waiting for him to tell her what she must do to become somebody's wife and somebody's mother. Why, cries The Monkey to Harpo, why must she always be involved with such hideous and cold-hearted shits, instead of with *men*? Why? Harpo, speak! Say something to me! *Anything!* "Oh, I know he's alive," The Monkey used to say, her little features scrunched up in anguish, "I just know it. I mean, who ever heard of a dead man with an answering service?" So, in and out of therapy (if that's what it is) The Monkey goes, in whenever some new shit has broken her heart, out whenever the next likely knight has made his appearance.

I was "a breakthrough." Harpo of course didn't say yes, but then he didn't say no either, when she suggested that that was who I might be. Apparently he did cough, however, and this The Monkey takes as her confirmation. Sometimes he coughs, sometimes he grunts, sometimes he belches, once in a while he farts, whether voluntarily or not who knows, though I hold that a fart has to be interpreted as a negative transference reaction on his part. "Breakthrough, you're so *brilliant!*" Breakie, or Through, when she is being my sex kitten and cat—and when she is fighting for her life—"You big breakthrough son of a bitch Jew! I want to be married and human!"

So, I was to be her breakthrough . . . but wasn't she to be mine? Who like The Monkey had ever happened to me before—or will again? Not that I had not prayed, of course. No, you pray and you pray and you pray, you lift your impassioned prayers to God on the altar of the toilet seat, throughout your adolescence you deliver up to Him the living sacrifice of your spermatozoa by the *gallon*—and then one night, around midnight, on the corner of Lexington and Fifty-second, when you have come really to the point of losing faith in the existence of such a creature as you have been imagining for yourself even unto your thirty-second year, there she is, wearing a tan pants suit, and trying to hail a cab—lanky, dark-haired, with smallish features that give her face a kind of petulant expression, and an absolutely fantastic ass.

Why not? What's lost? What's gained, however? Go ahead, you shackled and fettered son of a bitch, *speak to her.* She has an ass on her with the swell and the cleft of the world's most perfect nectarine! *Speak!*

"Hi"—softly, and with a little surprise, as though I might have met her somewhere before . . .

"What do *you* want?"

"To buy you a drink," I said.

"A real swinger," she said, sneering.

Sneering! Two seconds—and two insults! To the Assistant Human Rights Commissioner of this whole city! "To eat your pussy, baby, how's that?" My God! She's going to call a cop! Who'll turn me in to the Mayor!

"That's better," she replied.

And so a cab pulled up, and we went to her apartment where she took off her clothes and said, "Go ahead."

My incredulity! That such a thing was happening to me! Did I eat! It was suddenly as though my life were taking place in the middle of a wet dream. There I was, going down at last on the star of all those pornographic films that I have been producing in my head since I first laid a hand upon my own joint . . . "Now me you," she said, "one good turn deserves another," and, Doctor, this stranger then proceeded to suck me off with a mouth that might have gone to a special college to learn all the wonderful things it knew. What a find, I thought, she takes it right down to the root! What a mouth I have fallen into! And simultaneously: *Get out! Go! Who and what can this person be!*

Later we had a long, serious, very stirring conversation about perversions. She began by asking if I had ever done it with a man. I said no. I asked (as I knew she wanted me to) if she had ever done it with another woman.

". . . Nope."

". . . Would you like to?"

". . . Would you like me to?"

". . . Why not, sure."

". . . Would you like to watch?"

". . . I suppose so."

". . . Then maybe it could be arranged."

". . . Yes?"

". . . Yes."

". . . Well, I might like that."

"Oh," she said sarcastically, "I think you might."

She told me then that only a month before, when she had been ill with a virus, a couple she knew had come by to make dinner for her. After the meal they said they wanted her to watch them screw. So she did. She sat up on the bed with a temperature of 102, and they took off their clothes and went at it on the bedroom rug—"And you know what they wanted me to do, while they were making it?"

"No."

"I had some Planter's Peanuts in a can in the kitchen—and they wanted me to eat them . . ."

". . . Why?"

"Man, I don't know. I guess they wanted to know I was really *there*. They wanted to like *hear* me . . . Hey, look, do you just suck, or do you fuck, too?"

Thereal McCoy! My slut from the Empire burlesque—without the tits, but so beautiful!

"I fuck too."

"Well, so do I."

"Isn't that a crazy coincidence," I said, "us running into each other."

She laughed for the first time, and instead of that finally putting me at my ease, suddenly I *knew*—some big spade was going to leap out of the bedroom closet and spring for my heart with his knife—or she herself was going to go berserk, the laugh was going to broaden into mad hysterics —and God only knew what would follow. Eddie Waitkus!

Was she a call girl? Was she a maniac? Was she in cahoots with some Puerto Rican pusher who was about to make his entrance into my life? Enter it—and end it, for the forty dollars in my wallet and a watch from Korvette's?

"Look," I said, in my clever way, "do you do this, more or less, all the time . . . or what?"

"What kind of question is that! What kind of shit-eating remark is that! Are you another heartless bastard too? Don't you think I have feelings *too!*"

"I'm sorry—"

But suddenly where there had been fury and outrage, there were only tears. Did I need any more evidence that this girl was, to say the least, a little erratic psychologically?

Any man in his right mind would surely then have gotten up, gotten dressed, and gotten the hell out in one piece. And counting his blessings. But don't you see—my right mind is just another name for my timidity, my fears! My right mind is simply that inheritance of terror that I bring with me out of my ridiculous past! And that I hate. Which is my enemy! My right mind is only my cowardly, cringing, chicken-hearted self! That tyrant, my super-ego, should be strung up by his fucking storm trooper's boots! In the street who had been trembling, me or the girl? Me! Where was my boldness? My daring? My guts? Where was my courage to take for my own *in life*—and like a man!— what till then I had been content to daydream about, like a boy! Why was I all in a sweat once again—why did I believe that the shape of things to come was to be determined not by me *but by her?*

"Look," she said, blowing her nose and wiping away the tears with a Kleenex, "look, I lied to you before, in case you're interested, in case you're writing this down or something."

"Yeah? About what?" And here he comes, I thought—my *shvartze*, out of the closet, eyes, teeth, and razor blade flashing! Here comes the headline: ASST HUMAN RIGHTS COMMISH FOUND HEADLESS IN GO-GO GIRL'S APT!

"I mean like, what the fuck did I lie for, *to you?*"

"I don't know what you're talking about, so I can't tell you . . ."

"I mean *they* didn't want me to eat the peanuts. My friends didn't want me to eat peanuts. *I* wanted to."

Thus: The Monkey.

As for why she did lie, to me? I think it was her way of informing herself right off—semi-consciously, I suppose— that she had somehow fallen onto a higher type person: that pickup on the street notwithstanding, and the whole-hearted suck in her bed notwithstanding—followed by that heart-stirring swallow—and the discussion of perversions which followed that . . . still, she really hadn't wanted me to think of her as given over *wholly* to sexual excess and adventurism . . . Because apparently a glimpse of me was enough for her to leap imaginatively ahead into the life that might now be hers . . . No more narcissistic playboys in their Cardin suits; no more married, desperate, advertising executives in overnight from Connecticut; no more faggots in British warmers for lunch at Serendipity, or aging lechers from the cosmetics industry drooling into their hundred-dollar dinners at Le Pavillon at night . . . No, at long last the figure who had dwelled these many years at the heart of *her* dreams (it turned out), a man who would be good to a wife and to children . . . a Jew. And what a Jew! First he eats her, and then, immediately after, comes slithering on up and begins talking and explaining things, making judgments left and right, telling her how life should and should not be lived. "How do you know that?" she used to ask warily. "I mean that's just *your* opinion." "What do you mean *opinion*—it's not my opinion, girlie, it's the truth." "I mean is that like something everybody knows . . . or just you?" A Jewish man, who cared about the welfare of the poor of the city of New York, was eating her pussy! Someone who had appeared on educational TV was shooting off into her mouth! In a flash, Doctor, she must have seen it all —can that be? Saw and planned it all, right out there on Lexington Avenue? . . . The gentle fire burning in the book-lined living room of our country home, the Irish nannie bathing the children before Mother puts them to bed, and the willowy ex-model, jet-setter, and sex deviant, daughter of the mines and mills of West Virginia, self-styled victim of a dozen real bastards, seen here in her St. Laurent pajamas and her crushed kid boots, dipping thoughtfully into a novel by Samuel Beckett . . . seen here on a fur rug with her husband, who People Are Talking About, the Human Rights Commissioner . . . seen here with his pipe and his thinning kinky black Hebe hair, in all his Jewish messianic fervor and charm . . .

WHAT HAPPENED finally at Irvington Park: late on a Saturday afternoon I found myself virtually alone on the frozen lake with a darling fourteen-year-old *shikseleh* whom I had been watching practicing her figure eights since after lunch, a girl who seemed to possess simultaneously the middle-class charms of Margaret O'Brien—that quickness and cuteness around the sparkling eyes and the freckled nose—and the simplicity and plainness, the lower-class availability, the lank blond hair of Peggy Ann Garner. You see, what looked like movie stars to everyone else were just different kinds of *shikses* to me. Often I came out of the movies trying to figure out what high school in Newark Jeanne Crain (and her cleavage) or Kathryn Grayson (and her cleavage) would be going to if they were my age. And where would I find a *shikse* like Gene Tierney, who I used to think might even be a Jew, if she wasn't actually part Chinese. Meanwhile Peggy Ann O'Brien has made her last figure eight and is coasting lazily off for the boathouse, and I have done nothing about her or about any of them, nothing all winter long, and now March is almost upon us—the red skating flag will come down over the park and once again we will be into polio season. I may not even live into the following winter, *so what am I waiting for?* "Now! Or never!" So after her—when she is safely out of sight—I madly begin to skate. "Excuse me," I will say, "but would you mind if I walk you home?" If I *walked,* or if I *walk*—which is more correct? Because I have to speak absolutely perfect English. Not a word of Jew in it. "Would you care perhaps to have a hot chocolate? May I have your phone number and come to call some evening? My name? I am Alton Peterson"—a name I had picked for myself out of the Montclair section of the Essex County phone book—totally *goy* I was sure, and sounds like Hans *Christian* Andersen into the bargain. What a coup! Secretly I have been practicing writing "Alton Peterson" all winter long, practicing on sheets of paper that I subsequently tear from my notebook after school and burn so that they won't be found by anybody in my house. I am Alton Peterson, I am Alton Peterson—Alton Christian Peterson? Alton C. Peterson? And so preoccupied am I with not forgetting whom I would now like to be, so anxious to make it to the boathouse while she is still changing out of her skates—and wondering too what I'll say when she asks about the middle of my face and what happened to it (old hockey injury? Fell off my horse while playing polo after church one Sunday morning —too many sausages for breakfast, ha ha ha!)—I reach the edge of the lake with the tip of one skate a little sooner than I had planned—and so go hurtling forward onto the frost-bitten ground, chipping one front tooth and smashing the bony protrusion at the top of my tibia.

My right leg is in a cast, from ankle to hip, for six weeks. I have something that the doctor calls Osgood Shlatterer's Disease. After the cast comes off, I drag the leg along behind me like a war injury—while my father cries, "Bend it! Do you want to go through life like that? Bend it! Walk natural, will you! Stop favoring that Oscar Shattered leg, Alex, or you are going to wind up a cripple for the rest of your days!"

For skating after *shikses*, under an alias, I would be a cripple for the rest of my days.

With a life like mine, Doctor, who needs dreams?

BUBBLES GIRARDI, an eighteen-year-old girl who had been thrown out of Hillside High School and was subsequently found floating in the swimming pool at Olympic Park by my lascivious classmate, Smolka, the tailor's son . . .

For myself, I wouldn't go near that pool if you paid me—it is a breeding ground for polio and spinal meningitis, not to mention diseases of the skin, the scalp, and the asshole—it is even rumored that some kid from Weequahic once stepped into the footbath between the locker room and the pool and actually came out at the other end without his toenails. And yet that is where you find the girls who fuck. Wouldn't you know it? That is the place to find the kinds of *shikses* Who Will Do Anything! If only you are willing to risk polio from the pool, gangrene from the footbath, ptomaine from the hot dogs, and elephantiasis from the soap and the towels, you may possibly get laid.

We sit in the kitchen, where Bubbles was working over the ironing board when we arrived—in her slip! Mandel and I leaf through back numbers of *Ring* Magazine, while in the living room Smolka tries to talk Bubbles into taking on his two friends as a special favor to him. Bubbles' brother, who in a former life was a paratrooper, is nobody we have to worry about, Smolka assures us, because he is off in Hoboken boxing in a feature event under the name Johnny "Geronimo" Girardi. Her father drives a taxi during the day, and a car for The Mob at night—he is out somewhere chauffeuring gangsters around and doesn't get home until the early hours, and the mother we don't have to worry about because she's dead. Perfect, Smolka, perfect, I couldn't feel more secure. Now I have absolutely nothing to worry about except the Trojan I have been carrying around so long in my wallet that inside its tinfoil wrapper it has probably been half eaten away by mold. One spurt and the whole thing will go flying in pieces all over the inside of Bubbles Girardi's box—and *then* what do I do?

To be sure that these Trojans really hold up under pressure I have been down in my cellar all week filling them with quart after quart of water—expensive as it is, I have been using them to jerk off into, to see if they will stand up under simulated fucking conditions. So far so good. Only what about the sacred one that has by now left an indelible imprint of its shape upon my wallet, the very special one I have been saving to get laid with, with the lubricated tip? How can I possibly expect no damage to have been done after sitting on it in school—crushing it in that wallet—for nearly six months? And who says Geronimo is going to be all night in Hoboken? And what if the person the gangsters are supposed to murder has already dropped dead from fright by the time they arrive, and Mr. Girardi is sent home early for a good night's rest? What if the girl has the syph! But then Smolka must have it, too! —Smolka, who is always dragging drinks out of everybody else's bottle of cream soda, and grabbing with his hand at your putz! That's all I need, with my mother! I'd never hear the end of it! "Alex, what is that you're hiding under your foot?" "Nothing." "Alex, please, I heard a definite clink. What is that that fell out of your trousers that you're stepping on it with your foot?" "Nothing! My shoe! Leave me alone!" "Young man, what are you—oh, my God! Jack! Come quick! Look—look on the floor by his shoe!" With his trousers around his knees and the *Newark News,* turned back to the obituary page, clutched in his hand, he rushes into the kitchen from the bathroom—"*Now* what?" She screams (that's her answer) and points beneath my chair. "What is that, Mister—some smart high-school joke?" demands my father furiously—"what is that black plastic thing doing on the kitchen floor?" "It's not a plastic one," I say, and break into sobs. "It's my own. I caught the syph from an eighteen-year-old Italian girl in Hillside, and now, now, I have no more p-p-p-penis!" "His little thing," screams my mother, "that I used to tickle it to make him go wee-wee—" "DON'T TOUCH IT! NOBODY MOVE!" cries my father, for my mother seems about to leap forward onto the floor, like a woman into her husband's grave—"call the Humane Society—" "Like for a rabies *dog*?" she weeps. "Sophie, what else are you going to do? Save it in a drawer somewhere? To show his children? He ain't going to *have* no children!" She begins to howl pathetically, a grieving animal, while my father . . . but the scene fades quickly, for in a matter of seconds I am blind, and within the hour my brain is the consistency of hot Farina.

Tacked above the Girardi sink is a picture of Jesus Christ floating up to Heaven in a pink nightgown. How disgusting can human beings be! The Jews I despise for their narrow-mindedness, their self-righteousness, the incredibly bizarre sense that these cavemen who are my parents and relatives have somehow gotten of their superiority—but when it comes to tawdriness and cheapness, to beliefs that would shame even a gorilla, you simply cannot top the *goyim*. What kind of base and brainless schmucks are these people to worship somebody who number one, never existed, and number two, if he did, looking as he does in that picture, was without a doubt The Pansy of Palestine. In a page-boy haircut, with a Palmolive complexion—and wearing a gown that I realize today must have come from Fredericks of Hollywood! Enough of God and the rest of that garbage! Down with religion and human groveling! Up with socialism and the dignity of man! Actually, why I should be visiting the Girardi home is not so as to lay their daughter—please God!—but to evangelize for Henry Wallace and Glen Taylor. Of course! For who are the Girardis if not *the people*, on whose behalf, for whose rights and liberties and dignity, I and my brother-in-law-to-be wind up arguing every Sunday afternoon with our hopelessly ignorant elders (who vote Democratic and think Neanderthal), my father and my uncle. If we don't like it here, they tell us, why don't we go back to Russia where everything is hunky-dory? "You're going to turn that kid into a Communist," my father warns Morty, whereupon I cry out, "You don't understand!

All men are brothers!" Christ, I could strangle him on the spot for being so blind to human brotherhood!

Now that he is marrying my sister, Morty drives the truck and works in the warehouse for my Uncle, and in a manner of speaking, so do I: three Saturdays in a row now I have risen before dawn to go out with him delivering cases of Squeeze—the "soda-vater" Uncle Hymie distributes—to general stores off in the rural wilds where New Jersey joins with the Poconos. I have written a radio play, inspired by my master, Norman Corwin, and his celebration of V-E Day, *On A Note of Triumph* (a copy of which Morty has bought me for my birthday). *So the enemy is dead in an alley back of the Wilhelmstrasse; take a bow, G.I., take a bow, little guy* . . . Just the rhythms alone can cause my flesh to ripple, like the beat of the marching song of the victorious Red Army, and the song we learned in grade school during the war, which our teachers called "The Chinese National Anthem." "Arise, ye who refuse to be bond-slaves, with our very flesh and blood"—I do remember every word!—"we will build a new great wall . . ." And then my favorite line, commencing as it does with my favorite word in the English language: "*In*-dig-*na*-tion fills the hearts of all of our coun-try-men! A-rise! A-rise! A-RISE!"

I open to the first page of my play and begin to read aloud to Morty as we start off in the truck, through Irvington, the Oranges, and on toward the West—Illinois! Indiana! Iowa! O my America of the plains and the mountains and the valleys and the rivers and the canyons . . . It is with just such patriotic incantations as these that I have begun to put myself to sleep at night, after jerking off into my sock . . . My radio play is called *Let Freedom Ring!* It is a morality play (now I know) whose two major characters are named Prejudice and Tolerance, and it is written in what I call "prose-poetry." We pull into a diner in Dover, New Jersey, just as Tolerance begins to defend Negroes for the way they smell. The sound of my own humane, compassionate, Latinate, alliterative rhetoric, inflated almost beyond recognition by Roget's *Thesaurus* (a birthday gift from my sister)—plus the fact of the dawn and my being out in it—plus the tattooed counterman in the diner whom

Morty calls "Chief"—plus eating for the first time in my life home-fried potatoes for breakfast—plus swinging back up into the cab of the truck in my Levi's and lumberjacket and moccasins (which out on the highway no longer seem the costume that they do in the halls of the high school)—plus the sun just beginning to shine over the hilly farmlands of New Jersey, my state!—I am reborn! Free, I find, of shameful secrets! So clean-feeling, so strong and virtuous-feeling—so American! Morty pulls back onto the highway, and right then and there I take my vow, I swear that I will dedicate my life to the righting of wrongs, to the elevation of the downtrodden and the underprivileged, to the liberation of the unjustly imprisoned. With Morty as my witness—my manly left-wing new-found older brother, the living proof that it is possible to love mankind and baseball both (and who adores my older sister, who suddenly I am ready to adore too for the escape hatch with which she has provided the two of us), who is my link through the AVC to Bill Mauldin, as much my hero as Corwin or Howard Fast—to Morty, with tears of love (for him, for me) in my eyes, I vow to use "the power of the pen" to liberate from injustice and exploitation, from humiliation and poverty and ignorance, the people I now think of (giving myself gooseflesh) as *The People*.

I AM ICY with fear. Of the girl and her syph! Of the father and his friends! Of the brother and his fists! (even though Smolka has tried to get me to believe what strikes me as wholly incredible, even for *goyim:* that both brother and father know, and neither cares, that Bubbles is a "hoor"). And fear too that beneath the kitchen window, which I plan to leap out of if I should hear so much as a footstep on the stairway, is an iron picket fence upon which I will be impaled. Of course the fence I am thinking of surrounds the Catholic orphanage on Lyons Avenue, but I am by now halfway between hallucination and coma, and somewhat woozy, as though I've gone too long without food. I see the photograph in the *Newark News,* of the fence and the dark puddle of my blood on the sidewalk, and the caption from which my family will never recover: INSURANCE MAN'S SON LEAPS TO DEATH.

While I sit freezing in my igloo, Mandel is basting in his own perspiration—and smells it. The body odor of Negroes fills me with compassion, with "prose-poetry"—Mandel I am less indulgent of: "he nauseates me" (as my mother says of him), which isn't to say that he is any less hypnotic a creature to me than Smolka is. Sixteen and Jewish just like me, but there all resemblance ends: he wears his hair in a duck's ass, has sideburns down to his jawbone, and sports one-button roll suits and pointy black shoes—the very model of a Neapolitan pimp. But Jewish. Incredible! A moralistic teacher has leaked to us that Arnold Mandel has the I.Q. of a genius yet prefers instead to take rides in stolen cars, smoke cigarettes, and get sick on bottles of beer. Can you believe it? A Jewish boy? He is also a participant in the circle-jerks held in Smolka's living room after school, with the shades pulled down, while both elder Smolkas are slaving away in the tailor shop. I have heard the stories, but still (despite my own onanism and exhibitionism and voyeurism—not to mention fetishism) I can't and won't believe it: four or five guys sit around in a circle on the floor and at Smolka's signal, each begins to pull off—and the first one to come gets the pot, a buck a head.

What pigs.

The only explanation I have for Mandel's behavior is that his father died when Mandel was only ten. And this of course is what mesmerizes me most of all: *a boy without a father.*

How do I account for Smolka and *his* daring? He has *a mother who works.* Mine, remember, patrols the six rooms of our apartment like a guerrilla army in its own land—there's not a single closet or drawer of mine whose contents she doesn't have a photographic sense of Smolka's mother, on the other hand, sits all day by a little light in a little chair in the corner of his father's store, taking seams in and out, and by the time she gets home at night hasn't the strength to get out her Geiger counter and start in hunting for her child's hair-raising collection of French ticklers. The Smolkas, you must understand, are not so rich as we—and therein lies the final difference. A mother who works and no Venetian blinds . . . yes, this sufficiently explains everything to me—how come he swims at Olym-

pic Park as well as why he is always grabbing at everybody else's *putz*. He lives on Hostess cupcakes and his
own wits. I get a hot lunch and all the inhibitions thereof.
Though don't get me wrong (as though that were possible): during a winter snowstorm, what is more thrilling
while stamping off the slush on the back landing at lunchtime, than to hear "Aunt Jenny" coming over the kitchen
radio and to smell hot tomato soup heating up on the stove?
What beats freshly laundered and ironed pajamas any season of the year, and a bedroom fragrant with furniture
polish? How would I like my underwear all gray and
jumbled up in my drawer, as Smolka's always is? I
wouldn't. How would I like socks without toes and nobody
to bring me hot lemonade and honey when my throat is
sore?

Conversely, how would I like Bubbles Girardi to come
to my own house in the afternoon and blow me, as she
did Smolka, on his own bed?

OF SOME ironic interest. Last spring, who do I run into
down on Worth Street, but the old circle-jerker himself, Mr.
Mandel, carrying a sample case full of trusses, braces, and
supports. And do you know? That he was still living and
breathing absolutely astonished me. I couldn't get over it—
I haven't yet. And married too, domesticated, with a wife
and two little daughters—and a "ranch" house in West
Orange, New Jersey. Mandel lives, owns a length of garden
hose, he tells me, and a barbecue and briquets! Mandel,
who, out of awe of Pupi Campo and Tito Valdez, went off
to City Hall the day after quitting high school and had his
first name officially changed from Arnold to Ba-ba-lu. Mandel, who drank "six-packs" of beer! Miraculous. Can't be!
How on earth did it happen that retribution passed him by?
There he was, year in and year out, standing in idleness
and ignorance on the street corner, perched like some
greasy spic over his bongo drums, his duck's ass bare to the
heavens—and nothing and nobody struck him down! And
now he is thirty-four, like me, and a salesman for his wife's
father, who has a surgical supply house on Market Street
in Newark. And what about me, he asks, what do I do for
a living? Really, doesn't he know? Isn't he on my parents'

mailing list? Doesn't everyone know that I am the most moral man in all of New York, all pure motives and humane and compassionate ideals? Doesn't he know that what I do for a living is I'm *good?* "Civil Service," I answered, pointing across to Thirty Worth. Mister Modesty.

"You still see any of the guys?" Ba-ba-lu asked. "You married?"

"No, no."

Inside the new jowls, the old furtive Latin-American greaser comes to life. "So, uh, what do you do for pussy?"

"I have affairs, Arn, and I beat my meat."

Mistake, I think instantly. Mistake! What if he blabs to the *Daily News?* ASST HUMAN RIGHTS COMMISH FLOGS DUMMY, *Also Lives in Sin, Reports Old School Chum.*

The headlines. Always the headlines revealing my filthy secrets to a shocked and disapproving world.

"Hey," said Ba-ba-lu, "remember Rita Girardi? Bubbles? Who used to suck us all off?"

". . . What about her?" Lower your voice, Ba-ba-lu! "What about her?"

"Didn't you read in the *News?*"

"—What *News?*"

"The *Newark News.*"

"I don't see the *Newark News* any more . . . What happened to her?"

"She got murdered. In a bar on Hawthorne Avenue, right down from The Annex. She was with some boogey and then some other boogey came in and shot them both in the head. How do you like that? Fucking for boogies."

"Wow," I said, and meant it. Then suddenly—"Listen, Ba-ba-lu, whatever happened to Smolka?"

"Don't know," says Ba-ba-lu. "Ain't he a doctor? I think I heard he was a doctor."

"A doctor? *Smolka?*"

"I think he is some kind of specialist, that's what somebody said."

"Oh, can't be," I say with my superior sneer.

"Yeah, I think he lives up in Tenafly or someplace and is some kind of neurosurgeon."

"A *neurosurgeon?*"

But can't be! Without hot tomato soup for lunch on freezing afternoons? Who slept in those putrid pajamas? The owner of all those red rubber thimbles with the angry little spiky projections that he told us drove the girls of Paris insane with pleasure? Smolka, who swam in the pool at Olympic Park, he's alive *too*? And a neurosurgeon? Ba-ba-lu, you sound like my mother. You must mean plumber, or electrician. Because I will not believe it! I mean down in my *kishkas*, in my deep emotions and my old beliefs, down beneath the me who knows very well that of course Smolka and Mandel continue to enjoy the ranch houses and the professional opportunities available to men on this planet, I simply cannot believe in the survival, let alone the middle-class success, of these two bad boys. Why, they're supposed to be in jail—or the gutter. They didn't do their homework, damn it! Smolka used to cheat off me in Spanish, and Mandel didn't even give enough of a shit to bother to do that, and as for washing their hands before eating . . . Don't you understand, these two boys are supposed to be dead! Like Bubbles. Now there at least is a career that makes some sense. There's a case of cause and effect that confirms my sense of human consequence! Bad enough, rotten enough, and you get your cock-sucking head blown off by boogies. Now that's the way the world's *supposed* to be run!

SMOLKA COMES back into the kitchen and tells us she doesn't want to do it.

"But you said we were going to get laid!" cries Mandel. "You said you were going to get us blowed and everything!"

"Fuck it," I say, "if she doesn't want to do it, fuck her, let's go—"

"But I've been pounding off over this for a week! I ain't going anywhere! What kind of shit *is* this, Smolka? Won't she even beat my *meat*?"

Me, with my refrain: "Fuck it, if she doesn't want to do it, fuck it—"

Mandel: "Who the fuck is she that she won't even give a guy a hand-job? Is that the fucking world to ask of her? I ain't leaving till she either sucks it or pulls it—either one or the other! It's up to her, the fucking whore!"

So Smolka goes back in for a second conference, and returns nearly half an hour later with the news that the girl has changed her mind: she will jerk off one guy, and only with his pants on, and that's all. We flip a coin—and I win the right to get the syph! Mandel claims the coin grazed the ceiling and is ready to strangle me. He is still screaming foul play when I enter the living room to reap my reward.

She sits in her slip on the sofa at the other end of the linoleum floor, weighing a hundred and seventy pounds and growing a moustache. Anthony Peruta, that's my name for when she asks. But she doesn't. "Look," says Bubbles, "let's get it straight—you're the only one I'm jerking off. You, and that's it."

"It's entirely up to you," I say politely.

"All right, you can take it out of your pants, *but don't take them down.* You hear me, because I told him, I'm not doing anything to anybody's balls."

"Fine, fine. Whatever you say."

"And don't try to touch me either."

"Look, if you want me to, I'll go."

"Just take it out."

"Sure, if that's what you want, here . . . here," I say, but prematurely. "I—just—have—to—get—it—" Where *is* that thing? In the classroom I sometimes set myself consciously to thinking about DEATH and HOSPITALS and HORRIBLE AUTOMOBILE ACCIDENTS in the hope that such grave thoughts will cause my "boner" to recede before the bell rings and I have to stand up. It seems that I can't go up to the blackboard in school, or try to get off a bus, without its standing up and saying "Hi! Look at me!" to everyone in sight—and now it is nowhere to be found.

"Here!" I finally cry.

"Is that it?"

"Well," I answer, turning colors, "it gets bigger when it gets harder . . ."

"Well, I ain't got all night—"

Nicely: "I don't think it'll be all *night*—"

"Lay down!"

Bubbles sits sharply down beside me in a straight chair,

while I stretch out on the sofa—and suddenly she has hold of it, and it's as though my poor cock has got caught in some kind of machine. Vigorously, to put it mildly, the ordeal begins. But it is like trying to jerk off a jellyfish.

"What's a matter?" she finally says. "Can't you come?"

"Usually, yes, I can."

"Then stop holding it back on me—"

"I'm not. I am trying, Bubbles—"

"—'cause I'm going to count to fifty, wise guy, and if you don't shoot off that ain't my fault."

Fifty? I'll be lucky if it is still attached to my body by fifty. *Take it easy*, I want to scream. *Not so rough around the edges, please!*—"eleven twelve, thirteen"—and I think to myself, *Thank God, soon it'll be over—hang on, only another forty seconds to go*—but simultaneous with the relief comes, of course, the disappointment, and it is keen: this only happens to be what I have been dreaming about night and day since I am thirteen. At long last, not a cored apple, not an empty milk bottle greased with vaseline, but a girl in a slip, with two tits and a cunt—and a moustache, but who am I to be picky? This is what I have been imagining for myself . . .

Which is how it occurs to me what to do. I will forget that the fist tearing away at my flesh belongs to Bubbles— I'll pretend that it's my own! So, fixedly I stare at the dark ceiling, and instead of making believe that I am getting laid, as I ordinarily do while jerking off, I make believe that I am jerking off.

And it begins instantly to work. Unfortunately, however, I get just about where I want to be when Bubbles' work day comes to an end.

"Okay, that's it," she says—*and stops.*

"Oh, no!" comes my strangled cry. "More!"

"Look, I already ironed for two hours tonight, you know, before you even got here—"

"JUST ONE MORE! TWO MORE! PLEASE!"

"N-O!"

Whereupon, unable to stand the frustration—the deprivation—I reach down, I grab it, and POW!

Only right in my eye. With a single whiplike stroke of the master's own hand, the lather comes rising out of me.

I ask you, who can jerk me off as well as I do it myself?
Only, reclining as I am, the jet of sperm leaves my joint
on the horizontal, rides back the length of my torso, and
lands with a thick wet burning splash right in my own eye.

"You son of a bitch kike!" Bubbles screams—"You got
gissum all over the couch! And the walls! And the lamp!"

"I got it in my eye! And don't you say kike to me, you!"

"You *are* a kike, you kike! You got it all over everything,
you mocky son of a bitch! Look at the doilies!"

It's just as my parents say, comes the first disagreement,
no matter how small, and the only thing a *shikse* knows to
call you is dirty Jew. What an awful discovery! My parents
who are always wrong—are right! And my eye—it's as
though it's been dropped in fire—and now I remember
why. On Devil's Island, Smolka has told us, the guards
used to have fun with the prisoners by rubbing sperm in
their eyes *and making them blind.* I'm going blind! A *shikse*
has touched my dick, and now I'll be blind forever! Doctor,
my psyche, it's as difficult to understand as a grade-school
primer. Who needs dreams, I ask you? Who needs *Freud?*
Rose Franzblau of the New York *Post* has enough on the
ball to come up with an analysis of somebody like me!

"You sheeny!" she is screaming. "You Hebe son of a
bitch! You can't even come off unless you pull your own
pudding, you fairy bastard cheap Jew!"

Hey, enough is enough, where is her sympathy? "But
my eye!" and rush for the kitchen, where Smolka and
Mandel are rolling around the walls in ecstasy. "—right in
the—" erupts Mandel, and folds in half onto the floor, beating at the linoleum with his fists. "—right in the fucking—"

"Water, you shits, I'm going blind! I'm on fire!" and,
flying full-speed over Mandel's body, stick my head beneath the faucet. Above the sink Jesus still ascends in his
pink nightie. That useless son of a bitch! I thought he was
supposed to make the Christians compassionate and kind.
I thought other people's suffering is what he told them to
feel *sorry* for. What bullshit! If I go blind, it's his fault!
Yes, somehow he strikes me as the ultimate cause of all our
pain and confusion. And oh God, as the cold water runs
down my face, how am I going to explain my blindness
to my parents! My mother virtually spends half her life up

my ass as it is, checking on the manufacture of my stools—
how am I possibly going to hide from her the fact that I no
longer have my sight? "Tap, tap, tap, it's just me, Mother—
this nice big dog brought me home, with my cane." "A
dog? In my house? Get him out of here before he makes
everything filthy! Jack, there's a dog in the house and I
just washed the kitchen floor!" "But, Momma, he's here to
stay, he has to stay—he's a seeing-eye dog. I'm blind." "Oh
my God! Jack!" she calls into the bathroom. "Jack, Alex is
home with a dog—he's gone blind!" "Him, blind?" my
father replies. "How could he be blind, he doesn't even
know what it means to turn off a light." "How?" screams
my mother— "How? Tell us how such a thing—"

Mother, how? How else? Consorting with Christian girls.

Mandel the next day tells me that within half an hour
after my frenetic departure, Bubbles was down on her
fucking dago knees eating his cock.

The top of my head comes off: "She *was?*"

"Right on her fucking dago knees," says Mandel.
"Schmuck, what'd you go home for?"

"She called me a kike!" I answer self-righteously. "I
thought I was blind. Look, she's anti-Semitic, Ba-ba-lu."

"Yeah, what do I give a shit?" says Mandel. Actually I
don't think he knows what anti-Semitic means. "All I know
is I got laid, *twice.*"

"You *did?* With a *rubber?*"

"Fuck, I didn't use nothing."

"But she'll get pregnant!" I cry, and in anguish, as
though it's me who will be held accountable.

"What do I care?" replies Mandel.

Why do *I* worry then! Why do I alone spend hours
testing Trojans in my basement? Why do I alone live in
mortal terror of the syph? Why do I run home with my
little bloodshot eye, imagining myself blinded forever, when
half an hour later, Bubbles will be down eating cock on
her knees! Home—to my Mommy! To my tollhouse cookie
and my glass of milk and my nice clean bed! *Oi,* civilization and its discontents! Ba-ba-lu, speak to me, talk to me,
tell me what it was like when she did it? I have to know,
and with details—exact details! What about her tits? What
about her nipples? What about her thighs? What does she

do with her thighs, Ba-ba-lu, does she wrap them around your ass like in the hot books, or does she squeeze them tight around your cock till you want to scream, like in my dreams? And what about her hair down there? Tell me everything there is to tell about pubic hairs and the way they smell, I don't care if I heard it all before. And did she really kneel, are you shitting me? Did she actually kneel on her *knees?* And what about her teeth, where do *they* go? And does she suck it, does she blow it, or somehow is it that she does *both?* Oh God, did you shoot in her mouth? Oh, my God! And did she swallow it right down, or spit it out—tell me, what did she do with your hot come? Did you warn her you were going to shoot, or did you just shoot and let her worry? And who put it in—did she put it in or did you put it in, or does it just get drawn in by itself? And where were all your clothes?—on the couch, on the floor—exactly where, I want details! Details! Actual details! Who took off her brassiere and her panties—her *panties!*—did you? did *she?* When she was down there blowing you, Ba-ba-lu, did she have anything on? And how about the pillow under her ass, did you stick a pillow under her ass like it says to do in my parents' marriage manual? What happened when you came inside her? Did she come too? Mandel, clarify something that I have to know—do they come? Stuff? Or do they just moan a lot—*or what?* How does she come! What is it like! Before I go out of my head, I have to know what it's like!

Peyote

Bob Dawson

SQUINTING into the dark
I see an unresponding me
mirrored
over machine-green shrubs
linear as Euclid
inside the liquid of my window.
I scratch my eyebrow,
twitch
my shoulders, nod
punctilious yes's,
but the *me*,
bristle-chinned, squinty,
neck muscles knotted like lockjaw,
clinches his lips
and stares himself down.
He's immaterial,
has no senses, so
could only be spontaneous, a deaf
machine crashing down
whatever's in his path
(if he moves) until
caught
in a wedge he has no feeling
of the wedge. Gees, I
can't feel my knees, sings Dylan,
but my fingertips are my mind,
I can't think without skin-temperature,
I've been specialized behind my back
into a self and an image
of self, called
soul, a blind
thing, a thing to be
culminated, like a Methodist. Here

comes my missionary, promising
edible birthdays,
but his teeth
are rhinestone capsules and
he offers me pills for my poems;
then a broom
sweeps up behind me, a moustache
of bristles tasting the floor, it's
Genghis Khan! I
escape in my car wearing
only my reflexes
so I can't tell where I'm going . . .
but who's that tromping
in yellow leather
out of the Asia Grill?
Genghis!
All that collective
animal will
in pursuit of me!
He'd have to be born
with something on his mind!
The missionary
in the backseat mutters
"it's happening" and
"if it's happening
you must be meaning it to,"
giving me time this time
to zero in on his voice;
I cinch his whiskers
around his clerical collar and yank and yank
until he admits
that I
am Genghis Khan! Then
I mercifully finish him off
and skewer his head for a trophy.

Yesterday's Road

Josephine Herbst

In 1943, when I was in Washington on the German desk of our war propaganda agency, I was interrogated by two Investigators who asked, among other questions, why I had gone to the Soviet Union in 1930. The common-sense answer would have been, "Why not?" but common sense always looks treasonable in wartime.

The Interrogators were an Irish Catholic and a Jew: middle-aged, nice, family men who were only doing a job. They had nothing to do with the procedure which required each charge to be introduced with a curious wording, such as, "It is Reported that in 1930 you went to the Soviet Union." There were a good many of these charges, linked to the events of the thirties and the role I had played in connection with each, and, put to me in bulk, I was impressed by the record.

In that big, impersonal room with its clean tables, shiny chairs, and vacant windows opening on a wispy sky, the voices of the men, in ritualistic devotion to the recurring phrase, *It is Reported,* began to sound like an incantation and to cast a spell. The scenes that flashed to my mind's eye were more vivid than the factual line of the wording, which meant less than the subtitles on a Charlie Chaplin silent movie, where that anarchic and immortal lily of the field, the tramp, gives a backward kick at the impassive form of a slow-witted policeman before he flatfoots it around the corner and wings his way beyond. I might say that in the whirlwind of events, doors had slammed. The vagabond road to the twenties was blocked. The inquiring journeys of the thirties, made for evidence, not for "kicks," had ended in this office.

In a pinch you may remember the wildest scenes, blown up like dust from a distant explosion. As I remembered *Nach Paris* scrawled in chalk on the German boxcars, which I had seen only in photographs in Berlin, the jubilant *Soldaten* of the First World War Wehrmacht jamming the doorways on their way toward Paris. But their *Nach Paris* had metamorphosed into our Versailles, and our Versailles into their Berchtesgaden, and Berchtesgaden into a new world war. And thus, I was in Washington.

Should I call up, from the debris of the twenties, Rilke's impassioned line, "Choose to be changed. With the flame be enraptured!" Too literary for the present customers. But it had ignited the flambeau of the thirties, "Change the world," and no doubt about it, the world had changed. So had I. Should I try to go back to the crossroads where my own history intersected the history of our time? But every crossroad is a split diamond. And what would it get me? The real events that influence our lives don't announce themselves with brass trumpets but come in softly, on the feet of doves. We don't think in headlines; it's the irrelevant detail that dreams out the plot. You may have to go back to the blue bowl which held your infant bread and milk; or watch the sun shoot a dazzling arrow along the white table-cloth. Or listen for the squawk of the alarmed goose which once rode in a basket on the hard seat of a German third-class train. Or replay the scene where the doughboys glee-fully sang, "How ya gonna keep 'em down on the farm, after they've seen Paree," before they went back to the farm to burn wheat in the thirties, to sell corn for a nickle a bushel, and to defy, with a dangling rope, the sheriff who came to foreclose the old homestead.

I had been fired, abruptly, without being told the reasons why and at a moment when I was due to be promoted to the New York office or overseas. Though this particular in-quiry was to end with the approval of my qualifications by the Investigators, they now began to look more like auditors who tally up the assets and liabilities of the alleged bank-rupt before writing him off. I had the right of appeal, but I no longer wanted the post which now seemed to designate me more as a spook in a war poster than as an actor in a spectacular and moving pageant. What's more, I had no money to linger on in Washington to petition, to hang around in corridors and "present my case." Nor was I con-vinced that the paper bullets our outfit was firing over the airways could have any effect.

In those early days we were, of course, only tuning up, with a lot of raw recruits from the sticks as well as slick adepts from New York. My colleague on the German desk was a splendid young history specialist, trained at Princeton, and we both kept asking: Whom are we aiming at? The Nazis? The old Social Democrats? The Communists? The Junkers? Or that inchoate putty mass which can be pushed around and exists everywhere and nowhere? For if you hope to bend minds to a purpose, you must know to whom and to what you speak. We prodded, until one day we were summoned to an office and given a chunk of thick, typed "directives" to read, with the solemn proviso that we were to make no notes and must keep every comma incommunicado. A secretary was present as we sat sedately, and it was my mistake to laugh. Not that it mattered; I would have been fired anyhow. But who could help it? Even my more discreet colleague smothered a twitching mouth to mutter, "Quiet. There's a war on."

The directives, presumed to be of deep psychological import, were mostly for *hausfrauen* into whose unwilling ears we were to pour demoralizing suspicions concerning their absentee husbands. For wives with men on the Western Front: remember—not the French *poilu,* who had already officially capitulated—but the artful French sirens. Could a German housewife expect her man, on his return, ever to be quite the same again? Toward the East, the danger was equally insidious. Their women, too, might transform a potent warrior into a sex malingerer. But there were also paper bullets for the fighting men, who were to be twitched by their sexual roots and reminded that their home fire pullulated. Beware the horde of war prisoners and displaced persons—foreign types leaking in through crevices, who might be useful on the home front to spade the wife's garden, to plow, to feed the pigs, but many of whom were strong physical specimens. Could a woman's honor prevail over stark loneliness, dark winters, frost, the cries of the flesh? Did they want to come back from the gory front to find a stranger's chick hatched in their nest?

As propaganda, the directives struck me as about as effective as a loaf of our cottony bread. I knew a good deal about Germany, though not enough: I had lived there for two years in the twenties, had returned in 1930 and again in 1935 for the New York *Post.* I had learned something about actual war, that guns and bombs crushed more than a dozen eggs, when I was in Madrid in 1937 while the city was daily bombarded. As a woman, I felt a certain conceit in my awareness of the violent potentials simmering within situations and human beings. This stuff was silly. Hunger would have made more sense: older Germans remembered its pangs from the First World War; younger ones from the rickety legs of kids during the inflation. But *sex*—if I knew what I was talking about, damaged goods would have more appeal than empty arms, and the women knew it, the men knew it, and would be more likely to laugh than to weep at our piety. *Sex*—to *Germans*—who were pulverizing Jews and politicals, by the million!

I could remember some quoted lines from an old notebook where it was said that each man, according to his racial and social milieu and to the specific point in his individual evolution, is a kind of keyboard on which the external world plays in a certain way. All keyboards have an equal right to exist. All are equally justified. Something of the kind had even been built into our own Bill of Rights. But now these words sounded hollow, echoes from a departed summer twilight when the wooden croquet balls had jovially knocked against one another on the green lawn. In the convulsed knock of world upon world, could an individual keyboard hope to sound a single, clear, personal, or harplike note? In war, a mechanical master keyboard takes over, like some monster player piano, to drown out the piping of solitary and singular instruments.

The two Investigators and I might add up a column of facts and *It is Reported*s without agreeing on the final sum. Nor did childhood memories count; they might hopelessly entangle. The two of them had doubtless saluted our flag in local grade schools, as I had in Iowa when a militant principal tapped her little bell like a drum major; on Washington's birthday she marshaled the troupe of pupils in a body to the main hall, where the drum rolled, a trumpet bugled, and the beautiful flag was unfurled. We stood, rows of impressionable infants, to chant in unison, "I pledge my heart (hand on heart, ready to be broken) and my hand (outstretched hand, ready to be blown off) to my country." One Country, One Nation, Indivisible, and One Flag.

Drums. Star Spangled Banner. Shivery, exalted, my voice rang out. Did we also promise our heads? Not as I recollect it. I had my own fable, and fables speak.

But if the headpiece was inviolable, could it be granted immunity from the flesh? No head versus heart, mind versus flesh, here. Words, too, are carnal. My own *doppelgänger* might split an apple with me, take the core and give me the fruit, but more often it spoke in riddles. Or hinted that immersion in the vital present, an immersion, alas, achieved by an uncritical acceptance of the drift of things, could defeat the aims of any goal. Ready and intoxicating spontaneity had its price. I could feel the pinch of it in that office, and if I seem to be putting on bland airs now, from an experienced distance, I was becoming sick at heart at the time. As often as I had rehearsed risky situations, dramatizing myself in major important roles, I had neglected this smaller domestic opening for a minor part. I wasn't in a maniac Gestapo cellar, nor confronted by a merciless judge in a Moscow trial. The sadism of the parlor and gallery that the Surrealists had deliberately cultivated as a proof of their power to shock, and to delight, had passed over and beyond any of Max Ernst's bestiaries of animals with human heads, which now looked like benign beings compared with the factual evidence of the "real" world. But we were no police state, though it seemed we had engaged its footboys. The very politeness of my Interlocutors unhinged me, made me regard trivialities with concern. I noted with alarm one ink-stained finger of my gloves; another finger was ripped. A bit more of this and I would begin to simper, "Shall I pour the tea?"

Moments like this can relegate you to a dungeon with nothing to contemplate except your own abyss. I had no intention of retreating to the thirteenth century or to the fascinating eighteenth. Nor to call on Pascal, Plato, or Thucydides to the extinction, for instance, of Rosa Luxemburg, Madame Rolland, or Danton. Nor to apologize or stutter away my birthright or cede to strangers the ground rights to my own experience, my own mistakes. Or even to my own ignorance. To do so would close the debate. What I understood very well was that the dry rattle of all these *It is Reported*s might be calculated to reduce some of my best yesterdays to outworn slogans; telephone numbers of people who were no longer there, or were dead; and foxed files.

They could take *It is Reported that in Madrid, in 1937, you broadcast in behalf of the Spanish Loyalists,* turn it inside out, and find me involved in a conspiracy, where I saw only evidence of my own well-grounded reasons of the heart. Or what was I to make of the *Report* that I had signed a petition in 1932 protesting the violating of civil liberties in Detroit? No details were given and I couldn't remember what it had been all about. Or the one on the piece for *The New Masses* in 1935, when Batista was shooting students on the university steps, while in the mountains near Santiago peasants stood with machetes, behind virgin trees, to guard their land and what they took to be their rights from soldiers who were mounting the slopes in obedience to commands from the sugar planters in the valley below. I no longer wrote for *The New Masses,* nor would, nor *could.* But it had served my keyboard once, as my piece had doubtless served theirs. And I stood by the substance of it, which had its own life and veracity apart from either author or publication. I had only to remember the frail wishbone from a skinny chicken the mountain folk had shared with me, and which a child, who had never gone to school, had pressed into my hand at parting.

So I said, "Why do you keep saying, *It is Reported,* when it is a fact?" But what is a *fact?* Who is to interpret it? What ideas ride on its back? And a Protean Me wanted to break the cords that bind, and to soar, if only back to my attic, where there was some hope of getting to the source of things. If the truth about Me was what was wanted, they might better scrabble in the old Gladstone bag, near the window where the squirrel got in. Nothing within except a bunch of love letters, some tied together with a ribbon, others with string or a busted rubber band; some in ink, pencil, or typed; addressed to Madam, Mme., Mlle., Fräulein, Senorita, Mrs., or Miss. One clawed with a stern warning, *Destroy.*

Or they could fumble on the shelf where old newspapers were stacked, and where they might lay hands on copies of old little magazines such as *The Little Review* which I had carried to classes at Berkeley in 1917 instead of a ball of wool to knit a sock for a soldier boy; or the number that was banned when the editors printed a section of *Ulysses*. Or find *The Masses* before its editors were indicted for treasonable intent in opposing the Great War, and the magazine suppressed. Whatever happened to the seventy-year-old scholar with a shock of beautiful white hair, in a house in Berkeley, who had explained with enthusiasm what he believed to be the meaning of the Bolshevik take-over? Did he change his mind, or, like Victor Serge, stick with the Old Guard? They might stumble over a box of photographs to find a glum Hemingway in a stocking cap, with rod and reel. What could they make of Katherine Anne Porter, arms akimbo, posed with a rakish John Herrmann as a song-and-dance vaudeville team? I knew what they'd think of the jolly German soldiers in Madrid, lolling on the grass, who signed their first names on the back, but not their last. Or that one of Nathanael West and me as worthy old peasants on a wintry day, huddled in chilly coats: on his head, a sloppy hunter's hat; on mine, a shawl. While we brazenly held aloft a hammer and a sickle: he, the hammer; I, the sickle. Crossed, as duelists had once crossed swords. Or damning evidence: a photograph of me, taken in Moscow, 1930. Portrait of the Author, in a round cap, three-quarter view; eyelashes sloping downward over serious, downcast eyes; hand on table, open like an open book; expression watchful, listening, tender, and intense.

Were these courteous gents the hosts or were they my guests? It was nearing the cocktail hour. Why not take the deadweight out of facts and hand them a taste of mortal life? So I volunteered that they'd forgotten a thing or two, such as the day in Paris in 1935, when I had come out of Germany and had stood on the sidelines of the great funeral procession for Henri Barbusse. His body rode on a caisson, as it deserved to ride, for he had fought as a private in the First World War, and had written his antiwar novel *Le Feu* after he was demobilized. It had enlightened my green youth before our country came in as an ally. And that procession had been notable for me, not for its pomp, for it had none, but for the delegations from dozens of small towns, marching by the hundreds in formations of blue working-clothed ranks, and bearing homemade wreathes; and for the huge glass hearses, of the old-fashioned, ornate type, that were loaded within and without with great bouquets of wilting field flowers: blue cornflowers, red poppies, clover, and sheaves of golden wheat, which had been brought to the funeral train as it passed through Poland, Germany, and France on its way out of Moscow, where Barbusse had died; and for the construction workers standing as silent witnesses on the scaffoldings at the tops of buildings; and the women and children, crowded in windows along the miles where the procession passed on its way to Père Lachaise.

And among this throng had marched a band of exiles from Germany: poor, dismantled, and conspicuous for the absurd precision of their disciplined marching among the more loosely jointed, more happily assembled French. Had their discipline been of use only to make martyrs? Or to divide themselves? For some of the marchers were to show up in Spain in the International Brigade in 1937, claiming that if you wanted to see Berlin, go to Madrid. Nor had they foreseen in Madrid the fratricidal divisions to follow, or that concentration camps would await them in France after defeat, or death in the Moscow purges, or that they would flee to Mexico, Rio, or Buenos Aires, and some be denied America; or that some, brother against brother, might find themselves once more secretly at dagger's point with one another, but fighting together with the Resistance in Europe.

The two men listened—gentle, clerklike—and then let me go, toting up the figures to clear the bill of lading. Was their favorable verdict made out of pique against their rival investigators who had stolen their priority? I could not know, or care: the job was gone. I did not fancy that without me the war might be lost. I was as certain we would win as I had been that Hitler would not last his thousand years, nor the Russians crumple in two weeks as the Nazi tanks moved eastward. Not that I prided myself on superior diagnostic powers: of such, I had none. Often I had miscalculated and misfired; often engaged in internal combat while in combat without. One Me, a jaundiced eye on Progress, was a gloomy prognostician; the other, a congenital cricket, ready to chirp, "While there's life, there's hope." No, what most struck me was that my Interlocutors and I spoke the same tongue but lacked the elements of a common language. On my native soil, I was in a kind of no-man's-land, more strange than I had been when first I went to Germany and loved to drift anonymously with the crowd. And, just as I fancied then that because I could glibly read *Faust* in German I might hear and speak of Germany, so I had come to this outfit plumed with formal qualifications but unhanded by secret laws at cross-purposes with my own.

To blend our differences I would have had to sink myself in their total life, as once I had dissolved among Germans in the inflation days of 1923: when I had mingled with the rich in swank hotels and spas, or nibbled ersatz cakes with uneasy bourgeoisie in a pleasant pension on Kastanienallee while they regaled me with reports of outmoded delicacies, dishes now moribund: a dozen eggs, a pint of cream, split almonds, a fistful of orient spices, which took shape before their eyes, then exploded to their hysterical wonderment; or shared black bread and cabbage with students in their unheated *Studentenheim* in Marburg, where a youthful Pasternak had once climbed the steep, cobbled streets; or paid ten cents to take a train to Dresden to hear the opera, to look upon that Raphael Madonna that Dostoevski once complained had overenraptured Turgenev; or reveled at a different theater each night, where needy Germans strained to spend their paper marks before tomorrow made them trash and thronged for Ibsen, Strindberg, and Shakespeare, and for their own playwrights, who in fabulous stage settings set on fire the follies of their age, their bedevilment, their savaged predicament.

Or copied in my notebook, with a novitiate's pride, sage sayings: Georg Kaiser: *Berliner Tageblatt,* Sept. 4, 1923: On the poet as creator of the only history meaningful to man. "He orders the confusion. He draws the line through the hubbub. He constructs the law. He holds the filter. He justifies man." Or noted Werfel, hailing man as the name-giver, the one who expresses the unexpressed, lifts the world out of the unconscious and thus creates once more the cosmos. *Erkenntnis,* intellectual insight, was Heinrich Mann's motto; he claimed space for intellectual man to remake the social world according to the ideals of justice and reason. Shy and reticent, I circled around that circle about Herwarth Walden and his *Der Sturm,* where poets shucked off burdensome syntax, shed *Gemüt*, elevated the noun and verb to do their work of reshaping and reseeing, and brought the arrow of their desire to its mark, shorn of all circumlocution, description, diffuseness. And I was drowned in awesome reverence for the new, and then drew back in fright; read Gottfried Benn's poem "Happy Youth," in which a drowned girl's body serves as a nest for a brood of rats—the Happy Youth are rats, not men. And saw its constructs reveal an icy vision of total indifference to human woe and universal death, where devouring rats could frolic—and nonmen.

And then? I don't know why I forsook this intoxicating realm, but there were echoes from the very paving stones, sounds in the air and black birds in the sky, and I dived down, and for months lived cheek by jowl with the poor in gloomy tenements of Moabit and Wedding. And you can say that the poor won; and that I came out of Germany, in 1924, pro-German, for whatever that implies for those days. Nor could the dazzle of Paris, the rich, heady air, or falling in love; or idling along the quay with a modest, happy Hemingway, or calling hello to a ruddy-bearded Pound: none of this could wipe away that vital decisive stain, which blended deep and harsh and took its toll in years to come. What could my Interlocutors understand of this? The experience was my own; no outsider could subtract it from my totality. Who is to rob you except yourself? The heart must weigh the stone it earns.

II

By 1930 the road had lengthened out to reach to Moscow. Our government did not recognize the Soviet Union, no more than China now, but we could go to a writer's conference there provided the Russians approved our visas. John Herrmann and I sailed on the *Bremen*. We went third class, where there was no promenade deck, only a small space, about twelve feet by six, jutting out close to the water at the stern. This space was always packed with silent, intent men—looking back. "Third cabin" was a modern equivalent of the old-time steerage, and now held many immigrants who were sad to return, pushed out by the crunch of rising joblessness and by the crackdown, too, on all those who held views contrary to the Plan now engineered in the White House by the Man who was to tell us, year by year, that Prosperity was just around the corner and would soon appear.

We landed in Bremen and had to wait several days in Berlin, living cheap, hoarding the money we had raised, partly from selling books—a first edition of *Ulysses*, six of the early Paris copies of Hemingway's stories. Then, on a late October at six P.M., John and I stood, two posts, in a great train shed, while around about a crowd of Muscovites churned from up a flight of steps without, past us to their waiting trains. We tried to stop one, then another, but we had no speech they understood, until one man stopped in his tracks and moved back to tap on a pane of glass concealed by hurrying figures within the shabby waiting room.

Out popped a tall woman wearing a once elegant suit of English tweed; her fair hair was knotted in a heavy bun, and she came up to us to ask in English with a Russian accent what she could do for us. We showed her the address of the magazine to which we had been told to go first; she took us to the street, called a droshky driver and gave him the address; told us how much to pay him and no more; and away we went, clattering over cobbled streets, up high on a teetering back seat, while lower down the driver hunched in a heavy patched coat, a foot thick; and shouted to his horse, whose fat sides were warmed by his native shaggy barklike covering.

And so we rode on our elevated raft along a street which surged with faces all lifted up to us as we rode, or parted to our vehicle without once breaking the current of their stride. How can I once more gather up the look they gave toward us? Of swift astonishment, deep curiosity, nor stopped a second, but hurried on to catch their trains in the station we had left. The faces are what I remember, bearing down upon us in a thick, pale flood, or upturned to us, as eye met eye. If you've only known an indifferent shopping crowd whose attention drifts toward a show of radios, female finery, or a shiny car, you hardly know how alive a crowd can be, stripped bare of all excrescences; how attentive to the human thing, or how antennae are thrust out, invisibly, from you to them, from them to you, so that like insects in the dark you are drawn toward the scent of the stranger and his curiosity. Their clothes made an odd array: all shabby, shoes broken down, and some legs wrapped in neat rags or paper; men wore caps, women had dark scarfs, the tails hanging down the back like the pigtails of girls. But as to clothes, the Russians all looked more or less alike; male or female: all dun-colored, except for army men, whose uniforms were spick-and-span and could stand up to our best dressed man. The hollow murmur of many feet, and of our wheels on that street where no shop lights shone, was all the sound there was except for the crack of our driver's whip and a loud bray from his deep bass voice, shouting something as we passed. It was only later that I found out his bossy shout had been, "Make way for the delegation. Make way!"

We halted in a square where dead-eyed buildings stood and paid our man; got out with our two bags and typewriter; trudged inside the empty corridor. The elevator creaked, and we were the only moving bodies it seemed; our footfalls echoed as we walked. The door had a name on it; should we knock? We took the American way and boldly flung it open and went in. The room was dim; a long cord dangled a feeble bulb above a group of desks where four men sat. But on our entrance, they all rose up, and, like those faces I had once seen on a faraway Montana ranch, where hospitality was a necessity of life not to the travelers alone but to the settlers who pined for outside news, the four showed their suspended eagerness. John had barely said our names, and that we were Americans, when they rushed to us, so it seemed to me, like the old-timers in Russia must have run when they heard the troika bells on the lonely road, and welcomed the beginning of felicity. They threw their arms around us; we were kissed. We might have been a heavenly messenger who brings the *panis angelorum*.

Two were Russians: one, Dinamov, the editor of the *Gazette* and a professor at Moscow University; the other, a robust, dark youth, identified himself as a "specialist" in English and American literature. The other two were Hungarians: one ruddy, fierce, with stocky frame; the other, blond and frail, wore a curious rounded hole on his pale cheek, which puckered when he smiled or showed a glint of bone. He had been lined up against the wall when Hungarian Reds had been trapped in Budapest, and with a line of brother victims, shot down; they kicked him, but he lay still and waited, and then after dark crawled off through the woods and thus escaped to Russia; and to life, or so he thought.

But who could know what was to come? Not us, we knew so little. The room now buzzed with talk; yes, our names had been sent in but who could expect that we might really arrive? People were always promising things that never came to pass. And where to put us? Our new friends hardly knew; the hotels were packed. In a few days, a week, arrangements would be made for guests coming from afar for the Conference; and at once, we were pressed to be their guests and to go to Kharkov to meet the writers of the revolutionary vanguard. Someone telephoned; the Critic, as we came to call the specialist on American goods, volunteered that John should stay with him; they had so much to talk about. As for me, they had just the spot, in the apartment of an agronomist who spoke German, came home late at night, and to whom I could talk German and tell my needs. So far, we had been talking mixtures of English, German, and French, and by touch and look, added to the sense.

John left first, and thereafter, for some days, we met only to exchange views or to wander, hand in hand, through the streets. He told how the Critic's "place," described in advance as "commodious," had turned out to be a narrow cell, furnished only with books stacked to the ceiling and a tight bed too short for John's long frame; his feet stuck out. The Critic insisted his guest must take the bed, and he himself lay grandly on the floor, covered by an overcoat. At night a rat pounced out and was squelched when our Critic nonchalantly threw a shoe. But night for sleep was short; the Critic was all aglow with talk and tea; a little vodka too. He was translating Proust, not for general consumption, but for the knowing few. He failed to pass the Kafka test but was impressed that we had been fishing with Hemingway in Key West a few months before. Dreiser and John Dos Passos should have come. He loved success. *Ulysses* was too deep, he felt, for present days; the translation problems too austere for him. He must learn the idiom, and, on that first night, had insisted we send him samples of *all* our magazines on our return. Especially, the *Saturday Evening Post* and the detective story publications.

As for me, the huge apartment building where the agronomist had a nook had once been a fancy club for dissolute rich young men and had been gouged out in wedges to accommodate some of the more modest bureaucracy. An elevator landed us on the sixth floor; the door was opened by a little girl with a round, chubby face. She wore a kerchief on her fair hair, and a tough apron covered her from top to toe. My escort handed in a parcel which contained a hunk of precious butter and a jar of caviar for me. I stepped inside, but what to say? Our speech jangled odd sounds, we laughed, and from another room a plump woman sailed out, smiling, accompanied by an older, taller girl, slim and lovely, who asked me if I knew French; she was learning it. She would teach me Russian right away; she was dying to learn English; we could exchange. Right now, I must have something to eat. But first, a bath!

They took away my hat, my coat, my bag. There was a big open zinc tub in the room, near the fat kitchen stove on which pots steamed. The chubby one motioned me to undress, and the mother and her daughter withdrew. I undressed slowly and waited for privacy, but none came. The chubby one stood adamant; I was to get into the tub. I did, and knelt while she poured from a big tin pitcher a stream of warm water upon my head and me. I hadn't wanted my long hair washed, but washed it had to be. There was a tiny sliver of soap I feared would melt away, but it did not. I got out, there was a hot towel waiting, and I dressed, mounted a few steps from the kitchen to the dining room, where a beaded hanging lamp shone bright above a darned white tablecloth. My butter was set out, black bread and quantities of jeweled caviar. There was a fried egg, crisp and hot, a pot of tea, and so I began to eat, with a Russian lesson for dessert. A little boy with a thin, eager face joined us, leaning his chin upon the table. The mother worked away unraveling an old sweater to wind up its wool. My teacher would lift up a knife, say its Russian name; I would repeat, then give the English name; she echoed it and her little brother pantomimed. Before we parted for the night I knew the words for all the dishes on the table, how to say I would like some tea, thank you and good-bye, and how are you, and learned the name for where and what, for hot and cold, how to ask what time is it and what do you call this street.

The room where I was to sleep was choked with an enormous rubber plant resting against a tubercular window of sickly hue, and two narrow beds. I was to sleep in one; the chubby girl in the other. But the little boy had given up his bed for me; he was to sleep on two chairs pushed together, on which a fat pillow served as mattress, with a thick blanket flung over all. I protested it wasn't right to put him out of his bed; but his mien was proud, he smiled, and in Russian said what may have been, "Please, it's nothing." The room went dark, the children fell asleep; the moonlight filtered through the rubbery leaves to make a greeny pool, in which we all three floated, the night through, in our aquarium.

I only saw and talked to the agronomist once, when late at night he sat in the room beyond the kitchen at the top of the flight of steps and looked then like some tired man on a stool who has been made to sit too long and may fall asleep before he has finished his bowl of soup. But the second I mounted the steps between, he woke up with a smile to shake my hand and to ask, how did I fare, was there anything he could do? By this time I had nosed around and could have asked a dozen questions but refrained. Would he have told me of the vast collectivization plan then afoot, which would uproot flocks of human beings from their ground, to starve or die? I doubt it. Perhaps he himself was not in on the Plan, or what it foreboded. I knew far less, so told him of my youth in Iowa, where they raised corn and pigs and wheat. That was bait for him, he leaped at it, asked me a dozen questions about crops and machines; he had heard our farmers were not doing well.

The hour was late but in low voices we talked on and on. What was said? I don't remember his words, only that he unwound a drama of a vast and suffering land, with the unnamed protagonist an absent Machine that could do the work of many hands. I was not making judgments but sopping up and taking in; or tutoring my backward keyboard to new tunes. How to reconcile Rimbaud's *la Vraie Vie* with the Commune?

I only know those days were best before the delegations swept in; we could poke around, stare at pictographs in front of empty stores showing a fish, a loaf, a shoe to illustrate for the illiterate what was sold there once, but not now. Or at evening see the empty rooms light up with a lamp, a candle or two, while around a long table heads with caps or hooded with a shawl pored laboriously over a copybook, intent on the key which would release the clue. Or with an Englishman who spoke Russian and had lived there for months, visit a steel plant, the first I'd ever seen, doubtless the last: factories aren't my style. We moved around, electrified to see a great black bowl tip its scalding contents down, while a giant sheathed in leather wrestled with a huge red-hot snake which writhed until it was subdued to a long, dark shank for a train to glide upon. Or wondered when a little group of men, working at this and that, dropped their tools to follow us about, to press close. I'd ask, "What's he saying?" and they'd ask, was it true that in America every working man owned his own car? And, what did we think of Walt Whitman? Or, how did their steel plant compare with ours? Was Victor Hugo a revolutionary poet—what did we think?

Or once, wandering on the dim night streets with the Critic, we stopped to chat with a Russian night owl who stood with hands in pockets of a jaunty leather jacket and opined that he'd never had it so good, or thought to earn so much, except—alas—there was nowhere much to go and nothing much to spend it on. Or went with one of the Hungarians, as on a spree, to a factory meeting which turned out to be a poetry reading, and saw the intent faces, still as a clear flame, lighted up until the poem ended. One night we dropped into a basement den where the Critic promised other writers were sure to be. Rousing voices rumbled, tea was poured. We were introduced to a saturnine man, hunched in a black leather jacket. He was Leonid Leonov, a good writer, the Critic said, but like others of the older school, he found it difficult to make "the transition." The writer turned, bowed formally, and with an odd, faint, hostile smile, turned his back.

Where *were* the Russian writers? Did they hide? Mayakovski was already dead. Some years ago he had visited New York, had come arrogantly proud, bellicose, youthful, and intent. I had never met him, only felt the contagion of his presence: in an East Side dump he had enthralled a group of ardent youths and then departed, unheralded by the great, known by few:

> There's not a single grey hair in my soul;
> with nice old men I have nothing to do;
> the world shakes with my voice's roll,
> and I walk handsome,
> and twenty-two.

It was Mayakovski I had most hoped to meet; now he was dead, six months before: a suicide. But what of Babel or Pasternak? Gorki, too, was present only by his absence. Or what of the jolly pair who had written *The Golden Calf*? Or the ubiquitous Ilya Ehrenburg? Where was Pilnyak? Why was it that when the Conference at Kharkov began, the General of the Red Cavalry, Budenny, strode in like a hero, to great acclaim, but not Babel, who had ridden and fought with him? What was the cavalry without its bard, or Pushkin's statue in the square without Onegin?

Then the Germans streamed in, and, as you might know, order ruled. Our nonchalant strolling days were gone. Ludwig Renn, who had dropped his aristocratic *von* to take a name he coined, proved to be an inflexible as well as indefatigable lecturer on the pros and cons. John and I were now together again, in an old hotel, with delegates from twenty-two countries, so they said. But they said so much. The eight-hour day, the five-day week, the full employment as the rule: no beggars, no prostitutes. Museums, schools, nurseries. Under Renn's command the joy of riding on a streetcar strung with people swarming like bees was lost; he had to relate the history of the streetcar, its present degenerate state, its bright future as a going concern when more workers could be spared to build new cars again. Churches had become nurseries; here, too, we got a lecture on the bad air, which did not signify. A finger pointed at the rosy children who, in spite of clammy walls, thrived; they did. It almost seemed as if the robust kids should be carrying on their backs the tired mothers who fetched them away. Or we were taken to a big communal kitchen where hundreds of workers were fed; tasted the food and found it excellent; but got a lecture on the future Plan which was to rescue housewives from kitchen slavery to work in factories of shiny glass, and would restore to communal brotherhood the eating habits of individual man.

The Germans boasted more delegates than anyone else. All were said to have written books which were declared to be "important" or "brilliant." Anna Seghers was there; she might have posed for Dürer, with her brow and hands. She'd written a sensitive novel about some anarchists, called *The Revolt of the Fishermen*. But where was Brecht?

Ernst Glaeser, a guest like us, not a delegate, was described as a "kind of Hemingway." His novel *The Class of 1902* was antiwar; and so was Ludwig Renn's novel *War*, which he proposed to follow up with one called "Peace." But where was the dramatist Ernst Toller, who had been outlawed from his homeland for years? He'd been a leader in the Bavarian Red Revolution and his plays had drawn great crowds—some to riot, others to applaud.

You would think if pens were mightier than the sword, then War would have ceased. The twenties had been dominated by the theme that heroes were certain to back out; or to be blacked out by the catastrophe. By 1930 a last tide had swept in Hemingway's *A Farewell to Arms* and Robert Graves's *Goodbye to All That*.

But when the thirties came, Good-bye was turning to Hello, I'm here again. You realized in Moscow, and even more in Kharkov, that War was to be back on the track. It was as plain to see in Berlin or Rome as the sword that Ludwig Renn buckled on the night he made a speech, which he had won as a high-ranking officer in the Kaiser's Wehrmacht. Some held to a private view out of pride or indecision; some of the rich, loathing the wall-to-wall carpeted minds of their kind, moved sharply to the left; a few, who had the savor of the infinite in their mouths, wanted to see the worst of things, and hoped for the apocalypse. Violence had so detonated since the Great War that no one could be quiet anymore. Some took it all in stride; volunteered, so they said, for the duration, in the ranks of the social revolution.

We all bounced off to Kharkov in a train, with Ludwig Renn as a sort of paterfamilias to our car. The official delegation from the States had come; three ultraserious young men whom we had never met before and who looked us

up and down as if to say, How did *you* get in the door?
But neither did they think much of Mike Gold, the leader
of their group, when he blew in solo at Kharkov. The fact
was that the Russians loved Mike for his warm, breezy personality, and showed it. They also liked us. But it seemed
to me the faithful Three got little credit for their fidelity.
Outside of official recognition and the satisfaction of chores
done, they seemed to have little fun. Parties that went on
late at night with champagne, vodka, and caviar did not
note their presence. Nor did they approve of the sophisticated French, who brought a worldly gaiety, and Louis
Aragon and his Russian-born wife, Elsa Triolet.

Now don't expect me to relate all the pros and cons of
the debates that went on. It's all been done before. Nor was
I one who having sat on a park bench reading Marx was to
be rewarded by a sudden illumination. I had never read
Das Kapital but came to explore other works, both Engels
and Rosa Luxemburg, and to deplore that time was short
and I had a great background to fill in. But platform speaking never gave me much; I need books and quietude. And
the platform talk was barbarous as it trickled in translations.
There were some sentences which rang out, bright and
sharp, as when a handsome woman—from the Comintern,
it was said—got on the platform, and looking down, seemed
to direct her talk to me and John and Aragon, and to re-
prove some of the talk that had brayed for workers' correspondence as the substitute for literature.

There was no time in this era of great depressions or
threatened War to write long novels, poetry, or plays, the
others had said. What was needed was patient explanation
and reports from workers about their toiling lives; what
was required were stories of their struggles and their aim;
thus building the literature of the new class with the new
man. When one of the gloomy Three from the U.S.A. got
on the platform to orate, he added his bit to the harangue,
scolding that there was no time, no time; that what was
needed was plain talk—works like one already printed in
the States showing the life and death of a heroic worker.

I was trying to pay attention, to be serious, but at his
words, and quite spontaneously, I got up and pushed past
knees to leave the auditorium. In a drafty hall, I smoked a
cigarette. Aragon came after me, took my arm and said,

"We all know what your position is. You mustn't mind that kind of talk. It's a kind of infantile disease and will wear out." I said, "But it's so funny. Don't you see, the speaker is the author of the very work he extols anonymously."

But when the handsome woman from the Comintern looked down at us, she seemed to understand the more that was at stake. She reminded the stubborn group, who sat stiff-faced, that the great revolutionaries who had brought October to triumph had come from bourgeois strains. That when the proletariat won its goal there would be no bourgeois class, only a classless world, but that in Russia the workers had as yet barely had time to learn to read and write. That the favorite author of Marx had been Balzac. By the time the workers had mastered the world they were to make, what would the term proletariat mean?

The words struck. They might have come from the outlaw Trotsky, whose brilliant book on literature and revolution I had read, as I was to read his *History* after Max Eastman had translated it. But why was it, in reports written by the Faithful and printed back home, I never once heard mention of that speech or her name? Nor, for that matter, was Aragon's name ever brought to the fore or given the aplomb which would have added to the cause. I'll never know; there's too much I'll never know. But knew enough then not to try to write about what I had seen, except for one small piece for *The New Republic*, reporting the Conference in capsule.

What the Faithful wrote you can't call lies; they thought it truth. That's the way ideas take root. Their keyboards were struck by winds I could not feel or respond to; dogma to them was the needed arm, not anathema. But one thing sure is that the whole affair told me to beware, beware! Don't get me wrong. In those early years I went as far left as you can go. But I was wary of the chatter, no matter by whom. (I steered clear of our New York political elite, as much as I could, because they knew it all.) I thought, something overwhelming is at stake, but what? I can't find out here.

We had never before met Aragon. We had some mutual friends who had described his "white-toothed" smile, his "Roman nose." But what are mutual friends compared with a mutual climate of the mind, a rebel's idealism? Still our keyboards hardly chimed; at least not his and mine. You might say he was of the Paris school and I of Berlin. The Dadaists of the Café Voltaire had split into two camps, one to Paris, one to Berlin; one to become, in Berlin's terms, aesthetes; the other, in Paris's terms, political. So I, too, had been bent more toward the Berlin position, like the Dadaist who had said he needed only to take a single look at the starved and maimed hordes of Berlin to discard his Byronic cravat. The ironic thing was that the Berliners had shed their earlier coats before the Paris Dadaists, now turned Surrealists, took up the political role as 1930 rolled in.

Perhaps the Paris crowd had had their fill; had tired of wandering Paris streets, courting chance: the vertigo of the Unknown. Only vaguely aware of the great industrial strikes which paralyzed their country's economic life, they had wanted freedom; but the free man, as they conceived him, was not so much a man among the living as a dark angel—experimenting, destroying, and from whose ideal point of view all human ends pale into pure gratuity. The role of the terrorist, the spy, the saboteur, the traitor had become transformed. They had named Saint Just the Divine Executioner.

But who of our literary generation was not a Crime Snob of a sort? Who did not lean toward the underdogs, peddlers, thieves, prostitutes, beyond the call of duty: all the underbelly of the world, which looked so fat and smug on top? Perhaps we had gone to Russia because it had been so almost universally despised by the cautious and the respectable. But no surrender to either Nirvana or compulsive obedience.

Who of us had not dreamed of freedom, limpid affections, intensity above all, passionate friendships; and had not become as well, demanding, possessive? We wanted the universe; we wanted ALL. And leaning out from our traveling trains to wave Farewell, Good-bye, we rounded that long curve, back to War again.

Three Dream Songs*

John Berryman

Cantatrice

MISUNDERSTANDING. Misunderstanding, misunderstanding.
Are we stationed here among another thing?
Sometimes I wonder.
After the lightning, this afternoon, came thunder:
the natural world makes sense: cats hate water
and love fish.

Fish, plankton, bats' radar, the sense of fish
who glide up the coast of South America
and head for Gibraltar.
How do they know it's there? We call this *instinct*
by which we dream we know what instinct is,
like misunderstanding.

I was soft on a green girl once and we smiled across
and married, childed. Never did we truly take in
one burning wring.
Henry flounders. What is the name of that fish?
So better organized than we are oh.
Sing to me that name, enchanter, sing!

So Long? Stevens

HE LIFTED UP, among the actuaries,
a grandee crow. Ah ha & he crowed good.

That funny money-man.
Mutter we all must as well as we can.
He mutter spiffy. He make wonder Henry's
wits, though, with a odd

. . something . . something . . not there in his flourishing art.
O veteran of death, you will not mind
a counter-mutter.
What was it missing, then, at the man's heart
so that he does not wound? It is our kind
to wound, as well as utter

a fact of happy world. That metaphysics
he hefted up until we could not breathe
the physics. *On our side,*
monotonous (or ever-fresh)—it sticks
in Henry's throat to judge—brilliant, he seethe;
better than us; less wide.

Christmas, 1963

I AM interested & amazed: on the building across the way
from where I vaguely live there are no bars!
Best-looking place in town.
Only them lawyers big with great cigars
and lesser with briefcases, instead of minds,
move calmly in & out

and now or then an official limousine
with a live Supreme Court justice & chauffeur
mounts the ramp toward me.
We live *behind,* you see. It's Christmas, and *brrr*
in Washington. My wife's candle is out
for John F. Kennedy

and the law rushes like mud but the park is white
with a heavy fall for ofays & for dark,
let's exchange blue-black kisses
for the fate of the Man who was not born today,
clashing our tinsel, by the terrible tree
whereon he really hung, for you & me.

of paper, try to read it, but my mind is elsewhere, I am thinking of something else, I can't seem to get the gist of it, it seems meaningless, devoid of interest, not having to do with human affairs, drained of life. Then, in an hour, or even a moment, everything changes suddenly: I realize I only have to *do* it, hurl myself into the midst of it, proceed mechanically, the first thing and then the second thing, that it is simply a matter of moving from one step to the next, plowing through it. I become interested, I become excited, I work very fast, things fall into place, I am exhilarated, amazed that these things could ever have seemed dead to me."

Sleeping on the Stones of Unknown Towns (Rimbaud)

K. IS WALKING, with that familiar slight dip of the shoulders, through the streets of a small city in France or Germany. The shop signs are in a language which alters when inspected closely, MÖBEL becoming MEUBLES for example, and the citizens mutter to themselves with dark virtuosity a mixture of languages. K. is very interested, looks closely at everything, at the shops, the goods displayed, the clothing of the people, the tempo of street life, the citizens themselves, wondering about them. What are their water needs?

"In the West, wisdom is mostly gained at lunch. At lunch, people tell you things."

The nervous eyes of the waiters.

The tall bald cook, white apron, white T-shirt, grinning through an opening in the wall.

"Why is that cook looking at me?"

Urban Transportation

"THE TRANSPORTATION problems of our cities and their rapidly expanding suburbs are the most urgent and neglected transportation problems confronting the country. In these heavily populated and industrialized areas, people are dependent on a system of transportation that is at once complex and inadequate. Obsolete facilities and growing demands have created seemingly insoluble difficulties and present methods of dealing with these difficulties offer little prospect of relief."

K. Penetrated with Sadness

HE HEARS something playing on someone else's radio, in another part of the building.

The music is wretchedly sad; now he can (barely) hear it, now it fades into the wall.

He turns on his own radio. There it is, on his own radio, the same music. The sound fills the room.

Karsh of Ottawa

"WE SENT a man to Karsh of Ottawa and told him that we admired his work very much. Especially, I don't know, the Churchill thing, and, you know, the Hemingway thing, and all that. And we told him we wanted to set up a sitting for K. sometime in June, if that would be convenient for him, and he said yes, that was okay, June was okay, and where did we want to have it shot, there or in New York or where. Well, that was a problem because we didn't know exactly what K.'s schedule would be for June, it was up in the air, so we tentatively said New York around the fifteenth. And he said, that was okay, he could do that. And he wanted to know how much time he could have, and we said, well, how much time do you need? And he said he didn't know, it varied from sitter to sitter. He said some people were very restless and that made it difficult to get just the right shot. He said there was one shot in each sitting that was, you know, the key shot, the right one. He said he'd have to see, when the time came."

Dress

HE IS NEATLY dressed in a manner that does not call attention to itself. The suits are soberly cut and in dark colors. He must at all times present an aspect of freshness difficult to sustain because of frequent movements from place to place under conditions which are not always the most favorable. Thus he changes clothes frequently, especially shirts. In the course of a day he changes his shirt many times. There are always extra shirts about, in boxes.

"Which of you has the shirts?"

A Friend Comments: K.'s Aloneness

"THE THING you have to realize about K. is that essentially he's absolutely alone in the world. There's this terrible loneliness which prevents people from getting too close to him. Maybe it comes from something in his childhood, I don't know. But he's very hard to get to know, and a lot of people who think they know him rather well don't really know him at all. He says something or does something that surprises you, and you realize that all along you really didn't know him at all.

"He has surprising facets. I remember once we were out in a small boat. K. of course was the captain. Some rough weather came up and we began to head back in. I began worrying about picking up a landing and I said to him that I didn't think the anchor would hold, with the wind and all. He just looked at me. Then he said: 'Of course it will hold. That's what it's for.' "

K. on Crowds

"THERE ARE exhausted crowds and vivacious crowds.

"Sometimes, standing there, I can sense whether a particular crowd is one thing or the other. Sometimes the mood of the crowd is disguised, sometimes you only find out after a quarter of an hour what sort of crowd a particular crowd is.

"And you can't speak to them in the same way. The variations have to be taken into account. You have to say something to them that is meaningful to them *in that mood*."

Gallery-going

K. ENTERS a large gallery on 57th Street, in the Fuller Building. His entourage includes several ladies and gentlemen. Works by a geometricist are on show. K. looks at the immense, rather theoretical paintings.

"Well, at least we know he has a ruler."

The group dissolves in laughter. People repeat the remark to one another, laughing.

The artist, who has been standing behind a dealer, regards K. with hatred.

K. Puzzled by His Children

THE CHILDREN are crying. There are several children— one about four, a boy, then another boy, slightly older, and a little girl, very beautiful, wearing blue jeans, crying. There are various objects on the grass, an electric train, a picture book, a red ball, a plastic bucket, a plastic shovel.

K. frowns at the children whose distress issues from no source immediately available to the eye, which seems indeed uncaused, vacant, a general anguish. K. turns to the mother of these children who is standing nearby wearing hip-huggers which appear to be made of linked marshmallows studded with diamonds but then I am a notoriously poor observer.

"Play with them," he says.

This mother of ten quietly suggests that K. himself "play with them."

K. picks up the picture book and begins to read to the children. But the book has a German text. It has been left behind, perhaps, by some foreign visitor. Nevertheless K. perseveres.

"*A ist der Affe, er isst mit der Pfote.*" ("A is the Ape, he eats with his Paw.")

The crying of the children continues undiminished.

A Dream

ORANGE TREES.

Overhead, a steady stream of strange aircraft which resemble kitchen implements, bread boards, cookie sheets, colanders.

The shiny aluminum instruments are on their way to complete the bombing of Sidi-Madani.

A farm in the hills.

Matters (from an Administrative Assistant)

"A LOT OF matters that had been pending came to a head right about that time, moved to the front burner, things we absolutely had to take care of. And we couldn't find K. Nobody knew where he was. We had looked everywhere. He had just withdrawn, made himself unavailable. There was this one matter that was probably more pressing than all the rest put together. Really crucial. We were all standing around wondering what to do. We were getting pretty nervous because this thing was really . . . Then K. walked in and disposed of it with a quick phone call. A quick phone call!"

Childhood of K. As Recalled by a Former Teacher

"HE WAS A very alert boy, very bright, good at his studies, very thorough, very conscientious. But that's not unusual; that describes a good number of the boys who pass through here. It's not unusual, that is, to find these qualities which are after all the qualities that we look for and encourage in them. What *was* unusual about K. was his compassion, something very rare for a boy of that age—even if they have it, they're usually very careful not to display it for fear of seeming soft, girlish. I remember, though, that in K. this particular attribute was very marked. I would almost say that it was his strongest characteristic."

Speaking to No One But Waiters, He—

"THE DANDELION salad with bacon, I think."
  "The *rysstafel.*"
  "The poached duck."
  "The black bean purée."
  "The cod fritters."

K. Explains a Technique

"IT'S AN EXPEDIENT in terms of how not to destroy a situation which has been a long time gestating, or, again, how *to* break it up if it appears that the situation has changed, during the gestation period, into one whose implications are not quite what they were at the beginning. What I mean is that in this business things are constantly altering (usually for the worse) and usually you want to give the impression that you're not watching this particular situation particularly closely, that you're paying no special attention to it, until you're ready to make your move. That is, it's best to be sudden, if you can manage it. Of course you can't do that all the time. Sometimes you're just completely wiped out, cleaned out, totaled, and then the only thing to do is shrug and forget about it."

K. on His Own Role

"SOMETIMES IT seems to me that it doesn't matter what I do, that it is enough to exist, to sit somewhere, in a garden for example, watching whatever is to be seen there, the small events. At other times, I'm aware that other people, possibly a great number of other people, could be affected by what I do or fail to do, that I have a responsibility, as we all have, to make the best possible use of whatever talents I've been given, for the common good. It is not enough to sit in that garden, however restful or pleasurable it might be. The world is full of unsolved problems, situations that demand careful, reasoned, and intelligent action. In Latin America, for example."

As Entrepreneur

THE ORIGINAL cost estimates for burying the North Sea pipeline have been exceeded by a considerable margin. Everyone wonders what he will say about this contretemps which does not fail to have its dangers for those responsible for the costly miscalculations, which are viewed in many minds as inexcusable.

He says only: "Exceptionally difficult rock conditions."

With Young People

K., WALKING THE streets of unknown towns, finds himself among young people. Young people line these streets, narrow and curving, which are theirs, dedicated to them. They are everywhere, resting on the embankments, with their guitars, small radios, long hair. They sit on the sidewalks, back to back, heads turned to stare. They stand implacably on street corners, in doorways, or lean on their elbows in windows, or squat in small groups at that place where the sidewalk meets the walls of buildings. The streets are filled with these young people who say nothing, reveal only a limited interest, refuse to declare themselves. Street after street contains them, a great number, more displayed as one turns a corner, rank upon rank stretching into the distance, drawn from the arcades, the plazas, staring.

He Discusses the French Writer, Poulet

"FOR POULET, it is not enough to speak of *seizing the moment*. It is rather a question of, and I quote, 'recognizing in the instant which lives and dies, which surges out of nothingness and which ends in dream, an intensity and depth of significance which ordinarily attaches only to the whole of existence.'

"What Poulet is describing is neither an ethic nor a prescription but rather what he has discovered in the work of Marivaux. Poulet has taken up the Marivaudian canon and squeezed it with both hands to discover the essence of what may be called the Marivaudian being, what Poulet in fact calls the Marivaudian being.

"The Marivaudian being is, according to Poulet, a pastless futureless man, born anew at every instant. The instants are points which organize themselves into a line, but what is important is the instant, not the line. The Marivaudian being has in a sense no history. Nothing follows from what has gone before. He is constantly surprised. He cannot predict his own reaction to events. He is constantly being *overtaken* by events. A condition of breathlessness and dazzlement surrounds him. In consequence he exists in a certain freshness which seems, if I may say so, very desirable. This freshness Poulet, quoting Marivaux, describes very well."

K. Saved from Drowning

K. IN THE WATER. His flat black hat, his black cape, his sword are on the shore. He retains his mask. His hands beat the surface of the water which tears and rips about him. The white foam, the green depths. I throw a line, the coils leaping out over the surface of the water. He has missed it. No, it appears that he has it. His right hand (sword arm) grasps the line that I have thrown him. I am on the bank, the rope wound round my waist, braced against a rock. K. now has both hands on the line. I pull him out of the water. He stands now on the bank, breathing heavily.

"Thank you."

Montana Fifty Years Ago

J. V. Cunningham

GAUNT kept house with her child for the old man,
Met at the train, dust-driven as the sink
She came to, the child white as the alkali.
To the West distant mountains, the Big Lake
To the Northeast. Dead trees and almost dead
In the front yard, the front door locked and nailed,
A handpump in the sink. Outside, a land
Of gophers, cottontails, and rattlesnakes,
In good years of alfalfa, oats, and wheat.
Root cellar, blacksmith shop, milk house, and barn,
Granary, corral. An old *World Almanac*
To thumb at night, the child coughing, the lamp smoked,
The chores done. So he came to her one night,
To the front room, now bedroom, and moved in.
Nothing was said, nothing was ever said.
And then the child died and she disappeared.
This was Montana fifty years ago.

The Emergence of Rock

Albert Goldman

To experience the Age of Rock full-blast and to begin to grasp its weird complexities, one can't do much better than spend a Saturday night at The Electric Circus, the most elaborate discothèque in New York. Located on St. Marks Place, the main nexus of East Village otherness, The Electric Circus is up a flight of stairs from The DOM (one of the early landmarks of the rock scene which has since evolved into a "soul" club). One makes his way through a gaggle of very young hippies sprawled on the porch steps, and enters a long, narrow alcove where the faithful, the tourists, and those somewhere in between wait in line for admission in a mood of quiet expectancy, like people waiting to get into one of the more exciting exhibits at the World's Fair. Once inside, the spectator moves along a corridor bathed in ultraviolet light in which every speck of white takes on a lurid glow, climbs a steep staircase, and passes through a dark antechamber. Here the young sit packed together on benches and, already initiated into the mysteries beyond, stare back at the newcomer with glazed, indifferent expressions as though they had been sitting there for days. Then, suddenly, there is a cleft in the wall, and the spectator follows the crowd pressing through it into a gigantic hall that suggests a huge bleached skull. Its dark hollows are pierced by beams of colored light that stain the walls with slowly pulsing patterns and pictures: glowing amoeba shapes, strips of home movies, and giant mandalas filled with fluid colors. The scream of a rock singer comes at one, the beat amplified to a deafening blast of sound. Housed within this electronic cave are hundreds of dancers, a number of them in exotic, flowing garments, their faces marked with phosphorescent insignia, hands clutching sticks of incense. Some of the dancers are gyrating frantically, as if trying to screw themselves down through the floor; others hold up their fists, ducking and bobbing like sparring partners; while others wrench their heads and thrust out their hands as if to ward off evil spirits. For all of its futuristic magic, the dance hall brings to mind those great painted caves such as Altamira in Spain where prehistoric man practiced his religious rites by dancing before the glowing images of his animal gods.

Magnetized by the crowd, impelled by the relentless pounding beat of the music, one is then drawn out on the floor. Here there is a feeling of total immersion: one is inside the mob, inside the skull, inside the music, which comes from all sides, buffeting the dancers like a powerful surf. Strangest of all, in the midst of this frantic activity, one soon feels supremely alone; and this aloneness produces a giddy sense of freedom, even of exultation. At last one is free to move and act and mime the secret motions of his mind. Everywhere about him are people focused deep within themselves, working to bring to the surfaces of their bodies their deep-seated erotic fantasies. Their faces are drugged, their heads thrown back, their limbs extended, their bodies dissolving into the arcs of the dance. The erotic intensity becomes so great that one wonders what sustains the frail partition of reserve that prevents the final spilling of this endlessly incited energy.

If one withdraws from the crowd and climbs to the gallery overlooking the dance floor, he soon succumbs to the other spell cast by this cave of dreams. Falling into a passive trance, his perceptions heightened perhaps by exhaustion or drugs (no liquor is served here), the spectator can enjoy simultaneously the pleasures of the theater, the movies, and the sidewalk cafe. At The Electric Circus the spectacle of the dancers alternates with the surrealistic acts of professional performers. An immaculate chef on stilts will stride to the center of the floor, where he looms high above the dancers. They gather around him like children, while he entertains them by juggling three apples. Then, taking out a knife, he slices the fruit and feeds it to his flock. High on a circular platform, a performer dressed to look like a little girl in her nightie struggles ineffectually with a Yo-Yo. A blinding white strobe light flashes across her body, chopping her absurd actions into the frames of an ancient flickering movie. Another girl comes sliding down a rope; someone dressed as a gorilla seizes her and carries her off with a lurching gait. Sitting in the dark gallery, one watches the crepitating spectacle below; the thumping music now sinks slowly through his mind like a narcotic; eventually he closes his eyes and surrenders to a longing for silence, darkness, and rest.

II

LIKE THOSE fabled cities whose walls rose to the sounds of music, The Electric Circus and other such dance halls have been drawn into being and charged with their eclectic atmosphere by the magical power of the beat. The total-environment discothèque is principally an attempt to capture and concentrate, as in a giant orgone box, the multiple energies of rock, which have evolved during the past decade into a veritable witches' brew—part aphrodisiac, part narcotic, and part hallucinogen. There is no simple way of comprehending the extraordinarily rapid and complex development of the rock sound and culture. But perhaps the clearest way is to begin at the beginning and try to follow the principal trends of the music, along with their respective cultural ambiences and meanings, both in the Negro and in the white world.

Rock was born in a flashback, a celluloid loop doubled back inside a time machine. The date was 1954; the place was Cleveland, Ohio; the occasion, the first broadcast of Negro race records to an audience of white teen-agers. Alan Freed, a local disk jockey, made the experiment. Almost immediately, it became apparent that he had struck a nerve that was ready to vibrate. The records he played were known in the trade as "rhythm and blues." Ground out by tiny Negro record companies in the South, they were aimed at the black ghettos of the North. What they contained was a particularly potent strain of the same urban blues that had swept over the country in the late thirties during the vogue of the big bands. Indeed, if one can imagine an old Kansas City blues band crushed like a tin can so that nothing remains of it but top, bottom, and lots of rusty ragged edges, he will have a fair idea of how the early r&b combos sounded. Concentrating on essentials, these groups used a disproportionate number of instruments (electric rhythm and bass guitars, plus piano and drums) to hammer out the beat, while the solo performers, vocal or instrumental, worked way out in front, using a primitive style compounded of honks and cries and words bawled out like curses.

It was, therefore, an old and radically racial sound that Freed offered to his listeners in the Midwest, and later in New York: a sound that told of dirt and fear and pain and lust. But the white kids loved it; and soon, as if to signify that the music had been adopted by a new public, Freed changed its name to "rock 'n' roll," though even this new name came from an old blues, "My baby rocks me with a steady roll." The success of rock attracted white performers: the first r&b song recorded by a white singer was "Rock Around the Clock" by Bill Haley and the Comets. Haley initiated that process of white assimilation of Negro style that for many years has been a basic feature of the movement; but the tendency of early rock was to pull away from the heavy racial sound in favor of the lighter, swifter beat of hillbilly music, which was to be one of rock's more durable elements, and a subject matter (cars, Cokes, and heartaches) more suitable to white teen-agers. On this new wave of country blues, Chuck Berry and then Elvis Presley rode to fame. When Presley entered the army at the end of the decade, one expected the fad to recede and vanish. But the culture remained firmly rock-bound.

While rock was enjoying this first surge of popularity, Negro music was undergoing a series of changes among the most profound in its history. The music of the ghetto was being revived and recharged by powerful new performers bent on outdoing their white imitators, while its basic genres—blues and gospel—were coalescing to produce a new style of enormous strength and popularity.

The greatest of these singers—indeed, the greatest of all the basic rock performers—was Little Richard. Richard's records all sounded as if they were made in the Saturday night uproar of a turpentine logging camp. His raw strident voice was torn from his throat in a bawling, shouting torrent that battered and scattered the words until they sounded like raving. Behind this desperately naked voice worked a boogie-woogie rhythm section tightened to vise-like rigidity. The furious energy of the singing caught in the iron cage of the rhythm produced an almost unbearable tension. Instead of illustrating the words, which often spoke of pleasure ("I'm gonna ball tonight!"), the music conveyed the agonizing effort to break through to joy. (Or just to break through: Richard usually ended his chorus with the bloodcurdling scream of a man hurling himself over a precipice.) What Little Richard was saying musically—and the Negro ghetto with him—was not that he was having a good time, but that he had the right to one and would "cut" anyone who got in his way. His note was erotic defiance. As such, Little Richard represented a new type of Negro youth. Reckless and rebellious, he gave us the first taste of the voice that was later to holler, "Burn, baby, burn!"

Oddly enough, the other great performer who emerged in this period expressed a character of precisely the opposite sort. Ray Charles was the eternal Negro, a poor blind man crying out of his darkness, singing to assuage his pain. Yet as a musician he was far from being a traditionalist; in fact, in undertaking to mix gospel and blues he violated one of the strictest taboos of Negro music. Throughout modern times, gospel and blues had always been rigidly segregated expressions of the sacred and the profane. Blues worked cathartically, urging that everything painful be confronted, named, lamented, and exorcised in a lonely, impersonal, almost aloof style. Gospel had functioned in a completely opposite manner, one that overwhelmed unhappiness by a swelling evocation of the joys of life beyond the present world. Just as the blues was traditionally depressed, understated, ironic, and resigned, gospel was typically ebullient, extravagant, even at times orgiastic in its affirmation. The Negro community had preserved the solace of each of these traditions by maintaining a total separation between them. The singing of blues in church was forbidden, while the blues singer steadfastly confronted his troubles without ever looking heavenward.

That is, until Ray Charles and his followers stepped boldly over the boundary and ended the prohibition. One of the first effects of this revolution was an inversion of traditional modes. Not only did these singers perform minor blues in the style of plaintive dirges, such as one might hear in church; they also added blues lyrics to the hand-clapping, foot-stamping, tambourine-banging gospel shouts. On stage they adopted many of the mannerisms, practices, and rituals of the storefront Negro church. They testified, danced ecstatically, called for witnesses, appeared to be led from above, tore off their clothes, and fell and rose again like men in the grip of a religious revelation.

Charles's own manner was often that of the preacher: the voice deliberately crude, cracked, thickened with Southern Negro pronunciations; the style figured with cantorial embellishments. The effect was that of a man seized by emotion, spilling out his feelings with absolute candor. Typical of the original gospel-blues mix was "Yes, Indeed," one of Charles's most successful early numbers. The piece opens with soft church chords played on a harmonium; next, Charles gives out the text in his deep deacon's voice, a word or two—then the gospel beat, heavy and lurching, comes crashing in with a chorus of "Amen girls" hypnotically chanting after every phrase, "Yaas, indeed!" As the piece stomps through its traditional 16-bar course, the confidently rising intervals generate an aura of optimism that reaches its climax in a moment of pure "salvation." The horns riff joyously, the chord changes signal that we are coming home, and the lead voice sings: "Well, I know when it gets ya, you get a feelin' deep down in your soul, every time you hear that good old rock 'n' roll. Yaas, indeed." The lyrics tumble here to a dreadful anticlimax, just at the point where the music becomes most transcendent, for what would have been in the original a religious affirmation has been rubbed out and a pop music cliché scribbled in its place.

ONCE THE BARRIER was down between gospel and blues, the distinctions between other Negro musical traditions also began to disappear. Singers, composers, instrumentalists, and arrangers began to take what they wanted from a racial ragbag of Delta blues, hillbilly strumming, gut-bucket jazz, boogie-woogie piano, pop lyricism, and store-front shouting. The result—less a new genre than a mélange of musical materials—was called "soul."

When one thinks of soul today, the image that presents itself is of a monotonously revolving kaleidoscope loaded with dozens of factory-stamped, smoky-colored bits of gospel, rock, blues, jazz, pop, folk, rock, pop, blues, and so on in endlessly shifting combinations of this week's, last month's, tomorrow's "sound." The agency most responsible for this commercialization of Negro music is Motown, the General Motors of rock. Its founder, owner, and manager is Berry Gordy, Jr., a one-time assembly-line worker, who since the early sixties has been turning out hit tunes produced by teams of composers, arrangers, and performers, all working closely to the specifications of the Motown formula.

The basic ingredient of the formula is the beat. Pushing beyond the traditional "and *two* and *four*" style of drumming, Berry's arrangers trained the drums to bark on every beat. Then they strengthened and enlarged the new beat by overamplification and by doubling it with tambourine, tom-tom, cymbals, bass, and, eventually, anything that would bounce. Today, Motown rocks with a driving, slogging rhythm that rumbles up through the floor of a discothèque like an earthquake.

The other active ingredient of the formula is the "shout," a short, arresting phrase that flashes the song's message. This is underscored and embellished with every resource provided by Negro tradition and the Hollywood sound stage. The most primitive types of plantation music—the sounds of Jew's harps, tambourines, pipes, and quills—have been unearthed to fill the formula's demand for a "funky" core. Around this core have been wrapped some fairly complicated arrangements, entailing the integration of strings, symphonic percussion sections, choirs, and soloists.

Motown's effort to concentrate all the sounds of Negro tradition into a super-soul has often produced the opposite of the intended effect—a typically commercial dilution of the Negro essence. But sometimes Detroit's stylists, especially the gifted team of Eddie and Bryant Holland and Lamont Dozier, have updated tradition so skillfully that they succeed in adding a genuinely contemporary voice to Negro music. Not content to paste pop lyrics over old church tunes, this team has approached gospel in a sophisticated spirit, seeking to exploit its ritual of salvation without sacrificing the love story indispensable to the pop ballad. In their best work they can telescope into three relentless minutes the events of a whole evening in a storefront church without dislodging the conventional facade of the ballad.

"I'll Be There," the most admired song of Motown's The Four Tops, opens on a characteristically exotic note: pipes and slap bass evoking a movie image of Genghis Khan and his men trotting across the steppes of Central Asia. Then this mirage is suddenly blown away and we are down to the bedrock of soul: the drums pounding, the tambourines jingling, and the anguished voice of Levi Stubbs exhorting his sweetheart in the manner of an evangelist preacher:

> If you feel that you can't go on,
> Because all of your hope is gone,
> And your life is filled with much confusion,
> Until happiness is just an illusion:

"Reach out!" cry the wraithlike voices that have been trailing and echoing Stubbs. "Reach out for *me!*" he adds, distending the word with a flourish of emotion. Then for one suspenseful moment, all the voices cease, and we gaze into a void in which there is nothing but the nakedly writhing beat. Suddenly the emptiness is filled with the solemn sound of the "shout," "I'll be there," sung in unison by leader and chorus and accompanied by the exotic pipes of the introduction, which now assume their proper place as a kind of stained-glass window behind the singers. The final touch of religious excitement was added during the recording session: when the break in the melody opened for the last time, Levi shouted to the girl, "Look over your shoulder!" For a Negro audience this phrase summons up one of the most intense moments at a gospel service: the sight of some believer pointing wildly toward a corner of the church where he has caught a glimpse of the Holy Spirit.

Motown does a dizzying business with its exploitation of

classic Negro styles, and most of this business is done in the Negro ghettos (where nobody pays any attention to The Beatles). Generally, the success of the style is attributed to Negro pride, to the joy with which Negroes respond to the basic expressions of their culture. But the regressive, almost caricatured Negritude of soul, and even more importantly, the desperately naked avowal of suffering made in the more seriously expressive songs, suggest that this music celebrates blackness less for its beauty than for its strength as a revived resource against the white terror.

Soul's revival of gospel music has been accompanied by a return to archaic patterns of body movement which combine gestures of incantation and exorcism. In the currently popular boogaloo, for example, there is a complete pantomime of terror. The dancer's neck is twisted spasmodically as if by a lynch rope, his eyes roll up into his head, his hands shoot out past his face as if to avert a blow, and his whole body tips as though he were about to collapse. The imagery of anxiety in such a performance accords perfectly with the character of the words and music which excite it, and all three qualify drastically the notion that rock is simply the revelry of orgy.

III

NOT THE LEAST reason for the exaggeration of Negritude in soul music has been the emergence in recent years of rock groups composed of pale English boys. What The Beatles represented in their early unregenerate years was a Liverpudlian impression of Little Richard, Chuck Berry, and Bo Diddley, precisely the roughest, raunchiest Negro rhythm and blues men accessible through American records. When their manager, Brian Epstein, styled the boys' hair and dressed them in chic suits, he didn't comb any of the fuzz out of their sound. The result was that English dandyism was wedded to Negro eroticism, and every teenybopper in the Western world began to dream of possessing a mod moppet with soul. Other English groups have since become so adept at mimicking Negroes that the listener (white or black) can only identify the singer's race by the record liner. In fact, one may even prefer Stevie

Winwood or Spencer Davis to the ordinary Detroit sound just because the English product seems more authentic, less bedecked with the gaudy trappings of Motown. This authenticity is, of course, only skin-deep; it is a mask that the singer sustains only because his narrow expressive gambit does not oblige him to flex his features with a full range of expression. For three minutes, the length of a "45" side, he can hold this pose; but it is just as unnatural for him as the spraddling stance is for the model who is out to make a "smashing" appearance in *Queen* or *Vogue*. It takes only one record like Aretha Franklin's recent virtuoso treatment of "I Can't Get No Satisfaction," written by Mick Jagger of The Rolling Stones, to remind us of the great gap that exists between those who have soul and those who merely pay it the compliment of imitation.

Once Negritude had been synthesized so that it could be manufactured anywhere in the world, rock began to cast about for fresh game. But this was less a matter of the normal development of popular music than of the cultural disorientation of the rock generation. On the face of it, there was no reason why the music that developed from white imitations of Negro styles should not have continued to evolve along the same path that swing had followed in the forties. Starting with a basic style derived largely from Negro sources, the swing bands added more and more non-Negro elements until they had created a new pop sound. At that time, as today, there had been a dialogue between black and white, with plenty of give and take. Miles Davis, for example, borrowed the arranger of the most refined white band (Gil Evans of the Claude Thornhill band) to act as midwife at the birth of the cool. But rock was not destined to play with counters that were only white and black.

THE YOUTH of the swing era thought they knew who they were; today's youth has no such illusion. But lacking any clear-cut sense of identity has only made them more keenly aware of everyone else's. Rock is, in one sense, a direct reflection of their hunger for the essence of every people or period that displays a striking or exotic style. The Rock Age has assimilated everything in sight, commencing with the whole of American music: urban and country blues, gospel, hillbilly, Western, "good-time" (the ricky-tick of the twenties), and Tin Pan Alley. It has reached across the oceans for the sounds and rhythms of Africa, the Middle East, and India. It has reached back in time for the baroque trumpet, the madrigal, and the Gregorian chant; and forward into the future for electronic music and the noise collages of *musique concrète*.

By virtue of its cultural alliances, the Beat has also become the pulse of pop culture. The creators of the new milieu vie with one another in proclaiming rock the inspirational force of the day. A discothèque like The Electric Circus is a votive temple to the electronic muse, crammed with offerings from all her devotees. The patterns on the walls derive from Pop and Op art; the circus acts are Dada and Camp; the costumes of the dancers are mod and hippie; the technology is the most successful realization to date of the ideal of "art and engineering"; the milieu as a whole is psychedelic, and the discothèque is itself a prime example of mixed-media or total-environment art. The only elements of rock culture that are not conspicuous there are the literary ones: the underground newspapers that report the news and gossip of this world; the put-on critiques of the New Journalism; and the social and political rhetoric of the folk-rock singers, the finger-pointers, like Bob Dylan, Janis Ian, and Joan Baez.

As for the audience for rock, they are apt to manifest the same eager feeling for cultural essences that is revealed by the musicians. They like to fashion modish simulacra of cherished periods like the twenties, thirties, or the Edwardian Age; they are strong on certain ethnic types, like the American Indian and the Slavic peasant; their holdings in the East are large and constantly increasing—and they all can do a pretty good take-off on W. C. Fields. They like to dress up in cast-off clothes purchased in thrift shops or old theatrical costume warehouses; on Saturday afternoons they make King's Road in Chelsea the scene of one of the most extraordinary pageants ever seen on the streets of a European city. To describe their dress as "masquerade" is not quite accurate because, like all true decadents, they prefer to the pure forms those piquant mixtures of unrelated things that show wit and fancy as opposed to mere mimicry. Yet their ideal costume is not obviously hybrid. It aims to achieve the integrity of familiar things. The first glance at it elicits the sense of *déjà vu;* the second, a frown of perplexity. "What country do you come from?" is a query often directed at The Beatles' costume designers, a Dutch group known as The Apple, as they walk about London in their enchanting peasant drag.

As this mode of dressing makes clear, the time has now passed when it was enough to seize a single style and make it one's own—as Bob Dylan first transformed himself into an Okie or Monti Rock III into a Harlem Negro. Today, the grand cultural ideal is encapsulated in the tiny word "mix." The goal is to blend various exotic essences into mysterious alchemical compounds.

Take for example The Beatles' "Strawberry Fields Forever," with its mixture of hippie argot, classic myth, and baroque music. Grave Elysian flutes lead the way as the singers chant, "Let me take you *down*"; then, swooning on the wave of an Hawaiian guitar, the voices drift into their subterranean lotus land. Gradually, the atmosphere grows heavy and murky; the tone of the singers is stoned; their speech is muddled and ambiguous ("No one, I think, is in my tree; I mean, it must be high or low; that is, you can't, you know, tune in, but it's all right; that is, I think it's not too bad"). As the music advances in trance-like time, the baroque bass line presses relentlessly downward, the drums beat a tattoo, and trumpets sound like autos jamming. The song swells into a massive affirmation of meaninglessness— a junkie anthem. After a final crescendo, the end is signaled by the conventional fade-out; but this is swiftly countermanded by an unexpected fade-in which brings delicate Indian sounds bubbling to the surface of the heavily doctored soundtrack. The effect is magical—The Beatles sink into the ground in London and pop to the surface again at Bombay.

The more farfetched and unlikely the ingredients, the better for the mix; and likewise, the more arts and media laid under contribution, the greater the impact. The ideal is strongly reminiscent of surrealism, of Max Ernst's formula of "the fortuitous meeting of distant realities." It would be a mistake, however, to attribute any direct influence to such doctrines, no matter how prophetic they have proved to be. Life, not theory, and, more particularly, the electronic maelstrom that has shaped the sensibility of our youth best explain the syncretism of the present moment. Our youth are accustomed to being bombarded from every side by sounds and images that have been torn loose, distorted, and scrambled in a thousand ways. Nothing more is needed to suggest the frantic mix than the everyday act of twirling a radio or TV dial. It is not surprising that the archetypal image of so much Pop art is the fun house. Distorting mirrors, grotesque images, spooky vistas, traps, tricks, and shocks to every sense constitute in their aggregate a very brilliant metaphor for the contemporary experience. And, as if this were not enough, the youth have given their bizarre world one last crazy spin by turning on with anything they can get into their mouths or veins—narcotics, stimulants, hypnotics, hallucinogens.

EVERY CONTEMPORARY medium has evolved some version of the mix, whether it be called collage, montage, assemblage, or *musique concrète*. The form most often associated with rock is the light show. Two seasons ago, Bob Goldstein installed his "Lightworks" in a roadhouse called L'Oursin at Southampton, Long Island. To date the finest multimedia discothèque, Goldstein's club revealed a great deal about the potentialities of the mix. It was designed, like a giant Scopitone jukebox, to light up with a complete picture show every time a new record dropped on the turntable. The images that flashed upon its three towering screens (which were played contrapuntally, one against the other) were drawn from every source dear to the Pop sensibility. There were glass slides of New York's turn-of-the-century *haute monde*, film clips from Hollywood musicals of the thirties, twist films, old newsreels, poster patterns, and light paintings. The effect of this streaming phantasmagoria, which shuttled the spectator's mind back and forth along invisible tracks of association—from past to present, comic to sentimental, nostalgic to erotic—was that of a fantastic variety show, a Psychedelic Follies.

In such discothèques as L'Oursin, rock became a medium for producing a range of new sensations. Associating rock with images induces that sense of poring scrutiny, of lens-in-eye obsession, that is one of the most distinctive modes of contemporary sensibility. (Consider the excitement it generates in the central episode of *Blow-Up*.) Like the effect of LSD, that of rocking things is to spotlight them in a field of high concentration and merge them with the spectator in a union that is almost mystical. Few discothèque designers, to be sure, have Goldstein's taste and theatrical flair; most are content to break off bits and pieces of cultural imagery and embed them in the beat to produce a haphazard rock terrazzo. But the beguiling and tranquilizing effect of spending an evening in the contemplation of "Lightworks" assures us—far more than all the current theorizing—that the ideal of the synesthetic art work is perfectly valid and closer to realization today than at any time since its first statement in the writings of Wagner and Baudelaire.

IV

THE CONCEPT of a psychedelic variety show is strikingly akin to the form evolved by The Beatles in the last two years. Young men of imagination who have grown up in the cultural greenhouse of show business, The Beatles have developed their own exotic blooms of parody and hallucination. Like all the members of their generation, but to a far greater degree than most, they have fashioned themselves out of borrowed materials. Year after year they have added other idioms to their vocabulary, and now speak a language that is as rich as any in the history of the popular arts. The terms of their recent work are sophistication and ambiguity. But looking back over their history, one finds a logical progression toward these higher qualities, for the art of which The Beatles are masters has always had a complex and somewhat factitious character.

The story of The Beatles is pop culture's redaction of the myth of innocence and experience. When the famous four set out on their careers, they knew nothing of art or life. At home only in the rough-and-tumble world of the Liverpool cellar club or the Hamburg *Lokal*, they were a shaggy and ignorant crew. They could not read music, they could barely play their instruments, and their idea of a joke was to come out on the bandstand wearing toilet seats around their necks. Since then their careers and lives have mounted upward and outward in dizzying gyres that have swept them around the whole world of twentieth-century life and culture and set them on terms of respect and familiarity with some of the most sophisticated minds in the contemporary arts. In the course of their jet-age development, they have already been twice transformed bodily and spiritually; now they stand poised on the verge of yet another metamorphosis as the result of their studies with Maharishi Mahesh Yogi, the apostle of transcendental meditation.

It was their manager Brian Epstein who transformed these coarse rockers into the adorable Eton boys known to fame, a change of costume that proved to be the shrewdest packaging job in the history of popular music. It would be a mistake, however, to claim, as LeRoi Jones has done, that The Beatles owe their early success entirely to the Epstein formula; for paradoxically, just as their imitations of Negro rock began to achieve universal popularity, the boys began to modify their sound in obedience to the promptings of their own souls. What emerged was a sort of ancestral reverberation, echoes of ancient English music reaching back to a time before the New World had been settled. In his recent book *Caliban Reborn,* Wilfrid Mellers, the distinguished British musicologist, provides an interesting analysis of the traditional English elements in The Beatles' music, identifying bits and pieces that once belonged to the musical vocabulary of Giles Farnaby and of Orlando Gibbons, the master of the sixteenth-century madrigalists. From this analysis, it would appear that The Beatles stand in somewhat the same relation to their culture as do the Negroes and hillbillies to ours: they, too, play by ear, and what they hear is still attuned partially to a kind of scale and tonality that has long since been forgotten by literate musicians. If Mellers is right, the tension between the "illiterate" and "literate" elements in the work of these quasi-folk artists may be what accounts for their unique effect, the resonance in their simple songs of something deep and agelessly innocent. One might add that The Beatles' feeling for baroque music is characteristically British: it is Handel that sounds the affirmative note in "Strawberry Fields Forever," as it is the Purcell of the trumpet voluntaries that wells up with such purity in "Penny Lane."

The appearance in 1966 of their album *Revolver* signaled an important transformation of The Beatles. First, the album soured the milky innocence of "I Want to Hold Your Hand" and "Michelle" with the sardonic tone of the city citizen, personified in the acrid sounds and sarcastic lyrics of "Taxman." The second change was formal: instead of singing in their one basic style, The Beatles became virtuosos and produced a pastiche of modes.

"Eleanor Rigby," one of the two most impressive songs, is couched in a nineteenth-century string idiom, suggestive alternately of a country fiddle and a Beethoven string quartet. Its old-fashioned style, urgent, chopping rhythm, and lovely plangent melody provide a setting rich in sentiment for the series of genre pictures sketched in the verses. There is Eleanor Rigby, a solitary spinster picking up the rice after a wedding; and Father McKenzie darning a sock in his room late at night. They are the lonely people who live outside the modern world. The very thought of their existence wrings from The Beatles a cry of bewildered innocence: "All the lonely people! Where *do* they all come from? Where *do* they all belong?"

"Tomorrow Never Knows" is composed in an antithetical mode and provides this generation's answer to the poignant sense of human futility expressed in "Eleanor Rigby." A futuristic chant intoned by a robot voice over a hubbub of jungle noises, squiggling strings, and sore boil guitar riffs —all this underscored by the pounding of a primitive drum— the song mechanically announces its message like an electronic oracle. The message is that of the hippies:

> Turn off your mind,
> Relax and float downstream;
> It is not dying.

Revolver also contains a number of other "answers": a pioneer effort to assimilate the sound of the Indian raga ("Love You To"); a street chanty, widely interpreted as a comical drug song ("Yellow Submarine"); "For No One," which evokes the Edwardian parlor musicale, with Auntie Ellen strumming the cottage piano and Uncle Wembley winding the French horn; "Good Day Sunshine," a perky tune sweetly reminiscent of straw-hat vaudeville; and "Here, There and Everywhere," an exquisite ballad. Altogether this album offers a remarkable range of material, comprising the nostalgic, the futuristic, the hortatory, the contemplative, the Oriental, and the American. It also demonstrates a great expansion of The Beatles' resources of instrumentation and recording technique. For the first time, one really feels the presence of George Martin, the so-called "Fifth Beatle," a record producer and academy-trained musician of considerable sophistication who has supervised all The Beatles' recordings.

Revolver points the way to the variety mix, but it furnishes no general context for its excellent songs, and hence they gain nothing from being on one record. *Sgt. Pepper* remedies this deficiency by assembling its tunes inside the framework of an old-time band concert. Offering itself as a record of such an occasion, it harmonizes the stylistic eclecticism of its contents by presenting each song as an individual vaudeville turn. At the same time the opportunity is created to step beyond the artificial glare of the footlights and deliver with chilling effect the final revelation of "A Day in the Life."

The effect of this last song is like that of awakening from turbulent but colorful dreams to stare at the patch of gray that signals dawn in the city. What we awake to in the song is the modern oscillation between anomie and anxiety punctuated periodically by the sound of a dynamo that has just been switched on. This sound is itself the ultimate symbol of The Beatles' world. It represents the state of being turned on, of getting high and escaping from our deadened selves; but at the same time, its alarming crescendo of speed and power suggests an acceleration to the point of explosion (an implication underscored by the Beethoven-like chords of a symphony orchestra, portending doom). The end of the song is a single tonic chord struck on the piano and then allowed to float away for half a minute, like a slowly dissolving puff of smoke.

"A Day in the Life" is a skillfully contrived microcosm of the contemporary world. Called by one critic "the Beatles' *Waste Land*," and by another "a little Antonioni movie," its brilliance lies in the exquisite adjustment of its tone, calibrated finely between apathy and terror. Reflect-

ing meaning from every facet, the song not only evokes
the chug chug of a mechanistic society and the numbed
sensibilities of its anonymous inhabitants, but also sounds
with conviction the note of apocalypse.

V

THAT A SONG of such intellectual sophistication and artistic resourcefulness should arise out of the same tradition
that only a dozen years ago was spawning ditties like "Rock
Around the Clock" seems almost unbelievable. But the very
swiftness of the development indicates its real nature. Unlike other popular arts, rock has not been forced to spin its
substance out of itself. Instead, it has acted like a magnet,
drawing into its field a host of heterogeneous materials that
has fallen quickly into patterns. No other cultural force
in modern times has possessed its power of synthesis. Indeed, one of the common complaints of cultural critics has
been that there were no coherent movements to animate
and order the vast piles of cultural detritus under which
we seemed destined to smother. Evidently, the only impulse at all equal to the task has been the primitive power
of the beat.

Having assumed a role of cultural authority, rock has
not, as was feared, dragged us down into the mire of cultural regression. The Spenglerian anxieties have proven
once again to be unfounded. Rather than either lowering
or elevating us, rock has served to equalize cultural pressures and forces. It has cleared a channel from the lowest
and most archaic to the highest and most recent, and
through that conduit is now flowing a revitalizing current
of energy and of ideas. The result has been the elevation
of rock to the summit of popular culture and the accelerat-
ing expansion of its interests and resources.

Thus The Beatles have already journeyed so far from
their starting point in American rock 'n' roll that their relation to the tradition has become problematic, perhaps
irrelevant. In their steady drift toward the international
avant-garde, however, The Beatles, and the other English
groups like The Procol Harum that have followed in their
wake, represent only one end of the lengthening rock spec-
trum. At the other end, stand the new musicians who have

developed the sensuousness and violence of the original beat. Outstanding among these are the acid-rock groups of San Francisco and Los Angeles: groups with exotic names like The Grateful Dead, The Moby Grape, The Jefferson Airplane, Big Brother and the Holding Company, or Country Joe and the Fish. The California sound has sublimated the basic essence of rock and mixed it with the idiom of the hippies, the motorcycle gangs, and the surfers in a cultural fusion that is reminiscent of soul. Indeed, acid-rock is the closest approximation yet to an authentic white soul.

The finest of these West Coast groups is The Doors, four young Californians whose prior experience included college, jazz, and film-making school. The Doors think of themselves—as their name signifies—as the means or channel through which their audiences pass from ignorance to knowledge, from ordinary consciousness to ecstasy, from control and inhibition to revolt and freedom. They think of themselves as "erotic politicians" and as pioneers in a libidinal wilderness: "The world we suggest should be of a new wild West," proclaims Jim Morrison, the group's writer and singer. "A sensuous evil world, strange and haunting, the path of the sun. . . . We're all centered around the end of the zodiac, the Pacific."

Constrained in recording studios and falsified in their stage and TV appearances, The Doors need to be heard in their own milieu. They really do belong to the misty littoral of Southern California, facing the setting sun and leading a hippie tribe in their shamanistic rites. One can see Jim Morrison in the center of the circle, immense electric totems behind him, as he stands limply, his snaky body encased in black vinyl, his finely chiseled features framed in flowing Dionysian hair, his hands clutching, his mouth almost devouring the mike, as he chants with closed eyes the hallucinatory verses of "The End."

"The End" commences by evoking with solemn drones and shimmering metal the shadowy, consecrated atmosphere that surrounds the performance of an Indian temple dancer. But instead of sacred pantomime, we hear a voice—husky, pale, and weary—intoning words of farewell. Like all of The Doors' music, the theme hovers abstractly between sex, drugs, and death. What is ending: a love affair, an acid trip, the world? We cannot tell but it hardly matters. The emotion is produced by the ritual. First, the shaman or soul voyager launches himself with the aid of drugs and music into the spirit world; then he travels among its terrors, calling out his adventures to the awe-struck tribe. Sometimes his language is fragmentary and symbolic: he sings of an ancient snake, a gold mine, the summer rain. Sometimes the words are literal and dramatic, as in the climactic episode. "The killer awakes before dawn. He puts his boots on. He took a face from the ancient gallery. And he walks on down the hall. . . . And he came to a door and he looked inside." The Oedipal theme emerges with the cool violence of a Capote novel, " 'Father?' 'Yes, son?' 'I want to kill you. Mother? I want to—.' " The words explode into an incredible scream; the drums thunder and crash. But this is not the end. The tumult subsides, and the shaman croons like a seductive snake: "Come on baby, take a chance with us, and meet me at the back of the blue bus. Tonight, tomorrow night, blue bus, tonight, come on, yeah!" As he repeats the phrase with mounting urgency and indistinctness, the music—which has been coiling as if to strike—slips into a rocking raga and then races upward to an enormous crescendo. At the peak of the excitement, a sinister whine is heard (like The Beatles' dynamo) and then the sound erupts in crashing waves. Behind the uproar Morrison can be heard chanting hoarsely: "Kill! Kill! Kill! Fuck! Fuck! Fuck!" Then comes the end, not violently or cruelly but with a gradual subsidence into the dark and mysterious sounds of the beginning.

The mood of The Doors is revolutionary in that it represents a deliberate break with the mentality of the hippies—and for that matter, with that of the whole rock generation. Instead of "flower power" and "love, love, love," The Doors project real and undisguised anger. The seriousness of their anger varies from the Lear-like rage of "The End" to the deadpan mockery of "She's a Twentieth Century Fox," one of many songs that score off the modern woman. But the important point about this anger is its calculated violation of a taboo. For in the overthrow of so many old prohibitions, there has grown up a new structure of forbidden things and denied emotions—and the first of these is anger. By venting their rage in the ceremony of the tribe, The

Doors both express their own freedom and achieve their purpose as gurus, which is to confront their audience with the most basic unbearable truths. At the same time they achieve artistic effects that are finer than the adolescent moralism of Janis Ian or the monotonous, unmusical irony of Bob Dylan. They produce a purifying catharsis that leaves their audiences shaken but surer in themselves.

The Doors are no less revolutionary as musicians. Faced with the rigidifying conventions of hard rock, they have opened the door of free improvisation. The great moments at their recent concerts have been the extended treatments of tunes that were originally the constrictively patterned products of the rock formulary. By recovering the valuable skills that were lost to popular music through the abandonment of jazz, The Doors have begun to reestablish jazz on a rock foundation. But their development is completely independent of traditional jazz. The finest performing musicians on the scene today, their instrumental language owes more to Bach than bop and more than either to B movies. When The Doors jam, the effect is that of a mad organist tracing his fugue across an electric keyboard while beside him hovers a crazy chemist concocting psychedelics out of the sonorities of a steel guitar. Obviously, the boys have done a lot of their tripping in the vicinity of Hollywood.

Ultimately, what is most impressive about The Doors is the completeness of their commitment. Whether it be acid, sex, ritual, or rock, they are further into it than any other group. Perhaps this explains the air of dignity that accompanies all their actions. No matter how wild or strange this group behaves, one feels they are in the American grain—indigenous artists like Walt Whitman or Charlie Parker.

VI

BY PUSHING toward higher levels of imaginative excellence, rock has begun to realize one of the most cherished dreams of mass culture: to cultivate from the vigorous but crude growth of the popular arts a new serious art that would combine the strength of native roots with the beauty flowering from the highest art. In America this hope had been baffled time and time again by the failure of any of our popular arts (with minor exceptions) to achieve, after generations of development, the stature implicit in their beginnings. Like thundering geysers from underground, the geniuses of jazz, for example, have hurled themselves at their lofty goals only to fall back, spent by their unaided efforts. And this hope would have remained futile had it not been for the simultaneous emergence of two necessary conditions: first, the widespread assimilation through the mass media of the themes and technical resources of the fine arts; second, the tendency of serious artists today to exploit the myths and devices of the popular culture.

The difficulty of such a convergence of high and low modern art is well attested by recent history. On two memorable occasions in recent decades, a self-taught genius of popular music has sought unsuccessfully to study with a contemporary master. In the twenties George Gershwin approached Maurice Ravel in Paris, only to be told that there was no way he could improve what he was already doing so perfectly. Again in the forties, in New York, Charlie Parker implored Edgard Varèse to take him on in any capacity (even as a cook) in exchange for lessons in composition. But again the artist demurred—not because he lacked appreciation of Parker's gifts but simply because he could not imagine what two such sundered arts might have to contribute to each other. Today the situation is radically different—so much so that if John Lennon were to sit down with John Cage to discuss music, one wonders who would come away the wiser.

Homage to Andrew Marvell

Allan Kaplan

POEMS about America's cruelties are our patriotic fervor.
I wonder how to articulate my disdain for America with
    original fervor
as I rub your hand, keeping our love in its old habit of
    soaring
on wings "so strong, so equal, so soft,"
to use Marvell's words.
"You look as if I were a gorgeous peacock you just dis-
    covered strutting
through Central Park," you reply.
You think so? You *knew* me well—Once!
I am Andrew Marvell now and I'm shaking all over in the
    utter strangeness
of my head turning my heart into a
5-alarm blaze, fed by the generous ideas of my era.
So what you might do, apropos of today, is get up and say
    to me,
"You never really think of me. This is good-bye, *Andrew!*"
And I will wander into an Automat later, eat alone, then
    scribble these
words on a napkin: "Our love was begotten by despair
                      Upon Impossibility."

Crossbones

Leonard Michaels

At the end of the summer, or the year, or when he could do more with his talent than play guitar in a Village strip joint . . . and after considering his talent for commitment and reluctance she found reluctance in her own heart and marriage talk became desultory, specifics dim, ghostly, lost in bed with Myron doing wrong things, "working on" her, discovering epileptic dysrhythmia in her hips, and he asked about it and she said it hurt her someplace but not, she insisted, in her head, and they fought the next morning and the next as if ravenous for intimacy, and disgraced themselves yelling, becoming intimate with neighbors, and the superintendent brought them complaints which would have meant nothing if they hadn't exhausted all desire for loud, broad strokes, but now, conscious of complaints, they thrust along the vital horizontal with silent, stiletto words, and later in the narrowed range of their imaginations could find no adequate mode of retraction, so wounds festered, burgeoning lurid weeds, poisoning thought, dialogue, and the simple air of their two-room apartment (which had seemed with its view of the Jersey cliffs so much larger than now) seemed too thick to breathe, or to see through to one another, but they didn't say a word about breaking up, even experimentally, for whatever their doubts about one another, their doubts about other others and the city—themselves adrift in it among messy one-night stands—were too frightening and at least they had, in one another, what they had: Sarah had Myron Bronsky, gloomy brown eyes, a guitar in his hands as mystical and tearing as, say, Lorca, though Myron's particular hands derived from dancing, clapping Hasidim; and he had Sarah Nilsin, Minnesota blonde, long bones, arctic schizophrenia in the gray infinities of her eyes, and a turn for lyric poems derived from piratical saga masters. Rare, but opposites cleave in the divisive angularities of Manhattan and, as the dialectics of embattled individuation became more intense, these two cleaved more tightly: if Sarah, out for groceries, hadn't returned in twenty minutes, Myron punched a wall, pulverizing the music in his knuckles, but punched, punched until she flung through the door shrieking stop; and he, twenty minutes late from work, found Sarah in kerchief, coat, and gloves, the knotted cloth beneath her chin a little stone proclaiming wild indifference to what the nighttime street could hold, since it held most for him if she were raped and murdered in it. After work he ran home. Buying a quart of milk and a pack of cigarettes, she suffered stomach cramps.

Then a letter came from St. Cloud, Minnesota. Sarah's father was coming to visit them next week.

She sewed curtains, squinting down into the night, plucking thread with pricked, exquisite fingertips. He painted walls lately punched. She bought plants for the windowsills, framed and hung three Japanese prints, and painted the hall toilet opaque, flat yellow. On his knees until sunrise four days in a row, he sanded, then varnished floor boards until the oak bubbled up its blackest grain, turbulent and petrified, and Monday dawned on Sarah ironing dresses —more than enough to last her father's visit—and Myron already twice shaved, shining all his shoes, urging her to hurry.

In its mute perfection their apartment now had the expressive air of a well-beaten slave, simultaneously alive and dead, and reflected, like an emanation of their nerves, their own hectic, mainly wordless, harmony, but it wouldn't have mattered if the new curtains, pictures, and varnished floors yelled reeking spiritual shambles because Sarah's father wasn't that kind of minister. His sermons alluded more to Heidegger and Sartre than Christ, he lifted weights, smoked two packs of cigarettes a day, drove a green Jaguar and, since the death of Sarah's mother a year ago in a state insane asylum, had seen species of love in all human relations. And probably at this very moment, taking the banked curves of the Pennsylvania Turnpike, knuckles pale on the walnut wheel, came man and machine leaning as one toward Jersey, and beyond that toward love.

Their sense of all this had driven them, wrenched them out of themselves, onto their apartment until nothing more could make it coincident with what he would discover in it anyway, and they had now only their own absolute physical being still to work on, at nine o'clock, when Myron dashed out to the cleaners for shirts, trousers, and jackets, then dressed in fresh clothing while Sarah slammed and smeared the iron down the board as if increasingly sealed in the momentum of brute work, and then Myron, standing behind her, lighting a cigarette, was whispering as if to himself that she must hurry, and she was turning from the board and in the same motion hurled the iron, lunging after it with nails and teeth before it exploded against the wall and Myron, instantly, hideously understood that the iron, had it struck him, had to burn his flesh and break his bones, flew to meet her with a scream and fists banging her mouth as they locked, winding, fusing to one convulsive beast reeling off walls, tables, and chairs, with ashtrays, books, lamps shooting away with pieces of themselves, and he punched out three of her teeth and strangled her until she dissolved in his hands, and she scratched his left eye blind—but there was hope in corneal transplantation that he would see through it again—and they were strapped in bandages, twisted and stiff with pain a week after Sarah's father didn't arrive and they helped one another walk slowly up the steps of the municipal building to buy a marriage license.

My Father's Face

Hayden Carruth

Oʟᴅ ʜᴇ *was, but not yet wax,*
old and old, but yet not gray.
What an awkwardness of facts
gray and waxen when he lay.

Rage had held me forty years,
five alone have sought his grace.
Disproportioned, will my tears
quell at last his smiling face?

Awkwardly, at his behest,
I this queer rhyme try to make
after one that he loved best,
made long since by Willy Blake.

•

Cannot. In
my own way, half-inarticulate,
must sing the blues.

Oh, how he lay there
quiet as cast dice, crooked. They had given him
a face he never wore

smiling like anyone,
like God.
He, my own, who had smiled only

in the smear of pain—
as my hemlock smears in this wind
dripping with half-snow, half-rain.

Smoke flares from my stovepipe,
breaks sharply down, away,
blue, whipping the leafless alders, vanishing,

while I watch from my window, this shack
in a scrap of meadow
going to woods—

alder, chokecherry, yellow birch, ash,

and the one old hemlock leaning forth,
smeared in half-snow, half-rain, November and the North.

•

Southward, downcountry
was where he lay
and I stood

in a loathsome mass of bleeding flowers
that April. Sun flashed and was gone, cold.
We two there, lashed stiff in old antagonism,

yet altered. It was that new smile
fingered on him, official, patented,
like the oil that shone on the pale oak catafalque:

such means they use to publicize, to promote
a marketable death.
He was worthy, worthy!—

I blurted, tried to blurt
in the clench of a surprise of tears.
And then my anger shifted from him to them.

In that horror
of hurting flowers
where I stood and he lay

I, frozen, was turned around inside my years
as a shadow turns
inside the changing day.

•

Why couldn't they let him be himself?
Like all our family he smiled
with a downturned mouth.

No doubt professional death-tenders are required,
competence is required, yet I wish they had let him
lie as he had fallen,

old Darwinist smiling
at the light gone down in the south,
at the leaf gone down.

Strangely, the birds had come. Already
in cold twilight robins sang,
and he heard them, the simple but rich song,

like Blake's, melodious for a fair season to come,
he heard them and he fell down,

unable to last till summer.
It was a reversal.
At the wrong time, in April, light dwindled
and the leaf fell down.

But hearts burst any time.
He took it smiling
with a downturned mouth.

●

The old Socialist!
And his father before him.
Era of eyeshades, rolltops, late tracks in a snowy street,

a flare of shots maybe in the dark,
and the talk, talk: that man eating,
this man not.

It was all so blessedly simple.
Hate, hate the monopolists!
Ah, have I not, sirrah?—

but power of money has bought the power of heart,
monopoly eats the word, eats thought, desire,
your old companions now in the thick of it, eating—

is that betrayal? They fatten, but for my part
old hatred deepens,
deepening as monopoly deepens,

until my socialism has driven me to the sociality
of trees, snow, rocks, the north—solitude.
Strange outcome. Like so many.

I'll walk now; the woody meadow,
the firs, the brook, then higher to the birches.
I wish you were coming too.

●

"Alyosha left his father's house
feeling more depressed and
crushed in spirit

than when he entered it . . ." I walk,
going at last nowhere
in the snow and rain

that lock in air
and nap the gray rock with gray fur.
Beside me, among the ferns that confide

their green trust to the snow,
something stalks, or seems to stalk. A partridge?
Or my mind's shadow? Minute fires flow

in the lichened rock, and a yellow eye
blinks like a shuttered lens among the ferns.
Shadows and strange fires,

who can deny them, aspects of the cold world
and the father's house? We rebel
backward, ever backward, going

behind the ancestral impositions of reality.
To seek, to find—not to impose. So we say.
But it is a sad business.

•

Once he brought
to his blue house in the guttering chestnut forest—
oh, I remember this—

a pomegranate in his pocket.
But let me describe to you a killed chestnut tree.
Leaves, fruit, even the bark have long fallen

to the dark alien disease, and at last
the tree itself lies down
in a twisted, rising-and-falling

shape, and it never rots.
The smooth wood, pale and intense,
undulates

in a kind of serpentine passivity
among waves of witch hazel and dogwood
that wash along it

summer after summer after summer.
And so the killed chestnut has become
something everlasting in the woods,

like Yggdrasill. Tradition is not convention.
Tradition is always unexpected,
like the taste of the pomegranate, so sweet.

|●|

I must complete my turning.
With purpose, very coolly, I raise my vision,
snipping

a thread of the net that holds
everything together.
My splashing fears subside about my knees.

How easy! I wonder why
I took so long, learning
that to destroy

what could never be either right or wrong,
this net, this mere order
or any order,

is no real destruction—
look, I walk as I have always walked,
one foot in front of the other foot.

The rocks and birches take so warmly
to the purity of their restoration. I see this.
I have done it with one gesture, like that.

I walk in the tact of the ultimate rebel
graduated from conspiracy,
free, truly free, in the wonder of uncreation.

•

Well, the traditions of woods are sweet,
but something is withheld, something . . .
O my father, where is the real monopolist?

Can I, alien, avoid spreading
my dark disease? But you would say then,
seek its purity, deep at the root, radically.

If the orderly massacre of order creates an order,
then let it be new, even now, from the beginnings of things.
I am cold to my bones, my red hand clings

like a wind-plastered leaf to a white bole of birch,
the sky is speckled with snow-flecks
driven downwind, vanishing. It is all a song

vanishing down the wind, like snow,
like the last leaves of the birch
spinning away in harsh beauty. The hardhack,

clotted with snow, bends and rattles,
a sound like jeering in the driven twilight.
Why must the song be so intricate? What am I now,

what is my sorrow, has it not spun away?

Your face, snow-flecked, seems torn
downwind like the song of birch leaves.

•

Confused darkness turns a page. Wind slackens,
cold night is beginning, in the last light
the god of winter walks, gray and alone,

Odin, Windigo, St. Malachy, someone
with a downturned smile brushing the fir boughs,
shaking the dead reeds and ferns.

Snow thickens, leaning toward the south.
Could he come home tonight
to his house, his woods, the snow, the snow-light?

My thought sings into snow, vanishing.
At least I have two clear choices: to stamp
in deepening cold, half-blind, dragging

my feet in freezing ferns, determining
my way in darkness, to the ragged meadow,
the shack with the rusty stove;

or to stay where I am in the rustle of snow
while my beard clots and whitens
and the world recedes into old purity

and the snow opens at last to the stars
that will glisten like silent histories breaking
over a silent face, smiling and cold.

•

O thou quiet northern snow
reaching southward wave on wave,
southward to the land below,
billow gently on his grave.
Snowy owl that glides alone,
softly go, defend his rest;
buntings, whirl around his stone
softly, thou the wintriest.
Gently, softly, o my kind,
snow and wind and driven leaf,
take him, give to rebel mind
trust at last in this cold grief.

The First Street School

George Dennison

I

THE DISASTERS of primary education, both public and private, have been dealt with at length in many recent books. I would like to concentrate here on remedies, especially those we effected at the First Street School, which was a kind of public private school. We were privately endowed, and were chartered as a private school, yet our classrooms were open to the poorest families in one of New York's poorest neighborhoods. More than half of our children were on Welfare. They were able to attend without paying tuition. By and large we used standard materials and oriented ourselves toward a basic curriculum familiar to all teachers. We differed chiefly from other schools in this: that we understood education in the primary sense of growth. In my own experience, *all* true learning problems are problems of growth. They are not amenable to mere innovations in textbooks and in methods of instruction. The indispensable approach is environmental. It is essential to make a difference in the life of the child.

Let me illustrate this by describing Ramon, one of our older boys, as he comes to sit beside me for a reading lesson. He is twelve years old and has come to us from the fourth grade in the public school, quite normal but unable to read more than twenty words. There is a piece of paper in front of me, and on it a sentence of five words. The words are written again below the sentence in three columns, so that each word is repeated a number of times. Since Ramon is a chronic nonlearner, let us ask if these one dozen syllables are capable of producing the extraordinary behavior he exhibits.

He had been talking animatedly with some schoolmates in the hall. Now as he comes to join me his face contracts spasmodically, and the large gestures of his arms are reduced to almost nothing. There is no one near him, and he is absolutely free to refuse the lesson, yet he begins to squirm from side to side, as if someone were leading him by the arm. He hitches up his pants, thrusts out his lower lip, and fixes his eyes on the floor. His forehead is lumpy and wrinkled, like that of a man suffering physical pain. His eyes have glazed over. Suddenly he shakes himself, lifts his head, and squares his shoulders. But his eyes are still glassy. He yawns abruptly and throws himself into the chair beside me, sprawling on the tip of his spine. But now he turns to me and smiles his typical smile, an outrageous bluff yet brave and attractive. "Okay, man—le's go." I point to the sentence and he rattles it off, for his memory is not bad and he recalls it clearly from the day before. When I ask him to read the same words in the columns below, however, he repeats the sentence angrily and jabs at the columns with his finger, for he had not read the sentence at all but had simply remembered it. He guffaws and blushes. Now he sits up alertly and crouches over the paper, scanning it for clues: smudges, random pencil marks, his own doodles. He throws me sagacious glances, trying to interpret the various expressions on my face. He is trying to reconstruct in his mind *the entire sequence* of yesterday's lesson, so that the written words will serve as clues to the spoken ones, and by repeating the spoken ones he will be able to seem to read. The intellectual energy—and the acumen—he puts into this enterprise would more than suffice for learning to read. It is worth mentioning here that whenever he comes upon the written word "I" he is thrown into confusion, though in conversation he experiences no such difficulty.

Now by the standard criteria Ramon has a "learning problem" and "a reading problem." But has he? The fact is that these are the names given to those aspects of his troubles with which the schools have been willing to concern

themselves. "Concern" means without making any fundamental changes. A "reading problem" is not a fact of life,
it is a fact of school administration. If we want to know
what Ramon's problems are, we have only to look at
Ramon: shame, fear, resentment, rejection of others and of
himself, anxiety, self-contempt, loneliness. None of these
came into existence because of the difficulty of reading
printed words—which fact will be all the more evident if
I mention here that when Ramon came to this country at
the age of seven he was able to read Spanish and regularly
has read to his mother (who cannot read) the postcards
from his literate father who remained behind in Puerto
Rico. For five years Ramon sat in the classrooms of the
public schools, literally growing stupider by the year. He
failed at everything, and was promoted from one grade to
another to make room for those who were more or less
doomed to follow in his footsteps.

At the First Street School there were no tests, no grades,
no invidious comparisons; the children were free to refuse
lessons, and even to leave the classrooms. Obviously, not
all of Ramon's problems originated in school, but in this
setting his school-induced behavior was easy to observe.
He could not believe, for instance, that anything contained
in books, or mentioned in classrooms, belonged by rights
to himself, or even that it belonged to the world at large,
as trees and lamp posts belong quite simply to the world
we all live in; he believed, on the contrary, that things
dealt with in school belonged to school, or were adminis-
tered by some far-reaching bureaucratic arm. There had
been no indication that he could share in them but rather
that he would be measured against them and be found
wanting. Nor did he believe that he was entitled to personal
consideration but felt rather that if he wanted to speak
either to a teacher or a classmate, or wanted to move his
arms and legs, or even wanted to urinate, he must do it
more or less in defiance of authority. He had not refrained
from these things. He had been unruly—at the price of self-
contempt and a deepening alienation. During his first weeks
at our school he was belligerent about the most innocuous
things. Outside of school he had learned many games, as
all children do, unaware that they are engaged in "the

process of learning." Inside the school this ability deserted him. Nor had it ever occurred to him that one might deliberately go about the business of learning something, for he had never witnessed the *whole forms* of learning. What he had seen was remembering, reciting, copying, answering questions, taking tests—and these, alas, do not add up to learning. Nor could he see any connection between school and his life at home or in the streets. If he had heard our liberal educators confessing manfully, "We are not getting through to them," he would have winced with shame and anger at that little dichotomy "we/them," for he had been exposed to it in a hundred different forms. One would not say that he had been schooled at all but rather that for five years he had been indoctrinated in the contempt of persons, for this was the supreme fact demonstrated in the classroom and referred alike to students, teachers, and parents. For all practical purposes, his inability to learn consisted precisely of his school-induced behavior.

Now I would like to state axiomatically that the school-child's chief expense of energy is self-defense against the environment. When this culminates in impairment of growth—and it always does—there is little chance of reversing the trend by teaching phonics instead of Look-Say. The environment itself must be changed.

II

IN DESCRIBING Ramon I have given an extreme example of failure. Experienced teachers will recognize, however, that though the example is extreme it is by no means rare. The word "crisis" is justly applied to our schools.

But what of the failure that looks like success—or at least is rewarded as such? John Holt deals with this in *How Children Fail.* Writing of the better private schools, he describes how the "answer-producers" are rewarded, and how they seem to make progress, only to reveal again and again that they have learned very little. Their "parroting" is not learning—and behind the parroting lies an extraordinary fear of failure.

We use the word *conformity* as if we were speaking primarily of attitudes. One adopts the right attitude and thereby avoids embarrassment, ostracism, and censure. But these innocuous attitudes are not easily come by. They represent a painful process of self-suppression, especially of intellect, observation, and feeling. The answer-producers are not facing the world on their own two feet, alert to the evidence of their senses, but exist in a kind of passive dependency, accepting on authority not merely the idea of what is correct but accepting—disastrously—the framework of authority itself as if it were the world of nature. Where the end-product of abject failure like Ramon's is ignorance, frustration, and savagery, the end of rewarded failure is complacency, mindlessness, dullness—the soft blank face which blows neither hot nor cold. Here the meaninglessness of *national norms* is apparent. They are performance norms, "answer norms." If the "better schools" rank high in such scales, they are nevertheless, in their own distinctive way, engaged in the reduction of the human potential.

One might say, reducing these two typical failures still further, that the most familiar waste-products of our schools at present are complacency and rage. If we lived in a utopian democracy, we could undermine it in one generation by introducing a school system such as we now possess.

Obviously, no child's life begins and ends in school. Our way of life, as a whole, is berserk. When we take this broad view, however, we are struck immediately by the fact that our system of schools, precisely because it is a highly rationalized and delimited environment, is the one important environment susceptible to swift and radical change. There are powerful restorative effects at our fingertips. If we are to achieve them, however, we must begin by taking the schools seriously *as* environment, and by asking basic questions about their salient features. Two of the most prominent, from the child's point of view—and few parents are aware of it—are compulsion and the loss of relationship. The former means simply, "I must, whether I like it or not"—must go, must sit still, must listen, must attend to *this* instead of *that,* and so on. The compulsion, in the end, is physical, and few children have experienced anything like it in their own homes or among their friends or relatives. If we hear little complaining, it is because the children themselves fear that nothing can be done. In order to guess the extent of the child's resentment and loss of motivation (and frequently his apathy) it would be necessary to observe him in a school setting in which compulsion played no part; if, then, his behavior were radically different—and especially if he learned a great deal—we might guess at how many sighs were heaved previously in silence. This was precisely our opportunity at First Street, and I hope that some of my descriptions of the children will indicate how much of the world of childhood they regained simply through the removal of coercion. The second prominent feature of the public school—the loss of relationship—is as obscure to parents as the first. Parents are *in* relation with their children and cannot get out of it. They find it difficult to imagine the child's anonymity in an overcrowded classroom faced by a harried regular or a succession of harried substitutes. The very thing which reassures parents, namely the routinized, thoroughly controlled, official *look* of the schools, is the thing which creates hazards to the growth of the child, for the world of the child, quite abruptly, has ceased to expand through the familiar medium of persons with whom he is in relation. One of the first things he discovers is that his teachers are not in a position to show personal concern or to demonstrate the validity of their own lives. Even their judgment is rendered impotent by the demands of bells, superiors, and lesson plans. The child discovers, in short, that he is at the mercy of persons who possess authority but have been deprived of responsibility. This is an arid and confusing condition. It is compounded by the fact that his excited interest in the great swarm of classmates at his side plays absolutely no part in the structuring of the day at school. If he is made anxious by the minimization of his relations with adults, he is stultified by the loss of essential relations with his peers, his single greatest source of inspiration.

It becomes apparent then, when we take the schools seriously as environment, that even the most common practices represent disturbances in the continuum of persons.

III

WHY IS IT that the ordinary preschool environment of the home is so profoundly conducive to learning? For, as Whitehead points out in his *Aims of Education*, one of the greatest of intellectual tasks is routinely performed by infants under the aegis of mother and father:

> The first intellectual task which confronts an infant is the acquirement of spoken language. What an appalling task, the correlation of meanings with sounds! It requires an analysis of ideas and an analysis of sounds. We all know that an infant does it, and that the miracle of his achievement is explicable. But so are all miracles, and yet to the wise they remain miracles.

We can conclude either that infants possess special faculties—which they do not—or that the ordinary environment of the home actively supports the flowering of such faculties as all men originally possess. If this is the case, it would be wise to establish correspondences between the relevant features of this environment and the process of learning. Perhaps certain of these features can be incorporated in our schools. Obviously, mother-love cannot be, nor can the extraordinary "teacher/pupil ratio" of the home. But let us use Whitehead's example of the infant's acquirement of spoken language and ask how the various steps of this process relate to the environment of the home. All parents have observed it. All know that they have contributed to it. Few indeed, however, will insist that it was they who *taught* their children to talk. We can conclude immediately that *instruction*, of itself, is not the highroad to learning.

Crying is the earliest "speech." Though it is wordless, it possesses in prototype many of the attributes of true speech: it is both expressive and practical, it effects immediate environmental changes, it is directed to someone, it is accompanied by facial expressions and "gestures." All these will be regularized, mastered by the infant long before the advent of words. Two features of the growth of mastery are striking. The first is that the infant's use of gestures, facial expressions, and sounds is at every stage of his progress the true medium of his *being-with-others*. There is no point at which parents or other children fail to respond because the infant's mastery is incomplete. Nor do they respond as if it *were* complete. The infant, quite simply, is one of us, is of the world precisely as the person he already is. His ability to change and structure his own environment is minimal, but it is real: we take his needs and wishes seriously, and we take seriously his effect upon us. This is not a process of intuition but transpires in the medium he is learning and we have already learned—the medium of sounds, facial expressions, and gestures. The second feature is that his experimental and self-delighting *play* with sounds—as when he is sitting alone on the floor handling toys and babbling to himself—is never supervised and is rarely interfered with. Parents who have listened to this babbling never fail to notice the gradual advent of new families of sounds, but though this pleases them, they do not on that account reward the infant. The play goes on as before—absolutely freely.

Both of these aspects of the growth of mastery reflect the conditions found in the home. In the first, we see that the infant is born into the continuum of persons, and that this continuum is the medium within which learning occurs. In the ordinary home the continuum is one of maximum relation. From the infant's point of view, even though he be often frustrated, the ratio of effort and effect is high indeed. There are no breaks in the continuum in the sense that important demands meet no response. (When this does occur, we read of it in case histories of autism and schizophrenia.) Volition, too, is maximized, which is evident in both examples. In the second, however, we see that being alone, inventing, playing, following mere whim, in no way threatens the security of the continuum.

The role of imitation in all this is essential to any theory of learning. An infant of, say, fourteen months, not yet in possession of many words, will often enter vivaciously into the conversation of the parents, will look from face to face, join in the laughter, and "speak up" in sounds that are far from being words but which are spoken with very definite facial expressions and in rising and falling tones of voice. These will often be accompanied by hand gestures obviously copied from the parents. The infant seems to be imitating grown-up speech. But *is* this what he is doing? Parents are perhaps deceived because the sight is inevitably so charming, all that display of participation with so little content. They forget that among their own motives, the desire to charm, to enliven, to make a merry noise, is not insignificant. And they overestimate the content of what they themselves have said, for the truth is that the music of our ordinary conversation is of equal importance with the words. It is a kind of touching: our eyes "touch," our facial expressions play back and forth, tones answer tones. We experience even the silences in a physical, structural way; they too are a species of contact. In short, the physical part of everyday speech is just as important as the "mental" . . . and precisely this physical part has already, to an impressive extent, been mastered by the fourteen-month child. Moreover, when we raise the question of imitation, we tend to forget that the whole forms of our own coherent speech consist actually of a great many parts, all of them very intricate: sounds, rhythms, accents, tones, breathing patterns, facial expressions, gestures. When even a small number of these are present in an infant's "speech," we are already far beyond the stage of mere imitation.

But in truth there never was such a stage. The infant is surrounded by the life of the home, not by instructors or persons posing as models. Everything that he observes, every gesture, every word, is observed not merely as an action but as a truly instrumental form. This *whole life of the form* is what he seeks to master. It is what he learns. No parent has ever heard an infant abstracting the separate parts of speech and practicing them in isolation from the whole life of the form. It simply does not happen. Even in those moments that we might think of as instruction—when, for example, we are bending over the baby saying *wa-ter* to correct his saying *waddah*—our inevitable élan is that of a game; and in any event, as every parent knows, the moment this élan vanishes and mere instruction takes over, the infant will abruptly withdraw his cooperation. It is not only that he is not able to conceptualize but that we have removed the instrumentality he has all along been studying. He no longer recognizes the sounds as a *word;* and indeed, at this moment, they are not a word in the true sense but a conceptual device of pedagogy.

When we see the infant in action, then, it is impossible to say that any given expression or gesture is an imitation. What we mean is that we recognize its source. The fact that we observe it at all indicates that it has already been assimilated, or is well on the way. We are observing it *in use*.

A true description of an infant "talking" with his parents, then, must make clear that he is actually taking part. It is not make-believe or imitation but true social sharing in the degree to which he is capable. We need only reduce this complex actuality to the relative simplicity of imitation to see at once what sort of loss he would suffer. The vivacity, the keen interest, the immediate share in the ongoing intercourse of others, and above all the environmental effect—all these would vanish. His experience would be reduced to the dimensions of a chore, like that of an actor preparing a part. But in fact we cannot conceive of experience reduced to such dimensions. The infant, in short, is not imitating but doing. The doing is for real. It advances him into the world.

This very distinction between imitating and doing lies at the heart of John Dewey's thoughts on education. It is the root meaning of "learning by doing," which words, for many years now, have been little more than a catch-phrase signifying the filling-in of blanks in prepackaged experiments. Dewey's strength lies in his profound understanding of the whole forms of experience, the unity, in growth, of *self, world,* and *mind.* It was because of his perception of this unity that he insisted that school be based in the community and not in the Board of Education. (No myth has been more disastrous to American education than the notion that we have already availed ourselves of the thought of Dewey. Nothing could be further from the truth.)

These things, then, for the growing child, are maximized in the environment of the home: relationship, participation, freedom of movement, and freedom of volition with respect to the objects of attention. Knowledge is gained in immediately instrumental forms. The gain is accompanied by use and pleasure. The parents do not pose as models but are living their lives, so that from the point of view of the infant the model is life itself.

Before comparing this optimum environment with the usual environment of school, I would like to give another example from the home, one more deliberately educative, and one, again, with which most parents are familiar.

Let us imagine a mother reading a bedtime story to a child of five. And let us apply Dewey's holistic terms, bearing in mind that normal learning is not merely a function of intelligence, or of the growth of the self, but that self, mind, and world belong together as one fact. In Dewey's formulation, mind *is* the ongoing significant organization of self and world.

We can judge the expansion of self and world by the rapt expression on the face of the child, the partly open mouth, and the eyes which seem to be dreaming but which dart upward at any error or omission, for the story has been read before a dozen times. Where does the story take place? Where does it happen in the present? Obviously in the "mind" of the child, characterized at this moment by imagination, feeling, discernment, wonderment, and delight. And in the voice of the mother, for all the unfolding events are events of her voice, characteristic inflections of description and surprise. And in the literary form itself, which might be described with some justice as the voice of the author.

The continuum of persons is obvious and close. The child is expanding into the world quite literally through the mother. But the increment, so to say, *of world* is here another voice, that of the author, made durable in its observance of artistic form. Because of the form itself, there hover in the distance, as it were, still other forms and paradigms of life, intuitions of persons and events, of places in the world, of estrangement and companionship. The whole is supported by security and love.

There is no need to stress the fact that, from the point of view of learning, these are optimum conditions. I would like to remark on just two of their aspects, which might be described, not too fancifully, as *possession* and *freedom of passage*. The former refers to the child's relation to ideas and objects of perception. The latter refers to his relations with the persons already associated with such forms.

Both the mother, in reading the story, and the author, in achieving it, are *giving* without any proprietary consciousness. The child has an unquestioned right to all that transpires; it is *of* his world in the way that all apprehendable forms are of it. We can hardly distinguish between his delight in the new forms and his appropriation of them. Nothing interferes with his taking them into himself, and vice versa, expanding into them. His apprehension of the new forms, their consolidation in his thoughts and feelings, *is* his growth . . . and these movements of his whole being are unimpeded by the actions of the adults.

With regard to those aspects of the situation, then, that belong to learning and growth, we see first, that he is supported in his intuition that apprehendable forms are simply *of* the world and become his own in the act of apprehension; and second, that he is able to take for granted—with regard to the act of apprehension—that he has free passage among persons. Certainly there is effort on his part, but it is a true expense of spirit; that is, it is experienced as fulfilling action. The effort does not include self-defense against the environment. Nor is it accidental that he is blessedly unaware of himself. This follows from the fact that he is already accepted, already *included*, by his mother's act of giving, and by the absolute offer inherent in the literary form.

If we wished to retard his learning and complicate his growth, we could do it by the following steps: first, turn his attention back upon himself by letting him know that he is being observed, measured, and compared to others; second, destroy his innate sense of his own peerage among sensible forms by insisting that they are to be apprehended in standardized ways and that their uses are effectively controlled by others; third, make his passage among persons dependent upon the measurements to which he has been subjected; fourth, apply physical coercion to his freedom to move, to express his feelings, to act upon his doubts, to give or refuse his attention—all of which will effectively convince him that learning is an act of disembodied will or of passive attention, neither of which he can find within himself; fifth, present him with new forms in a rigidly preordained order and quantity, so that he will give up utterly the hope of the organic structure which proceeds outward from his own great attraction to the world.

But we need not extend this list. It is obvious that I am

describing the ordinary school. The results of such methods, *in extremis*, can be seen in the behavior of Ramon as he sits beside me for a lesson. His attention is so centered in himself—in his fear of failure, his resentment, his self-contempt—that quite literally he cannot *see* what is under his nose. The words on the paper, the words of the teachers, books, pictures, events of the past—all these belong to *school*, not to the world at large, and certainly not, by prior right, to himself. His passage among persons—among teachers and schoolmates both, and among the human voices of books, films, etc.—is blocked and made painful by his sense of his "place," that is, by the measurements through which he must identify himself: that he has failed all subjects, is last in the class, is older than his classmates, has a "reading problem," etc. He is under coercion of all kinds and no longer knows what it means to express his own wishes simply and hopefully, or to *give* his attention, or to take seriously his doubts and special needs. As for the organic unity of self, mind, and world, he is so fragmented, so invaded by an environment too much for his feeble defenses, that by any serious standard he must be described in terms of crisis.

There can be no doubt that Ramon's experience of public school contributed to his astonishing insufficiencies. There is no doubt, either, that his life at home and on the streets created problems as well. At the First Street School we could do little about the poverty of his home or the violence of the neighborhood, but by making radical changes in his school environment we were able to reverse his long-standing habit of failure and take him through considerable changes in personality.

But now, taking this point of view, namely that much classroom behavior represents a defense against the environment, I would like to look again at two familiar kinds of failure—the "parroting" that Holt found in the better schools (but which occurs in slum schools as well), and the rebelliousness which is common in slum schools but which in fact occurs everywhere. And I would like to ask if there is not some element in both which represents a desperate search for health, a true effort, however confused, to preserve the integrity of the self. I believe that there is such an element. It comes through as a kind of plea, and the plea itself offers decisive clues for remedy.

IV

THE CHILD who parrots, who gives the answer he believes is wanted, gives it because he esteems the wanting, not the answer. The answer means little to him. He is convinced that nothing is expected but performance, and of course the correct answer *is* performance in the sense that his grade follows from it, his standing in the class, and usually his peace of mind at home. In proceeding thus, he is evading the material, but even more importantly he is excluding himself from true interchange with his teachers and classmates. He is afraid to reveal himself, as he must reveal himself if he is to make the material his own by asking his own questions, raising his own doubts, and going at his own pace. In effect, he has rejected himself, obviously in order to avoid rejection by others. But this is only part of the story. For he has accumulated a great deal of evidence which indicates precisely that his own individual needs and style are not wanted; they are an inconvenience, a source of trouble to others and eventually to himself. Furthermore, he has seen that answer-producing is rewarded, that the letter *does* pass for the spirit. This is the way of the world, or so he supposes. And so, not cynically but simply in error and timidity, he tries to bring himself into harmony with it. The fact of harmony, after all, is a primary criterion for the functioning of the self. It overrides other criteria, such as loneliness and anxiety. Nor is this harmony illusory. Rather, the fact is that this world the child has intuited is itself, as a whole, a confused and anxious world, though abounding in material comforts. Here, of course, we are describing the troubled sleep and the soft beds of suburbia. And so it is not contradictory that such children—seemingly secure in the group—remain lonely and anxious. If their anxiety seems out of proportion in their frequently sheltered lives, it is nonetheless real. One false move, one deep revelation of need, threatens not merely a corner but the whole of that little world. A child in this dilemma cannot be helped by innovations in teaching methods, or by improved curricula, or by weekly conferences with the school psychologist. It is essential to make a radical change in his environment, if only to create a true haven. Specifically, a way must be found for him to relate to his elders without having to disavow his own animal and intellectual needs.

As an example of the rebellious child, I would like to describe Maxine, one of the children at the First Street School. She was a rosy-skinned eight-year-old, robust and active, with flashing black eyes and a great deal of wit and awareness in her face. Her intelligence was obvious to everyone, but she had been threatened with expulsion at the public school because of her disruptive behavior. For at least six months at First Street she was "obsessed by sex" and bodily functions. She provoked "sexual" advances from the older boys, the elevens and twelves.

I have been putting the word *sex* in quotation marks. There was a great deal of animal excitement in her behavior, yet it was hardly sexual in the mature sense of the word; that is, her activity did not tend toward genital satisfaction. Nor was she simply curious about sex. She would not have been satisfied by mere explanations. The sexuality normal to her age—which is certainly not a-genital but is diffuse and permeates the physicality of play as élan and tonality rather than as eroticism per se—had been complicated, as had everything else in her personality, by the fact that she was both more infantile than her age-mates and more advanced. She was infantile in her extreme dependence on adults and her insecurity among sibling rivals; she was advanced physically and intellectually and in her vivid sense of her own powers. Thus she was able to manipulate situations but never to her own advantage. Nor could she ask directly for what she wanted, for no matter what she wanted, it brought her into conflict with herself. As was true of many of the children in the school, sex was terribly confused in her mind with violence and contempt of persons. She had surmised, as do so many Americans, that no other obsession is quite so native; yet she had gathered, accurately enough, that it was essentially forbidden. Add to this a profound ignorance of the simple facts of birth and the body, and that her mother had remarried and that another baby was on the way, and you have the picture of a difficult and highly-charged little girl.

Now let us imagine Maxine in a regular classroom. (And let me mention here that *every* child is plagued by apparently special problems and by unmet needs.)

She is quite capable of concentrating for short periods of time. She learns rapidly and well. But the lesson is going on and on. The wooden chair is burning her energetic little fanny. She feels herself vanishing in this swarm of children, who are not only constrained to ignoring her but seem to be flowing toward the teacher, interposing a mass of rivals between herself and her one source of security. The deep confusions of her life are knocking at her forehead—and who better to turn to than a teacher? She does it indirectly. She runs across the room and hugs her favorite boy, and then punches him, and then yells at the teacher—who is now yelling at her—"Do you have a boyfriend? Does he lay on top of you? Where do babies come from? I mean *reallllly*." She wants to say the magic word—and she does say it: *cunt*—which invokes a whole world of power, heat, and confusion. Obviously it is powerful, it makes the grown-ups jump. But pleasure, fertility, violence, are all mixed up here, and she wants desperately to sort them out. And there is her new daddy, and something he has done to her mother; and there is the forthcoming rival.

All these are the facts of her life. If we say that they do not belong in a classroom, we are saying that Maxine does not belong in a classroom. If we say she must wait, then we must also say how long, for the next classroom will be just like this one, and so will the one after that.

"I have a new daddy. He loves me as much as my old daddy. Do you believe that?"

Maxine was too vigorous—and too desperate—to suppress all this. Inevitably it brought her into conflict with her teachers at public school. The teachers, however, made no effort to answer her questions or accommodate her needs. Nor were they able to demonstrate, in their actions, that the discipline they called for represented their own loyalty to rational imperatives. The integrity of individuals does, after all, convince children, just as it convinces adults; it provides a rationale for discipline and self-discipline, for it demonstrates the fruits of both. But it was only too evident that the teachers had given away their integrity in order to hold their jobs. They were unable to make moral judgments and implement them. All that was left was the naked conflict of wills—and Maxine entered this conflict all sails to the wind. Naturally enough, her behavior was self-defeating. Yet it had the virtue of placing her life smack in the center of her relations with adults.

Two aspects of her behavior were profoundly self-protective. First, she was not willing to abandon her animal and psychic needs (nor to suspend her skeptical judgment of adults); and second, she drove unremittingly toward the kind of encounter which leads to true relation.

Where the parroting child is typically rather bland, Maxine was electric and vital. Other of our rebellious children were similarly alive. But the story doesn't end at the age of nine. The rebellious child is starved for true performance and for relationships with adults. His development is arrested. He postpones, and eventually comes to fear, vital impulses of curiosity and emulation. Frustrations accumulate, and he is led down blind alleys of inner conflict. Lacking skills, knowledge, and, ultimately, confidence, the weight of the world lies heavy indeed.

Both parroting and rebelliousness, then, display components which are self-protective. Each style, in its way, wards off a more dangerous collapse. Each is driving toward reality of encounter, that is, toward true relation.

The parroting child is saying, "I need to feel secure in the group and within the framework of authority. I am willing to suppress certain needs in order to achieve this." Our response must be to make his security independent of his performance, so that "artificial learning" will no longer loom as the one method of safety.

The rebellious child is saying, "My life must be included." And we must answer, "Of course! Your life, really, is what it is all about."

V

I HAVE BEEN using the words *reality of encounter, continuum of persons, relation.* All these are vital aspects of environment. When a teacher conceives of his task as mere instruction, the accomplishment of a lesson, and when he addresses himself to his pupils as to containers of varying capacities into which the information must be poured, the children will not find reality of encounter or enter into very supportive relations. The environment militates against their doing so. Testing, grading, seating arrangements according to the teacher's convenience, predigested textbooks, public address systems, guarded corridors and closed rooms, attendance records, punishments, truant officers—all this belongs to an environment of coercion and control. Such an environment has not consulted the needs of normal growth, or the special needs of those whose growth is already impaired.

If the environment of the home is optimal for the great tasks of learning that belong to the early years, it is no longer so by the age of four or five. A larger community is essential, a larger body of peers, and persons of special skills. Yet in order to obtain these, it is not necessary to abandon utterly the environmental qualities that proved so marvelously supportive to the first tasks of learning. Some of them, certainly, can be carried over to the environment of school. At the First Street School, we made much of freedom of choice and freedom of movement; and of reality of encounter between teachers and students; and of the continuum of persons, by which we understood that parents, teachers, friends, neighbors, the life of the streets, form all one substance in the experience of the child. We abolished tests and grades and bells and lesson plans. We abolished Superiors, too—all that petty and disgusting pecking order of the school bureaucracy, which contributes nothing to the wisdom of teachers and still less to the growth of the child. We abolished homework (unless asked for); we abolished the routines of punishment and reward; we abolished the category "truant." And now, lest the apprehensive reader wonder whether what was left very much resembled a school, let me hasten to point out that some of our children covered as much as three years' work in one; and that even Ramon, whom I have discussed, reversed his long-standing habit of failure. This is especially noteworthy in that half of our children came to us from the public schools with severe "learning and behavior problems."

Since we removed so many of the external sources of

order, it might be well to mention here that we were not, on that account, thrown into chaos, but were put into contact with factors which might be called *internal* sources of order. In the broadest terms, I mean simply this: that children *do* want to learn. They are powerfully motivated by nature; this motivation, properly respected, is a trustworthy source of order. Similarly, there are adults who do want to teach, who find themselves and expend their love in precisely this function. They too are strongly motivated, and their motivation is a source of order.

VI

I WOULD LIKE to put this last point in more specific terms. Here are three familiar kinds of unruliness: first, the children talk among themselves, paying no attention to the teacher and interfering with the attention given by others; second, the unruly ones nag at the teacher and sabotage his efforts; third, the children struggle or fight over some object, a pencil, a book, a candy bar. In the crowded classrooms of the public schools, things of this sort, countered by efforts to stifle them, are endlessly disturbing. Even in smaller classes they prove to be difficult if the teacher is much devoted to formal discipline.

Now here are some incidents I observed at First Street:

(1) Marilyn and Nora, the former nine, the latter eleven, both Puerto Rican, begin talking to each other during the lesson in arithmetic, paying no attention to Susan, their teacher. To make matters worse, several of the other children begin to listen to them. Instead of calling the class to order, however, Susan, too, cocks an ear. Nora is talking about her older sister, who is eighteen. Their mother had bought a voodoo charm, and the charm had been stolen. Dodie, a Negro girl of nine, enters the conversation, saying in a low voice, "Voodoo! It don't mean nuthin'!" "What kind of charm?" says Susan. "A charm against *men!*" says Nora—and now the whole class begins to discuss it. Sandra, a Negro girl of nine, says in her broad, slow way, "Phooey! I bet she stole it herself. I know somebody I'd use that thing on." Susan agrees with Dodie that voodoo probably doesn't

work, "though maybe it has a psychological effect."
"Yeah," says Nora, "it makes you afraid." The discussion
lasts ten or twelve minutes, and then all return again to
arithmetic.

(2) Ramon bursts into song or jumps up and
executes dance steps during our sessions in reading. This
has nothing to do with exuberance; it is compulsive and
frantic. But it is essential that he do it. The honest effort
he is putting into his work arouses an intolerable anxiety,
and he needs to boil it off and to feel the vigor of his
body so as to reassure himself that he is "all there."

(3) Nora and Maxine are howling and screaming,
pushing and punching, one with endlessly voluble Carib-
bean fury, the other with the wide-open, full-throttle
voice of New York emergencies, cab drivers in a traffic
jam, bargain-day shoppers at Klein's. Each claims possession of a piece of red corduroy cloth, a queen's gown in
their theatrical game, now in its fourth day. Children and
teachers alike are impressed by the ardor of this conflict,
and by the obvious issue of justice, for the gown cannot,
in fact, belong to both, though both are shouting, "It's
mine!" "Where did it come from?" cries the teacher.
Nora repeats, "It's mine!"—but Maxine, who now has
tears in her eyes, yells, "My mother gave it to me!" "All
right, we'll call Maxine's mother and find out." There is
immediate silence, broken only by Maxine's voice, now
much lower (pointing her finger at Nora): "You'll see,
boy." Now fifteen children gather around the telephone
—the conclusion of which conference is the teacher's an-
nouncement, standing up: "It belongs to Maxine. Her
mother gave it to her." Nora hands it over, and Maxine
limits her triumph to: "See! I told you, didn't I?" All the
other faces have that grave, almost stoical child-look of
Important Issues Really Settled.

There is no such thing as uncaused behavior; and children, far more than adults, are transparently close to the
causes. When these causes are included in the business of
the day, the children are quick to make use of the consideration shown to themselves. In doing this they inevitably put
themselves into relation with the natural authority of adults,
for precisely this authority is what they are making use of.

The nature of the authority is obvious. The adults are larger, are experienced, possess more words, have entered into prior agreements among themselves. When children are convinced of the possibility of justice, such differences as these take on a positive, and not merely a negative, character. The adults are protectors; they are repositories of certitude, approval, novelty, skills. In the fact that they have entered into prior agreements, the child intuits a seriousness in the life that surrounds him, and he is not indifferent to its benefits and demands.

These two things—the needs of children and the natural authority of adults—taken together are the large repository of what I have called internal sources of order. The child is always *finding* himself, moving toward himself, as it were, in the near distance. The adult is his ally, his model, and his obstacle (for there are natural conflicts, too, and they must be given their due).

It is not difficult, then, even with unruly children, to give a coherent, organic shape to the enterprise of the classroom, though it is essential, obviously, to depart widely from the confines of the lesson. It should be borne in mind, however, that normal growth is not a step-by-step progression but includes fits and starts, momentary regressions, plateaus, and sudden leaps. Nothing is less realistic than imposing a uniform continuity upon all, as if to say that growth must look like growth every hour every day. This is bad faith and impatience. Month by month, year by year, the real pattern is discernible. Rousseau's old dictum is profoundly true: ". . . the most useful rule of education is: Do not save time, but lose it."

Nora is the child I was referring to when I mentioned three years' work accomplished in one. Maxine, too, underwent spectacular changes. After a year and a half, she was reading two to three years above her grade level and had become relatively cooperative with her classmates and teachers. We *lost time* with these children prodigiously. By far the greater part of every day was given over to free play, and to trips, and to such lively scheduled classes as singing and dancing.

Here is a description Susan wrote of Nora:

This child from a Spanish-speaking home entered the school generally doing first-grade work at the age of eleven. She spoke adequate "school English," but did not know the vocabulary for common household objects. Her school failure had given her a resentful conviction that she was "stupid." Actually, she was quite intelligent. She used to settle all disputes with her fists, steal, and wantonly destroy property. When she left, after a year and a half, she could be trusted with large sums of money, showed respect for other people's possessions, and —most important—had stopped trying to beat everybody up. By the time she transferred to a public school in the Bronx, her English vocabulary had increased a hundred-fold. She was doing advanced fourth-grade work in all subjects and expressed a desire to go to college.

A Passion to Learn

Paul West

I

EXCEPTIONAL CHILDREN come in two kinds, advanced and retarded. Both, like jugglers and mystics and astronauts, are astounding, especially the second kind, of which I've had a close view for six years. Amanda West, the daughter who is my theme, didn't seem unusual—not to mention exceptional—until she was two. Slow to speak, she was cautious about starting to walk; but once she had walked she ran like a bird preparing to take off. She fell in love, as well, with water and umbrellas, and in the presence of either orated vehemently (although nonverbally) to herself. Water she preferred in puddles on the living-room floor or in baths, but she also liked it in rainspouts, saucepans, and lavatory basins. Umbrellas—which, I think, exerted the stronger spell—she collected with casual relentlessness. She never had fewer than a dozen. They were her trees, really: a plastic-leaved, tin-branched orchard of them, which every night had to be rolled up firm and laid across her bed, and every morning landed in a cascade on ours when she came heavy-footedly in, hooting for them to be opened. Then, with half-blind eyes, down to the living room where we spread them over the floor like Pan and Company afforesting a bare mountain while she, red-cheeked with elation, danced among them, catching occasionally the beads on the rib-ends and skimming the canopies half-around, but never trampling the handles or ramming a fist through the fabric.

She would stand, do a preliminary skip to get her timing right—a one-two-three with her big toes creased downward as if to scratch earth—and then flow into a joyous high-kneed pounding, her long hair a flash, her arms providing her with a tightrope-walker's balance, her eyes unobtainably fixed on an upper corner of the room, where she saw what no one else saw. She looked and smiled, and danced the more wildly for it, fueling her semi-tarantella from the presence in the vacancy.

Fred, we began to say, domesticating the ghost: *it's Fred again*. And so, each morning, with a flim and a flam, and a flim again, followed by a swift series of flim-flams, she danced spread-eagled, lithe, and bony, chirping on an empty stomach.

We began to wonder, hard as it was even to begin to do it, if she wasn't deaf or autistic. Or.both. To think a thing is to make it so, whereas to deny it is to abolish it—especially on the Isle of Man, Amanda's home, island of witches, banshees, and temperamental goblins. But being not altogether pagan, we kept on wondering until the day we took her to the mainland, to the Manchester University Audiology Clinic. It was winter, the sea heaving and pumice-gray; so we flew in a BEA Viscount, lurching through the rain, and Amanda, at each plunge or sideslip, let out a birdcall of delight.

Born on the island, she had never been off it—never been Across to England—and now, leaving it for the first time, she seemed isolated in a new way. Her three words—"baba," "more," and "ish-ish"—she had used heroically, intending meanings we missed and being credited with others that we invented. I listened to the lax, feathered whine of the engines, wondering what noise they made to her as she sat smiling into the clouds. I'd heard, I told myself, on humid days, the squeak of my sinuses filling, and then a pop of contraction on a day of high pressure, with all the sinews and membranes tugging and fluctuating in a mucous orchestration. But that was nothing to what I imagined for Amanda's head: a tinnitus of bad bells, a frying noise, which in combination drove her to cup a hand over her right ear and rock heavily to that side as if trying to shake something loose or back into place or—thought ended: the

two-foot doll that bathed with Amanda in the teeth-chatter-
ing English bathroom and that we brought with us on the
plane, slipped sideways from my casual hug, and a cache
of bathwater spilled into my lap. My fault, I said; you
can't blame a stark-naked doll.

When we landed, Amanda whooped down the steps from
the plane. It was still raining, but we had two umbrellas,
both hers. The only trouble was that she didn't want them
open or up; they had to be carried before us like totems,
one red, the other green, every loose fold clamped tight by
a rubber band. Two umbrellas, kept from getting wet, made
good folk stare; but good folk knew nothing of umbrellas,
water, and Amanda. In the taxi, however, she opened up
the red umbrella and sat in an indifferent silence, an erect-
sitting being of utter trustfulness, heedless of the roof-lining
she might puncture, and with no more idea of where she
was going than of where she had come from. Out of the
taxi, she insisted, with a plangent squeak, on the umbrella's
being folded again and rebound in its rubber band. Then
she was ready to march with us past the porter's lodge
(empty), wrongly up steps to the Department of Law and
down again, and finally into a waiting room stocked with
heavy, ridable toys, and equipped with tiny toilets whose
still water she inspected and approved.

Called for, we went left into the laboratory (one wall of
which was a one-way window facing a lecture room).
Amanda stared at the people, the things, and, it seemed, at
Fred, whom she has always been able to find anywhere. She
grew busy and began to chirp. When, to her exact satisfaction, she had arranged the umbrellas and the doll on a low
table, she turned to the experts with a patronizing smile.
We sat and watched—her mother at one end of the room,
myself (still feeling damp) at the other—helpless on the
perimeter and unable to smoke. There was some tinkering
with a green box, all dials, and a chart. The door snicked
open, admitting an authoritative-looking face which
beamed and vanished. Then testing began with overtures
of friendship from the studious-mannered man whose
trousers looked as if he kneeled a lot. The calm woman in
patent-leather high heels clicked a tiny clicker, but Amanda
did not turn. They gave her a doll then and tried her from

behind with a duck quack, a whistle of low pitch, several rattles, then a small tom-tom. Abruptly, not having turned, she ran to the table, slammed one doll alongside the other and hooted, with finger pointed, for the red umbrella to be opened. There were nods; the umbrella opened, sprang taut, was set in her hands, and she squatted, drawing it down over her as if sheltering under a thin, frail mushroom, slipping out a hand to adjust a downslid sock, and beginning to make again the birdcall (as if a curlew tried to bleat) which had driven countless local dogs into emulative frenzy, provoked birds into surpassing themselves (searching for a bird, they never saw *her*), and scared all the cats away.

Private under the panels of vinyl, she sang with mounting fervor, the umbrella stem between her legs. No one moved. It was clear that she was going to be given her leisure, allowed to collect herself. In succession she fluted her voice upward in an ecstatic trill, twirled the umbrella like a color disc without once catching the rim or the plastic against her face (a perfect, sheltering fit it was), peeped out to giggle just a bit fearfully, hoisted the umbrella up and away behind her in a pose from *The Mikado*, and then hid again beneath it. We had seen her face shining with heat, seen her only long enough for that.

Now they tapped on her roof, flicked middle finger hard off thumb against the fabric, and brought their mouths close to the surface, calling her name. Out she came, astounded at something heard: not her name, because she didn't know it, but something—a retaliating and envious dog, a curlew weary of being competed with, a cat returning to venture a duet—amplified and vibrating in the umbrella above her, but only faces and maneuvering mouths to make it. Us. Us only; so she concealed herself again, tilting the canopy forward.

What brought her out again and kept her out was the xylophone. She abandoned the umbrella for it, fondled it a while, then beat the living decibels out of it, a Lionel Hampton Lilliputian who struck away and then canted her ear close to the trembling bars, her eyes widening in half-piqued recognition that *this* was what we'd flown her across the sea for. She banged on it with her wooden hammer a few times more and let it fall the two-and-a-half feet to the parquet, wincing once in the wrong direction as it hit.

After calls, hums, hisses, pops, buzzes, barks, bays, and several indeterminate ululations, all from behind her, they did the left side while she smiled at a distracting monkey puppet over on the right. My hands were holding each other too tightly; her mother, twelve yards down the room, looked pale, her maternality shut painfully off and her own hand beginning gestures that ended halfway, the fingers tongue-tied.

"Now," said the studious, kneeling man, his kindly face tense, and snapped two wooden bars together. A slapstick, I thought; like the split lath of the harlequin. But whatever was going on, it wasn't low comedy. What he said next, after a fractional shake of his head to the woman in heels— the professional pair's exchange of glances crossing the parental one—sounded like:

"Right down the track." The headshake was a zero in mime.

Amanda smiled at the puppet, offering her hand to put inside it. They let her, working through all the modes of sound, but not to a crescendo, only to a punctuational drum-tap which she ignored. And then, as the light waned —that legendary dank Manchester light swollen with soot and rain and absorbed by tons on tons of Victorian brick and tile—they switched sides, this time beguiling her with a model farm at which she sat, cantankerously checking the cows for udders (as a country girl should) and stationing Clydesdale horses at the water trough. Brilliants of wet formed along her narrow nose, and she heard not the snap-crack of the wooden bars: not the first time, anyway. But when it came from a yard closer—these testers gliding about the room like prankish Druids—she flinched, directed an offended stare in a vaguely right-hand direction, and went back to her farm. Again and again they worked from the right, varying the angle and the sound. Again and again, with just a few moments of preoccupied indifference, she jerked her head sideways, beginning to be cheerful as she discovered the routine: beginning to play.

Suddenly there was no farm. It went into a gray steel cabinet against which Amanda kicked and at which she took a running kick as her eyes began to pour (tears whopping enough, I thought, to merit nostrils for conduits) and her birdcall harshened. As she swung, both-handed, the xylophone at the locked handle of the door, I got up, stuck out a hand as I half-fell in a skid on the polish. I took a tonic sol-fa smack in the forehead as she swung the instrument backward again, farther than before, the better to mangle the steel between her and the authentic cows, the horses a-thirsting.

"Ap," I sort of said through the plong and the blank crash, not seeing well. "You might as well get it out again."

"Naughty girl," her mother said unconvincedly as Amanda laugh-cried, pitching the xylophone over her shoulder without so much as a look. I have seen her dispose in the same way of bus tickets, mail, money, books, food, scissors, and plates. The oubliette is anywhere behind her.

"She'll soon—" I heard, but the rest was drowned by a scream of unmitigated anger while Amanda pounded the cabinet with both fists.

"Strong!" called the man who kneeled a lot, busying himself with earphones attached to the many-dialed machine. "She's a grand temper."

"You've seen nothing," I told him. "Yet." I knew how, in the Cleopatra-Clytemnestra rages to which she entitled herself, she could butt her head through a firm window (one so far, without bloodshed, but there were long blond hairs on the splinters of glass). Or pound her uncallused hand down through the crisp and warm pulp of a loaf not long out of the oven, once burying her hand and bringing her arm up with a bread mallet wedged on her wrist, crying "Ish! Ish!" which is anthem, plea, and threat in one.

But it wasn't "Ish" she came out with this time; it was the first of her calls, "Baba—babababa," uttered with pauses only long enough for everyone present to shout the same phonemes back at her. If you didn't, she increased the volume, blustering and raucous. It was the most comprehensive aural version of herself. So the clinic-room, soundproof of course (there is even a sign just inside the entrance requesting silence), became a barnyard for a while. Turning wet-eyed, grime-faced, to each of us in turn, she babbled at us, coercing, commanding, appealing;

and in turn and sometimes in unison we babbled and brayed back, short only of a cock-a-doodle-doo, the hymn of a pig wallowing or even farrowing in hot lava, and a moose drowning in a swamp of caviar. This, so that the testing could go on; one farmyard for another.

In the beginning is the test, and in the end comes a remedy of sorts. But how, I wondered, can they even begin —overworked but obliged not to rush; never short of children to work with, one in six being somehow deaf and usually not deaf only—until they too have run their fingers across the crowns of her blunt, curiously thick teeth, have seen her dance a full hour among the umbrellas, have night after night studied her fanatical attention to the placing of her slippers within an invisible outline which is there and symmetrical for her beneath the chest of drawers in her bedroom.

"You haven't—" I began to say on our third trip to the clinic, seen her do the living things; give Creation a run for its money. Not at home. They hadn't seen her, like a gross Ophelia, distribute around the house—on the window ledges, in the wardrobe between two decent suits or dresses, on the rim of the letter box, on the Christmas tree itself—pork sausages on butcher's hooks or threaded on wire coat-hangers. Or eat the sausage raw, oblivious of worms. Or, in hydrodynamic delight, rip off shoes and socks to plant her bare feet on the TV screen whenever it showed water. Or (I stopped: they were calling her name again and she wasn't ever going to answer) sit naked and warbling for an hour in a washbasin of cold water. Or green her face with eye-shadow, eat nail-varnish, coat the windows with lavender furniture polish, jump down five stairs fearlessly, mimic (by waving a stiffened arm) men carrying umbrellas, chant into a toilet pedestal after choking it with a whole roll of tissue, chew cigarettes, cover herself with Band-Aids when there wasn't a scratch in sight, climb any ladder and refuse to descend, slide pencils up her nose, use a rubber hammer on the doctor's private parts, drink from her potty, wade into a sewer-inspection chamber the plumber had opened, eat six bananas in six minutes, wind and play an alarm clock at her right ear time and again, shave her face and arms and legs with instant lather and bladeless razor, threaten enormous dogs by advancing upon them with a reed in hand, cut her own hair at random, dissolve soap in a tin basin, rock so hard that her hair touched the floor on either side, sit motionless and rapt in front of a mirror, voluminously autograph walls, tear samples from the dictionary or a book of Picasso prints, stare unblinking into 150-watt bulbs, run, run, run everywhere, heedless of gesticulating and half-felled adults and the sanity of drivers.

"Mandy . . . *Mandy* . . . MANDY," they said, upping the decibels as she gazed from them to the red finger spinning across the dial and back again. When she heard them, her expression changed, fixing in atavistic wonder. Funny, it was as if we were watching the face of sound itself while she, flushed and nervous, heard something visible. After an interval they let her use the microphone herself, and she began to boom and call in an almost continuous orgy of sound, confronted for the first time with her own share of the missing continent: a Columbus of euphony dumbfoundedly exclaiming at the glories of exclamation itself, every bit like the man in Xenophon who kept shouting *thalassa!* when he saw the sea. I myself felt a bit like shouting; I'd never heard anyone hearing before. And since then I've known a good many firsts with her—things which, up to then, I'd done without really experiencing them, or which she herself thought up and I myself had never dreamed of doing. Some of the latter are grotesque and sometimes rather revolting as well; I try not to do them, but usually Amanda prevails, imperious queen with her dithering court. I do as I am told. Most people would. You have to; that's where the education begins.

II

SHE QUICKENS in you the sense of life; makes you grateful for what's granted, what's *taken* for granted. A handicap so severe drives you through fury, then through an empty, vengeful indignation, to two points: first, when, in the absence of explanations medical and reasons cosmic, you ignore the handicap to make it go away; second, nearer to common sense, when you welcome it in as her special gift and, while trying to eliminate it, learn its nature by heart as a caution to yourself, and study the voracious subtlety of her compensations—as when she, unlike most of us, smells at a pencil newly sharpened, inhaling from the beechwood its own soot-sour bouquet, or traces with addicted fingers the corrugations on the flat of a halved cabbage before eating it raw with the same naturalness with which she drinks vinegar, steak sauce, and mayonnaise, and sniffs glue. I too, now, have tasted ink (a flavor of charred toenail), coal (a rotted iron-and-yeast pill), bark (woolly and raw, suggesting vulcanized crabmeat), leather (a taste here not of the meat or fat next the hide but of the fur once outside it and of seaweed-iodine).

Tasting—testing—with her, I have found new ways into the world. She discovers what she discovers because she has lost what she's lost. I tag along on her voyages, and together we sneak into the randomness, the arbitrariness, of the universe as distinct from its patterns. Without her—although I have in my time delighted in *The Compleat Angler*'s bald and bland arcana, in insect and fungus books, in Jean Rostand's reports on tadpoles and toads—I don't think I would be delving, as I now am, with strangely relevant irrelevance, into the behavior of slugs, mushrooms, cicadas, and flesh-eating plants, or into a way of death called atherosclerosis, the result not (I learn) of saturated fats yielding cholesterol but of unsaturated fats—much used in the paint and varnish industry—varnishing our insides with lipofuscin. Because she brandished it at a big dog, I found out about Great Reed Mace (*Typha latifolia*), often wrongly called the bulrush, but rightly, I reckon, thought sexy. The black six-foot stem is a long cheroot, topped by a yellow spike, and, as my *Observer's Book of Wild Flowers* says, "the closely packed pistillate flowers forming the 'mace' consist of a stalked ovary, with a slender style and a one-sided, narrow stigma, and enveloped in tufts of soft, brownish hairs."

I keep two books, one for what Amanda does, one for what I find out while waiting for our first conversation. She ate a dandelion flower some time back; one day I'll try her with the leaves in oil and vinegar, that good salad. I have a lot to tell her which, thank goodness, I've been late in learning: the hyena isn't quite the scavenger he's supposed to be, whereas the almost extinct American Bald Eagle is a scavenger out and out. And so on; it's a question, really, of finding a life-style, of opening up for myself a universe into which she fits. So I try to devise for her the biggest memberships possible, now and then blundering from wishful thinking into wishful biology, but at other times enrolling her in majestic clans we'd stare at if we knew about them, just as some of the inhumanly ordinary on the earth have stared at her.

Take the shark, created perpetually with two inexplicable handicaps: it has no swim bladder, so must keep on the move or sink; its fixed, paired fins have hardly any braking effect and no motive power, which means that it finds difficulty stopping or reversing. A shark, therefore, is compulsive and a bit helpless; no one knows why. But all sharks are handicapped thus; whereas what I am casting around for is a handicap not just inexplicable but also affecting a minority only. Trying again, I come up with such samples of a partly mismanaged universe as so-called "waltzing" mice, which have an abnormality of that part of the inner ear concerned with balance; the hereditary deafness found in white dogs like Dalmatians and Bull Terriers; *Gentian acaulis,* which for reasons unknown refuses to flower in good soil but does well where the acid and lime counts are high; holly, whose greenish flowers are sometimes bisexual, although sometimes male and female flowers exist on *separate* plants (which is why they tell you to plant hollies in groups); uranium 235, old faithful of an unstable and vulnerable isotope which is as it is because it isn't otherwise; the particle for which, it seems, there is no antiparticle; flawed crystals in which one atom is where another should be or where no atom ought to be at all; the so-called incoherence of natural light, traveling as it does in brief packets of energy in random directions at uncorrelated times, compared with the light from an optical maser; acridines, believed to produce mutations which consist in the deletion or addition of a base or bases from the DNA chain. Such is the beginning of my list: Amanda's alibi, not so much an excuse (the popular sense) as her being genuinely elsewhere while the universe put a foot wrong with that mouse or this crystal, but suffering a similar misadministration that relates her more closely than most people to Nature; a Nature I never really noticed until it bungled.

As a factory, Nature—the more familiar end of the universe—is more reliable than the best baseball pitcher ever, but less reliable than the London Underground. To be sure, where it falters it sometimes lowers its guard usefully: U 235 gives us the chain reaction, or at least the possibility of it; the misbehaving particle may teach us something about the "elementariness" of particles (e.g., are two different particles equally fundamental or is one merely an "excited" state of the other?). The imperfect crystal tells physicists a great deal about the mechanical properties of solids. And the deaf—also, perhaps, in this case, the autistic and/or brain-damaged—child, from whom I have wandered briefly only to hunt out some of her peers and analogues, is equally instructive, preparing you for the next phase, in which you find what I will call the superior intricacy of one child at the deaf-blind unit at Condover in England: a child born without eyes or ears and with all internal organs so garbled that sex cannot be determined. Yet he/she knows how to get angry, is eager to sniff at things and people alike. Something on the lines of "Age 6—80 decibel hearing loss—IQ 120" says nothing much if you are willing to learn something more; neither does "Age 7—hearing nil—sight nil—sex?—IQ minimal" if you have a passion to learn (I intend the ambiguity). How you proceed from the statistics depends on who and what you are, how much of Nature you're willing to look at; but, pretty certainly, there will be some desperation in your proceeding. Which, given such standard desirables as warmth, light, and some health, may not be a bad thing. It's a bit like writing the prospective novel—being a prospector for fiction in uncharted areas —inasmuch as you don't know where you will end up or how.

To put it topically, locally: you run the home around the child. You learn her ignorances until they are yours. You steal her condition from her by risky analogies, like the mystic borrowing the lover's terms, like the lover borrowing the mystic's. You give your Amanda a glut of olibles, tangibles, edibles, and visibles: all the perfumes of Arabia; all the grades of sandpaper, leading up to a feel at an elephant; all the fluents from goat's milk to mercury; all the spices from cinnamon to chili; all the zoos, parades, Dufys, flags, unwanted *National Geographics*, French colonial stamps, travel posters, and rainbows you can muster. Always a color camera: preferably Polaroid, because she doesn't like to wait.

Against all this—the stark handicap and any voluptuously zany sharing in it—set a thought neither apocalyptic nor original. Ten years after the atomic explosion on Bikini Atoll, birds were sitting on sterile eggs; turtles, instead of going back to the sea after laying their own eggs, pressed on to the island's interior where they died of thirst. Their skeletons remain, thousands of them, evidence of a gratuitous handicap we might have had the brains to do without.

III

IT IS three years since that first visit to the clinic when powerlessness hit home to us. The strain told on Amanda too. She fetched a shovel from the garden to destroy with: lighting fixtures, windows, crockery, clocks. Strong always, she lifted and swung it with ease, pouting with birdcall. It took her two years to reject the shovel, to change from indefatigable and destructive hobgoblin into a girl who, gaining a word a month only to lose it the month after, developed luminously beautiful, big, Nordic features. Capable, without warning, of histrionic graciousness of manner (as if all the pressures lifted at once and the noises in her head stopped), she enjoyed her increasingly frequent visits to the clinic (toys, earphones, EEG apparatus), ate mightily, hardly ever caught a cold, thumped obliviously past staring or derisive children, and rebaffled the experts. Deaf, yes; "stone" deaf (in that melodramatic inversion of the pathetic fallacy) in the left ear; autistic, perhaps, but that's a vague word like "romantic"; brain damage not ruled out; amblyopia mentioned, with an ophthalmologist joining her team.

At five she left the island for the last time, blasé by now about Viscounts, to live near the clinic and the school associated with it. I signed out a speech-trainer, donated by the

Variety Artists' Federation, on which she had a daily lesson, dealing sometimes in words, sometimes in sheer noise. She did her jigsaws like an impatient robot, began to lip-read, and gradually built up and kept a tiny vocabulary enunciated with almost coy preciosity, intoning "more" like an aria, raising "hair" into "har," curtailing "mouth" into "mou," lengthening "nose" into a three-second sound, but all the same *talking* although she still didn't know her name. Nicknames accumulated: Moo, from Mandy-Moo; Birdie, from her call; Tish from "ish-ish"; Lulu (developed cunningly from the two-syllable, high-pitched call with which her mother called her in; Yee (which sound she herself had substituted for Baba); Proof, from the condition called Manda-proof, she being the only thing or person invulnerable to herself, or so we said; and, strangest of all to strangers, Boat (her word for water—until she got *worbar*—shouted while paddling her feet on the TV screen). Epic formulae, these, while she went incognito.

During one spell, she averaged only three hours' sleep a night, erupting at midnight with umbrellas and jigsaws, then fetching a guitar, one mechanical top, several model baths, a dish brimming with soap dissolved, a length of iron piping, and a purloined fruit-knife, with all of which to while the night away until she could go out. And always wet. She became frenetic, twitched more than ever, during this waiting period: all that soothed her was running water, the swing in the garden, and ghoulish faces I pulled while pursuing her up the stairs. She partnered everyone at the lavatory, exclaiming "Oh" in exaggerative dismay at anyone's being under the vile necessity and then seeking to examine the deposit. But, we noticed, her "Yee" was less strident, less insistent; a month later, it had become a delicate, diffident greeting to be answered just as quietly, and she became drier, banged her head less, was less obsessed by the grotesque or the effluvial, gave up rending the day's newspaper, lost her passion for knives, began to draw faces and bodies that had two eyes, not one, with two legs instead of a barbed-wire entanglement of blue ball-point. She even drew a bath—always the long throne of her joy—with a Mandy in it.

She took the intelligence test and passed it before, after

forty minutes' concentration, she flung the next puzzle across the room and mounted a full-size tantrum. The children's hospital lost her file, and two starch-bosomed nurses lost their cool when she screamed twenty minutes solid because they took from her the model jet kept to calm little boys during EEG tests. She thought it was a present.

"I'll buy it," I said against the screams. "It's worth it." No, that was out of the question; it was part of the equipment—it was government property. She vanished into the pathology lab, and was there found admiring fetuses, tumors, and cysts in their quiet jars, a true humanist explaining to her what was what. We got her a jet at the airport, and, later, a helicopter, a new swing, a miniature cooking set in Bavarian iron, building blocks, card games, a thousand candy cigarettes, as many lollipops and ices: a surplus for purposes of habilitation.

Out of the clutter has come a girl who can make beds, bake bread, fry bacon, iron and fold clothes, hoover the carpets, mow the lawn (she calls escalators "bo" now), set a table, adjust the TV, fell apples from the tree by swatting it with a tennis racquet, tune her own hearing-aid, on her best days say "roundabout" as "rounabou" and "elephant" as almost that (it's otherwise known as "NO-o-se"), and on most days recite her own name. She cried and shuffled not at all when she began at the school for the deaf, a day-girl, almost six. She dotes on baths, Scotch tape (which she calls *yap*), steaks, and tenon saws, has become unoffendably gregarious, has learned to spit, looks through illustrated magazines with an anthropologist's gravity, has discovered how "No" doubles her range of concepts, and, I realize, sees Fred less and less. The Martian, we call her, or Miss Rabelais. Photogenic, long and agile, she has about forty words all told, a schoolbag and a homework book, which is all penumbra to the darkness of Amanda invading the house with a big shovel, sometimes a coal hammer, and that unfailing drooped-eyelid leer.

One special thing left a new light shining. Her class of nine children, working by the loop that amplifies sound identically for them whichever way they turn, was told to draw a spider's web. All drew but Amanda, who sat abstractedly apart, aloof from this planet. No one saw her move—and, being ambidextrous, she could have done it with either hand—but when the teacher got to her, Amanda was *yee*-ing gently beside a perfectly delineated web, all done in one unbroken line, with a spider at center. It's a prized school exhibit now, which she can bring home at year's end, when, presumably, she will bury it unsentimentally in her crate of junk in which, I once thought, she meant to bury us all, outclassed by her energy, thwarted by her privacy, heartsick at Nature's misbehavior, and as short of new expedients as of sleep.

One day, home from school with her homework book in which the teacher uses the special alphabet ("home" is "hoem"), she will extend *yee* into what I think it is, what it has been all along. I mean *yes*, and so will she, even if she's as incoherent as daily light, as vulnerable as uranium 235, and has an atom where an atom shouldn't be.

Epithalamium

John Knoepfle

CROSSING Illinois
from Chicago to Savanna
on the Burlington line
the braying diesel
steelily halted between two hills.
The conductor had the cause,
the president of that great
Illinois line
was wedding in his spats
and his tails O
and I think this was done
at eleven on the dot in the morning O
wasn't that fine
all the trains that were running
on the Burlington line
stopped between hills
when he got married O
but it would have been better
if they locked their wheels
on those moonhoned tracks
when he was striking twelve O
oh yes that great president
of the Burlington line
when he took off his spats
and slipped off his tails
and he was all aboard
ringing in the midnight O.

Survival

M. F. Beal

LILLIAN TWITCHED the white nylon dress from the
shower head and fluffed the skirt briskly. With small grunting explosions of breath and snatches of hummed sound
she twined slip straps, tucked hems, waistlines even; tied,
buttoned, and zipped herself into her day's routine, watching all the time the ragged crest of firs beyond the window
and their illuming tips. Dawn, then suddenly day and sun
and a stirring wind. She released one last satisfied throat-
sound, then flicked off the light and strode from her room-
and-a-half to her Burger Hut. The slam of the birch door
punctuated her engagement with the day.

"Whew!" she spat, pausing. It was still night in the Hut.
The long counter was islanded by stale smoke, white
enamel surfaces glaring stingingly; a stale patter of grease
slicked from the grill. The floor, impenetrably scuffed
and mounded at the door with red mud, had a look of
failure. A lone customer stirred his coffee in grating
circles.

So she shouted hello to Helen, somewhere behind frying
bacon, hotcakes, and the lone coffee drinker, and began
to clean for the day, or at least to tidy. She turned off lights,
nodding as surfaces were again reduced to function. She
swept with orderly strokes, humming on the downbeat,
shoes squeaking. She watched the highway, went out with
the wire broom and swept toward the road shoulder, inspected passing cars and glared as they passed, knowing
their occupants needed a good hot breakfast as she began to
sense her own emptiness. Finally, a small headache creep-
ing up, she unreeled the hose, watered red and white
petunias, flushed the walkway and went in for breakfast.

The customer looked from his plate and nodded as she
planted elbows around her coffee cup and tried the first

sips with a great taking-in of air. "Uhm." The radio played a war song, vaguely familiar. She thought for just an instant of Harry. There was kitchen clatter, then car sound. Pursing her lips, turning curiously, she saw the purple and cream Plymouth pull up to the house next door, this time with a U-Haul.

That guy, she thought, looking over the partition at Helen. Must be broke . . . Why doesn't he . . . "Say," she said aloud when Helen saw her staring, "fix me something, will you? Don't tell me what, just—something." She sipped the cooling coffee. Must be broke, moving in with her. He never will learn . . .

The customer rattled the morning paper and hunched back over the ruins of his breakfast.

"What's happening?" she asked. The radio buzzed with the DJ's insistent voice. She flicked it low. "What's happening?"

The customer looked up, back down. "Oh, more of the same."

"Yeah?" She slid down the counter toward him and he looked up, startled. Helen brought her breakfast as she stared at the newspaper around his arm. "Thanks, hon," she said, turning to the eggs and hashbrowns. With obvious hunger she began to fit them between her dark wet lips.

SHE DRANK her second cup of coffee and stared at the purple and cream Plymouth parked in front of Helen's house. It belonged to Helen's ex-husband. The day before as Helen worked her shift she said he'd called again, wanting to come see her. Helen asked Lillian what to do. Helen was a pushover; married twice to the guy and twice divorced and still willing to listen when he called. Lillian couldn't get across to her that she had to give up on a bad thing. So this morning he came, bright and early, carrying something or other under his arm. Well then, at least he wasn't broke. Thank God for small favors.

As she watched the car, her own husband's hard-to-remember face flitted through her mind and she tried to fix it for a moment; hadn't seen or heard from him in nearly fifteen years, since two weeks after he left her and Harry, so whenever she thought of him it was of an aging boy with still-curly hair and a mad grin bursting to display his strong, even white teeth. She sucked egg residue from her molars and sipped again, reflectively.

"That's disgusting," the customer was saying sharply, batting the paper with a folded five-dollar bill. "How come they put stuff like that right on the front page?" It was a picture of an oriental face bundled about with print fabric and splayed, stick arms. A woman, one guessed, because below the shut dead eyes a smaller child's face watched with erupting tears.

"Yeah," she said, running her ragged red nail across it as if to pin down or make contact with the message.

"And it says here it's just a setup, anyhow, propaganda," the customer said, and paid.

She made change but failed quite to grasp how a picture of a dead woman could be propaganda. "Izzen it awful," she mumbled, flicking the radio dial loud and calling out: "Bye now," as the door shut tinkling.

Harry was dead. It was months already since his coffin had been returned.

THE TINY TRANSISTOR belched magically, a cornucopia of noise. The DJ, a grown man's larynx surrounded by a teen-age mind, rambled about "oar tewn" and "lewcal proide" and how it would be "gosh, great" if we all got out to line the highway when the visitors from Neuhoftal, "oar sister city from across the waves" arrived in their motorcade.

Motorcade brought a sudden tinselly feeling to Lillian, a recollection of colored floats and summer sun: "Let's see, where did I put those signs they gave me?" She dumped her empty cup into the tepid suds behind the counter where it drifted down clattering. "Uhm." Sifting through dusty inked cardboards, adding-machine tapes, and ball points, she finally found the C of C offerings:

WELCOME
SISTER CITY DELEGATION
from
NEUHOFTAL, GERMANY

When she had set them against the heating flyspecked glass, she ran outside to inspect; the motorcade would pass right by, see her place . . . behind her the DJ's voice mounted: "and I got to thinkeen, wouldn't it be noice if we could greet these visitors with just a word or two in their own language, just sometheen simple, hello in German . . . so you out there who know German, give us a call, will you? And here's the German National Anthem . . ."

To the opening strains, as if cued, the purple and cream car pulled away from the curb and she could see the face of Helen's ex-husband squinted in concentration as he crossed traffic. Her eyes traced his passage, her scalp heated, and she realized she was still mad from last night. Twice married, twice divorced, almost forty; the business with Helen and her husband had been going on for . . . eleven years, as long as Lillian had her Burger Hut. And last night suddenly she found herself unable to feel Helen was just a mixed-up kid. Her own involvement in the thing came to her too; she saw how she'd been used by them both. She felt the righteous fatigue of the victimized. The answer was clear: forget the bastard. Find someone who'll realize what he's got. She got nowhere pressing this solution; it was not the direction which interested Helen. Helen's passivity frustrated her, yet excited her protective instincts. Still when Helen finished cleaning the grill the night before, Lillian was tired to the bone. "I'm just a doormat," she said to herself.

The DJ was having a phone interview with a quavery-voiced old man: "*Willkommen*, that's what my dad used to say. He was from the old country, he was from . . ." he rummaged his memory for a moment, uselessly, then the DJ asked him to spell it, to pronounce it.

Lillian bagged the newspaper with one hand and lined it even at the end of the counter while with the other she ran the rag in damp circles. The photo of the dead woman and the crying baby held her eyes: how did she die? She bent closer to look for darker gray spotting which might be blood but it was unclear what was the print of the dress and what the wound. Harry, on furlough before being shipped overseas, told her about wounds, about how the wounded he'd talked with said they never felt the one that hit them. His sergeant, who had a bayonet scar running down and across his chest from shoulder to hip, said he'd felt a series of sharp blows, had run on past the Japanese who'd done it, then found himself on hands and knees . . .

Helen came from the kitchen, took off her apron, and sat at the counter with a cup of coffee. She had on a bright pink dress and looked very young; from the radio a woman's voice sharply countered the DJ's: "I don't know what the correct form of greeting in Germany is now, but it used to be 'Heil Hitler'!" the phone clicked firmly. A car pulled into the Burger Hut lot and disgorged a man, woman, and child. As she took their order for burgers, she sensed Helen behind her rising to return to the grill; on impulse she turned, smiled: "Why don't you stay put, dear, I'll run this order." She was rewarded by a blank look as Helen wandered, obedient, to a seat. She felt somehow that she had protected herself from further violation.

The frying of the order and setting of places, cutting of beefy tomato slices, spearing of pickles, took her time. She wiped the ketchup and offered it, poured coffee, and milk for the little girl. Then, almost an afterthought, took Helen a fresh cup. Behind the kitchen partition the patties sizzled, filling the room with their tentatively meaty odor; humming wafted like steam, as if in the act of cooking Lillian realized herself. She spread buns with soft butter, took them in and set them on warmed plates, removed the finished burgers swiftly and slid them in front of the waiting family. She watched eagerly as they bit in.

"Good burger," said the man, after a moment. The woman nodded.

Lillian licked her lips and smiled. "Oh, I love a good burger," she said, richly endowing the *u* of burger. "I'm real fussy about the burger I serve. People come all the way from Portland . . ." Satisfied, she drifted away, to Helen and the cooling coffee; Helen, perched sullenly over the cup, looked up and smiled unwillingly but Lillian dismissed her temper: "Well, hon, want to talk?"

And so Helen told her:

He had called last night after she got off about coming by. She didn't know what to think. She told him they were through, really through this time—just what she and Lillian had talked about. But he sounded miserable. She remembered they'd had more than one good time together and she hated, anyway, to hear anyone that miserable. Wasn't that right?

Lillian sucked her coffee without comment.

This morning he came by earlier than she thought he would and caught her in her housecoat—oh, everything had kind of been beyond her. He brought a red shorty gown. She hadn't liked that, it was compromising. But after all, he said, it wasn't as if . . . He had a new business deal with a fellow he'd met a few weeks before: his own car and fifteen hundred to cover operating expenses, twenty-five hours a week collecting from coin-ops. One-twenty-five a week right now, more as new users were added to the route. It sounded really good this time. There was, of course, the past . . .

But her eyes glowed. Lillian sipped coffee and saw Helen warm to the excitement of remarriage. He got to her, thought Lillian. That son of a bitch. But it was hopeless to remind her how it had been.

"It's your life," she said shortly, and not even that could put Helen off: "Oh wouldn't it be wonderful if this time we worked things out?"

"Hey, who are you trying to kid? It hasn't worked twice; you've got to forget it and go on."

She got up to refill coffees for the family and to talk about french fries, about how she made her own instead of just using frozens; and when the little girl had loiteringly finished her milk and the bill had been paid, Helen was back in the kitchen. She felt bad. The sun was climbing; on the radio the DJ talked in terms of a half hour and played the German National Anthem again: "Now wouldn't you be threlled if you were going into Neuhoftal and they were playeen the 'Star Spangled Banner'? So I think it's kinda noice if we . . ."

She gathered herself and moved briskly into the kitchen. "Helen?"

Helen looked up from dishes, focusing milkily.

"Helen? Let's make a nice plate of deviled eggs."

SHE HUMMED as she set things out, pleased with her briskness. She worked well, and working satisfied her; she forgot in it, passed over the bad and incomplete. Once it had bothered her to do filthy work: cleaning the Men's and Ladies' had been agony. Then gradually she had seen how it was all the same, a contribution. It had to be done. She would do it well, would incorporate it and make of it something explanatory. If anyone asked, she could say how clean toilets were part of the Good Burger.

The DJ reminded them of the passage of time; he had a reporter stationed down the line and by phone traced the visitors. Lillian began to hurry. She saw, beyond specked windows, early parade watchers: two boys and a small girl in a droopy pinafore. Coffee. Buns warming for burgers. Fresh cream in the pitchers; refills on ketchup, mustard. Sugar. Salt. Onions to chop. Moisture stood out on Lillian's lip; Helen abandoned her humming.

Then as she sliced down hard she felt the blade sever flesh; her stomach turned, blood spurted. Lillian stared unbelieving at her thumb even as her lip rode up over her teeth. "Uhm."

Helen came over, stared, fumbled at it with napkins. "God, so deep. Press it." The blood was very red, thick. It hurt. Lillian thought of how Harry had said wounds did not hurt. Well maybe big ones. They blotted and drew the napkins away, inspected, blotted. They ran cold water over the wound, then finally, when Helen located the aid kit, wrapped it well with gauze and adhesive. "It'll be wet in a minute," Lillian said, laughing shakily. "Oh I know," said Helen.

She went back to work, her thumb throbbing. Harry.

She had not seen him; the coffin was sealed. At one point she was desperate to know what, just what, had happened. He died of multiple fragmentation wounds. What were they? She ached steadily behind the eyes. You could not keep them out of it. A long time ago she had talked with an older woman whose two sons died in the Second World War. "You could not keep them out of it," the woman said, without much force. Later, when Harry left school to join, claiming it was only a matter of time before they got him anyway, she understood what the woman meant and adopted it for herself. "You can't keep them out of it."

Yet again the German National Anthem came on, and this time after the last strains the DJ announced triumphantly the visitors were entering town. "So get out there, welcome them folks. Show them you're glad to see them. *Willkommen,* that's the exprayssion. *Willkommen.*"

It was true; passersby had stopped, sensing a commotion down the long street. Without thought, Lillian and Helen took off their aprons and went out. People stood two deep at the curb, their excitement stirring the air; cars filled with cruising teen-agers pulled to the sides and halted, young faces gaped from the windows, as much at the footbound onlookers as at anyone who might suddenly arrive. They stared at each other in a confusion of transistor voices chiming the same message, wondering at a sense of history. Lillian longed for something to hold on to, perhaps a flag. Down the highway voices swelled; they strained to hear. Their eyes caught movement; the sun, glinting, hit them in its reboundings from glass and chrome. A Motorcade! Red firetrucks and grinning firemen; ambulances with frosted sides; the mayor's car; chief of police; motorcyclists, leather-clad; a float by the Elks: *"Willkommen!"* and pretty girls and a deeper, nearer voicing.

They strained at the sounding syllables as it all drew near, caught and held the sounds: Villl ko mmennnvil komm men villll kkoommm mmeeenn so their throats took it up: VILL KOO MMEN VILL KOO MMEN . . .

THAT LUNCHTIME the Burger Hut took in one hundred fifty-four dollars, and Lillian, returning from the bank, realized with astonishment her accounts, savings and checking, held over nineteen thousand dollars. Nine of it was from Harry's insurance; there had been the eight hundred dollars used for his funeral, the rest she had. But ten thousand she had made on the Burger Hut. Suddenly she understood she would not have to worry about money. If she needed anything, she could go out and get it, and not think twice about expense. She fingered the hem of her sweater as she wondered what she might need or desire; oh, some stockings, of course; some underpanties, a new lipstick. But what else? She could not think of any other desire that had enough force to excite her imagination. Still she would have to do something with all that money.

With a dull feeling she remembered how, when Harry was small, she had wanted things: dresses, shoes, jewelry, a car . . . once she slid halfway into a nasty affair over a mouton lamb coat. Then that all seemed to pass and it had been instead a question of meeting bills and keeping ahead of creditors when she couldn't; teeth to be fixed, never-ending lunch money, money for movies, notebooks; then date money. Finally money for college. Now all that was permanently ended; she herself could not quite understand how so much money had come her way. They said the war had cut down unemployment. It was true she had more business lately.

She helped Helen set up for the evening and then let her take off a few hours before her evening's work; with a cup of coffee and the final edition she settled herself to wait for late-afternoon coffee-breakers.

The first thing she noticed when she opened the paper was the photo of the dead oriental woman with her crying child. She briefly thought she was seeing it for the first time; the hours collapsed as if it was still morning. Then she shook herself, realized it was simply a rerun, leaned closer to study it again.

It told her nothing new; it was imperfection: dull, hazy, confused. How did the woman die? The big wounds did not hurt, Harry said. Her finger throbbed under the damp gauze. The woman never felt a thing. The child's face was as if split in two, unhealable. *How did the woman die?* Stick arms utterly destroyed thrust from the rag bundle dress whose pattern was so obscure you could not make out the wound's sign.

In the last week before his senior year, on a cool evening as they drove home, a four-point buck ran in front of the car and Harry stopped dead, pulled out his Winchester levering the action, and fired in an instant, bringing the deer down in midleap. They walked together into the rhododendrons, she saying again and again over her heart's pounding: "You got him. I saw him go down."

The buck lay bedded and still breathing in thick bracken, red blood sprouting lazily, bright petals on dry ferns. *What will we do?* she asked herself as he bucked upward and fell back over and over, looking at them and dragging himself on windbroke legs. "What will we—?" Harry slit the brown throat. The hair parted white, then ran pink-red like the sprouting petals; a sheet spilled on Harry's wrist, a black clot of hemorrhage slid to the ferns. The buck kicked and was still. They stood back together, briefly appalled by death.

In his last letter Harry said: "I know it's not a nice thing to talk about but yesterday I killed a VC. He was six feet away and I figured I'd better cut him down before he got any closer."

When the buck's ribs were still, and quickly as the dusk fell, Harry cut the white belly and spilled the ropy guts onto the ground. Bits of fir needles, bracken, dust clung as they rolled and oozed; the deer's dulling eye unblinkingly collected its own freight.

There was an odor. Lillian drew back, placed herself beyond the sense of it touching her, but still she saw her son's arm in the deer's gaping chest, prizing first the liver to steam in the cooling air, then the frothy lungs.

"Got him right here, see?" he asked with a craftsman's awe. "He went right down, wouldn't have gone more than ten feet before he bled to death. Probably never felt a thing."

She was amazed there could have been so much inside the body; the heap of viscera glinted in the last light as Harry's boot touched it. He kicked duff and it dulled, reduced to indistinguishable refuse.

"There," he said, shouldering the deer, grunting under it. "You'd never know anything had happened, would you?" He was grinning, blood was on him, dark streaks down his arms and in black moons around his nails. That was the next to last time she saw him.

HEY, LIL, wake up." The lights snapped white.

"Oh," she said, coming alive, lips recurving over licked teeth. "Hi." It was Helen, returning. "Say," she said as Helen tied her apron, ". . . fix me something, will you?" She went on firmly, ". . . don't tell me what, just . . ."

"I know, a surprise."

She watched Helen's face as it bobbed above the grill and the sizzling of food brought an evening warmth to the Hut. Her face seemed bland, resolved; Lillian wondered briefly what Helen had been thinking. She poured herself another coffee, straightened salts and peppers, and sat before the cup. She felt strange yet. Maybe she needed a vacation. But she could not think of any place to go.

Suddenly she knew something bad was going to happen; it welled up like tears. I'd better get out, she thought, rising and walking swiftly to her room-and-a-half, shoes rapping the floor with a panic beat. *My God.* She felt faint. She found herself in her darkened bathroom, a ghostly face in the mirror. She snapped on the light.

Her face swam up like the face of a stranger and to still the pounding in her temples and throat she leaned on the sink, close, almost eye to eye. It was as if she asked *Who are you? What are you doing here?* She saw how terror had blurred all the planes of the face in the mirror—terror, advancing age, and ignorance; how it had all settled the fine wrinkles around the eyes into unbelieving blankness and set the fine recurving lips loosely in rouged laziness. *I have just been going on and on,* she realized with terror. *On and on. And all these things have been happening.*

Tears burst from her. Her mouth hung, a cry pushed up behind her teeth and she held it, watched the face in the mirror, closed her eyes and let it come, impersonal. At first it was thin, small, but it rose larger and came again. She cried and cried. Her whole face ran wet, jerking, slippery with tears and mucus, loud; she cried, tears burst again, her shoulders jerked, shook, twisted but without relief: *my God I will not feel better when I stop this time* she thought in panic. Her wet face chilled, split again with new grief.

So she stopped, exhausted.

IT WAS DEADLY dark outside but she could hear fir limbs chafed by an awakening breeze. She hung to the lavatory rim as her clock beat out the time; she listened for what seemed hours. Something calm and cold was building itself in her and slowly she understood parts of it; as in a ceremony of puberty, she was passing from one world to another. All she had left behind: courtship, marriage, childbirth, abandonment, even the loss of her son, came swimming up again. These are all I have, she thought wonderingly. I've tried to do right and it's all been taken from me.

Then she knew how the woman had died, she had died in pain and final understanding of the violation of her body; she had died knowing her body was broken. Harry, too. He had in the last moments understood life was amnesiac, death real.

"Lillian?" The opened door slashed the strong life odor of food across the room. Oh yes, she thought. Helen. My surprise. "Right there."

She realized Helen was coming into the room. "Hey," Helen's voice asked, "what's up?" Helen stood behind her. "Oh, Lillian. It's Harry, isn't it."

Lillian patted at her hair and tried to move but an overwhelming weight held her to the lavatory basin; she felt she knew what she was going to hear:

"Oh, Lillian, I've thought it over and I realize you're so right about me and him. I've got to give it up, I've got to go on. You and I, we've both got to go on, we've got to live."

Lillian felt something deep in her throat respond even as her scalp crawled with a sense that things were slipping from her, that as fast as she learned she forgot. *No* she thought. No. But the incantation faded and instead came the image *surprise* and she thought *Friday; probably Helen's cooked fish and chips.*

Women

May Swenson

Women should be pedestals
moving pedestals
moving to the motions of men
Or they should be little horses
those wooden sweet oldfashioned painted rocking horses
the gladdest things in the toyroom
The pegs of their ears so familiar and dear
to the trusting fists
To be chafed feelingly
and then unfeelingly
To be joyfully ridden
until the restored egos dismount and the legs stride away
Immobile sweetlipped sturdy and smiling
women should always be waiting
willing to be set into motion
Women should be pedestals to men

Satiriasis

Robert Garis

Mike nichols' *The Graduate* is an ambitious, intelligent film that has some powerful moments and some good jokes. But like much of the satire that is currently in vogue, it seems to me almost meaningless in its overall effect and so false in feeling and in tone as to become actively unpleasant. These miscalculations are deliberate in the sense that they are the byproducts of Nichols' failed attempt to go beyond the spirit and method of ordinary dramatic realism. In short, *The Graduate* is still another demonstration—not that we need one—that this much-abused art form can't easily be laid aside.

By dramatic realism I mean the kind of representation of human behavior that engages your sympathy closely with the pleasures and pains, the decisions and the failures to make decisions, of a "believable" human being. It is the most familiar and popular mode of dramatic art, and its popularity is understandable and well deserved. Debased and degraded since the eighteenth century by the entertainment industry; snubbed by radical critics of both the right and the left, by both Eliot and Brecht; denounced as in its very nature dishonest to formidable realities of modern political and social life—dramatic realism still speaks from and for valuable and central human interests which I take to be permanent. And in the important movies of our time this dramatic mode has been virtually reborn. The way Bergman keeps your sympathy engaged with the actress and the nurse in *Persona* could hardly differ more widely from the way Godard engages your sympathy with the "children of Marx and Coca-Cola" in *Masculine-Feminine;* Bergman's controlled intensity couldn't be further in tone and spirit from Godard's affectionate spontaneity. Yet both movies are essentially dramatic realism. Similarly, the main point of *Blow-Up* is Antonioni's precise shaping of your subtly ambiguous sympathy with the young photographer.

Dramatic realism, then, still has a lot of life in it. And this is doubly fortunate, for it still provides the most convenient and efficient way of sustaining and intensifying interest in a long movie or play or novel, of making the work seem to hang together, move forward, and arrive somewhere. If an artist can get his audience involved with one of his characters, his major structural battle is all but won, though other problems may, of course, remain. Now this kind of convenience may seem, to artists interested in other modes, a somewhat undignified, even unfair characteristic of dramatic realism; and they have a good point. For our impulse to extend sympathy to believable characters is so habitual that very trashy works of art can set it in motion, as those addicted to junk fiction or to the late movies on TV can testify. Sympathy can be very powerful but sentimental and undiscriminating; escapist art would be impossible if this weren't true. Brecht had a more specialized objection: he feared that even the noblest and most discriminating kind of sympathy for a character's suffering in bourgeois realistic drama would weaken the audience's impulse to change the social conditions responsible for that suffering. In any case, whether sympathy is good or bad, discriminating or not, it is clear that there are modes of art which can legitimately reject it as simply inappropriate to their aims; and it has been pointedly, even violently, rejected by a mode that has become increasingly popular and influential today, the art of outrageous satire with a serious, often political intention. But the practitioners of this art have therefore had to manage without a very convenient organizing device. It hasn't been easy. *Dr. Strangelove, MacBird!, Catch-22, The Sot-Weed Factor, How I Won the War:* all of these join in a principled repudiation of the kind of sympathy aroused in dramatic realism, and all of them share the same basic flaw—an incapacity to sustain interest, a lack of forward movement, a kind of generic thinness and repetitiousness.

I had better say outright what will in any case be pretty obvious, that I would be unlikely to admire any of these works even if they did manage to hold my interest. I can follow the usual arguments offered in their defense: that certain terrible facts about our world—Auschwitz, the bomb, Vietnam—seem inaccessible to dramatic realism, a form appropriate to the liberal imagination, which has dealt weakly with these terrible lunacies and may indeed have bred a trained incapacity to deal strongly with them. Perhaps then no *individual* drama can represent our largest realities. And I can see some point to the contention, when I hear it in the abstract, that an aggressively trivial and silly kind of joking might be the only way to handle these realities, since it would be so striking an indication that they are beyond the reasonable, liberal, sympathetic imagination. But after all this plausible reasoning, the actual works themselves still have the same old puerility: the large, terrible facts have not been handled. On this question there can, of course, be no rational debate. All you can do is cast your vote.

But rational debate ought to be possible about the question I am more pointedly concerned with, the question whether *MacBird!* and the rest of these works don't in fact fail disastrously to sustain that initial impulse, puerile or not. But I have yet to meet an admirer of *MacBird!* who will even inspect the possibility that ninety-nine percent of the lines in that play actually boast of their laziness. With art of this kind it's all or nothing—and that for me is a good enough sign that there is in fact nothing there. Self-congratulating laziness has become a form of political activism, a kind of artistic "slowdown"—perhaps the last vestige of respect for organized unionism in the radical left.

Miss Garson's laziness is uniquely complete, as she herself has all but admitted. The almost pathological long-windedness of Heller's and Barth's novels is laziness of quite another kind; I view it as these writers' unconscious awareness that their writing can't have a significant ending. *Dr. Strangelove* sustained a trickle of interest by routine suspense about that bomb, but couldn't invent enough to do with its very expensive equipment. Two of Peter Sellers' roles—the President and Strangelove—barely exist, and I couldn't believe until the picture was over that a little something more wasn't going to be done with that huge strategy room; it made a wonderful effect when you saw it first, but you weren't allowed to see it often enough even to appreciate the ingenious technological expertise, or even the money, that made it. Lester's *How I Won the War* is more advanced than *Dr. Strangelove* in its complete disregard for any pretense of forward movement, and its aggressively boring repetitiousness. The tedium of Michael Crawford's unvaried leaps and squirms and pratfalls seemed just what Lester wanted, and I think I got the point. But the waste of Lennon's talents after a few tantalizing glimpses was an effect that escaped me.

One would like to feel more sympathy for Lester, Kubrick, and these other satirists, since the job of sustaining interest in their jokes asks for a degree of inventiveness that even Dickens could hardly have supplied. But that such inventiveness is in fact asked for seems the last thing to have crossed these artists' minds; and they were right, in a way, because it apparently doesn't cross the minds of the large audience that is in touch with this kind of art, as I so clearly am not.

BUT I WAS, and still am, very much in touch with the satirical skits that Mike Nichols used to write and perform with Elaine May some years back: I know the records almost by heart. These skits weren't of course very ambitious by any standards, certainly not in comparison with things like *Dr. Strangelove* or *How I Won the War*. In the first place they were very short—the longest is under ten minutes—so that Nichols and May never faced the challenge of sustaining interest in single large-scale situations. And they were far from being interested in large themes. In fact Nichols and May quite obviously started out with a kind of verbal horseplay, mimicking foreign accents, doing takeoffs; and some of the parodies are much closer to dressing-up than to satire. Even topical interest wasn't very strong. The takeoff on *Brief Encounter*, for instance, was long out of date when the record came out, and the skit about the English style of adultery is really the same routine slightly varied: these marvelously funny things are hardly more worth the name of satire than one's own ventures in making fun of the English—they are simply immeasurably better. "The Von Brauns at Home," the only skit that touches on politics, might be called risqué, in comparison to the large-scale, hard-core political pornography which may have been what seemed to Robert Lowell close to genius in *MacBird!* On psychiatry, presumably a more "relevant" and important subject than most of their choices, Nichols and May somewhat compromise the severity of their attack by never for a moment trying to disguise their personal malice and the pleasure they are taking in gratifying it. There isn't much keen cold impersonality in evidence here, nor is there in "Mother and Son," "Telephone," or in "Out of Africa," in which a Mrs. Doris Finch confronts Dr. Schweitzer.

Yet these not very serious motives and circumstances produced some wonderful satire. For if Nichols' and May's guiding impulse was rarely more ambitious than the impulse to exercise a talent for mimicry, that motive guaranteed the spontaneity and the accuracy of their choices of subject. When Nichols and May tackled psychiatry, or name-dropping, or the telephone company, it was because they knew there was something in it for them, something funny *they* could find to say, and they were nearly always right. And then, though there was never a development in length, there was a remarkable development in depth. Improvisation was the beginning; but what started out as improvisation, or the mere self-display of two very funny people, was then extraordinarily enriched in nuance of intonation, in wildness of fantastic invention, until the final result came to be really important, despite its informal beginnings. You knew it was important because you wanted to hear the skits again and again, not because they had a big theme for a subject. I am not saying that satire with a big theme is necessarily fraudulent, but that it is difficult to carry off and very likely to be marred by the laziness about detail which a big theme can in fact encourage. And I am saying too that important art can develop unexpectedly out of what began as mere entertainment. This is easy enough to see about the art of the past—about Dickens for instance—but with our contemporaries it seems difficult for some reason to avoid making rigid distinctions between art and entertainment, as all the recent fuss about the Beatles clearly enough shows.

When the bad news got around that Nichols and May were no longer working together, I couldn't help wondering whether part of the reason for their decision might not be that their skits hadn't received the right kind of attention and encouragement from the right people. *Dr. Strangelove* and *How I Won the War* are long, expensive movies, intended for an audience of millions, therefore more newsworthy, obviously, than Nichols' and May's three records, their occasional TV appearances, their one Broadway show; also Kubrick and Lester attracted serious interest because they were adventurously using the new satirical style to deal with the Bomb and war in one of the mass-media. But these circumstances didn't make these ambitious enterprises automatically important in and for themselves, just as the inevitable publicity about *Rhapsody in Blue*—jazz comes to the Philharmonic—didn't make that fine piece more important than Gershwin's show music. But many people at the time thought it did: it is easy to lose contact with your own private experience when you come up against this question of what's really important in art. People in the Jazz Age had a kind of psychomotor knowledge that Gershwin's show tunes were important before they had the head-knowledge of it: they put the records on the phonograph over and over again long before they were ready consciously to say that what they were doing was listening to good music. And I think something of the same thing may have been true of the Nichols and May records which were liked and admired, by the people for whom I played them, more than almost any other theatrical works of the early sixties; yet it was perhaps hard to believe that something one heard for fun at a party, and heard on the phonograph besides, might be really good and important. And I think this fact may have had something to do with Nichols' and May's decision to go into some other branch of the theatrical business.

Whatever the reason, and however regrettable the decision, Nichols and May are now working independently, and those of us who admired the records have naturally followed their careers with high interest and hope. The results to date haven't been very encouraging. Elaine May's acting in *Luv* seemed to me so distressingly bad that I hadn't the heart to investigate her second try. She must certainly have been badly directed in this movie, every element of which was also a disaster; but it did seem too that her style might be simply wrong for the movie-medium, and it was undeniable that she lacked the capacity to sustain an impersonation—I don't remember ever having seen so wildly unintegrated a performance. As for Nichols, who has given up acting entirely and given up writing at least officially, I have seen none of his stage work and I couldn't tell much about where he was going from *Who's Afraid of Virginia Woolf?* It seemed recklessly ambitious to take on, as his first movie assignment, so famous a play and so notorious an acting team; and then it seemed intelligent, but cautious, to produce the careful, modest, rather anonymous conventionality that one in fact saw in this movie. It is true that there were some almost eerie echoes of the Nichols and May skits in the intonations of Elizabeth Taylor, Sandy Dennis, and George Segal, but this indication of Nichols' presence was the opposite of encouraging, since it suggested that he could do only his one kind of thing, lacking the flexibility, the objectivity, perhaps the sheer knowledge of other styles that a professional director needs. On the other hand, Burton's superb performance presumably owed something to Nichols' direction, and Burton paid him a handsome tribute, the sincerity of which there is no reason for doubting; so it seemed that Nichols could function impressively with gifted actors, and therefore the Nichols-May intonations in the other performances may have been due to the fact that the other actors needed total, almost hypnotic coaching in order to perform creditably at all. For all these reasons one couldn't feel that Nichols was operating very freely in *Virginia Woolf,* but this isn't true of *The Graduate.* Calder Willingham and Buck Henry are credited with the screen play but many of the lines suggest that Nichols collaborated with them, and one can safely take the whole spirit and tone of this movie as the product of his own choices.

THE FIRST choice was the story itself, for *The Graduate* is not, like *Virginia Woolf*, the inevitable screen version of a famous play, but a free choice, since the novel by Charles Webb on which it was based is by no means well-known. The story is worth inspecting in itself as a sign of Nichols' interests. It concerns a young man named Benjamin, who is spending a bored and depressed summer between college and graduate school with his parents; he gets involved in an affair with an older woman, Mrs. Robinson, the wife of his father's business partner, then falls in love with Mrs. Robinson's college-age daughter Elaine; in the end he gets the girl, though only by kidnapping her just after she has been railroaded into marrying another man. Now the characters, the setting, and the theme of this story offer plenty of chances for the kind of satiric comment you would expect from Nichols: there is a lot to be done with life in southern California, the generation gap, the affluence of the older generation, the identity-crises of the younger. And Nichols offers some amusing and pointed things on these subjects, although far less than I expected, and nothing of the genuine brilliance of the Nichols-May skits. The story line in itself, however, is by no means just the string to hang satiric episodes on that you might have expected; it is a real story, involving to an obvious, even aggressive extent, dramatic conflict and choice. The substance of the action—Benjamin's unusually complicated love life—is deliberately far-out; and it wouldn't be the easiest thing in the world to render these conflicts and choices in the inward mode of dramatic realism, to engage and control our close sympathetic involvement with Benjamin in this bizarre dilemma. Yet dramatic realism is nevertheless the mode one would expect; that, or its direct opposite, a brilliantly cold farcical disengagement. Nichols has tried for something in between. He carefully and thoroughly prohibits close sympathetic involvement with Benjamin or clear understanding of his motives; yet, we are encouraged not only to like Benjamin and respect him but to take his problems and his conflicts and his choices seriously. It is an interesting strategy because of its apparent difficulty, almost impossibility; yet even my outline of Nichols' strategy raises the question why any artist should go to so much trouble. What's to be gained from doing things the hardest way? And when one sees the movie, the answer turns out to be that nothing is gained, and a lot lost. For Nichols' departure from the mode of dramatic realism doesn't finally seem to have been motivated by anything more dignified than an interest in a more fashionable tone. His strategy is mechanical and negative, not the necessary condition of new insight, and the sadder fact is that it simply doesn't work: our feelings get out of hand because Nichols has so artificially refused to pay enough attention to them. *The Graduate* isn't a new way of looking at experience, but a bad and false way.

At the beginning I admired the intelligence in some of these negative choices—the choice, for instance, to avoid Salingeresque intensity of charm and pathos. Benjamin, as Dustin Hoffman plays him, is neither theatrical, exhibitionistic, nor flirtatious in his adolescent anxiety, and there is something like real dignity in his heavy, closed-in face and his rather stolid and inexpressive body. And I liked too the way this dignity was carried through in his understated speech, which likewise lacks any Salingeresque brilliance of accent. This quiet style was a good preparation for making you take him seriously. I admired the way Nichols shows that Benjamin's father is a bore and fool without getting all wrought up about the false values he represents; and it was oddly moving, and seemed real, that this bore and fool should be married to a woman so much his superior in tact, warmth, and wit. Then, as Benjamin's affair with Mrs. Robinson got under way, I was briefly relieved to see that I was going to be spared both the American soap opera of the woman's guilt and the French soap opera of the young man's initiation into love. In sum, these intelligent choices, however negative, seemed to promise an impressively adult and quiet tone, a way of taking life that wouldn't be solemn or easily shocked or unrealistically anguished, though of course not deeply moved or deeply moving either.

And this tone did prepare me for some of the more drastic avoidances that follow. But preparation isn't the same as justification, and though I was not surprised to see that

Nichols was uninterested in building up deep understanding or involvement, I couldn't see that his procedures were
yielding very valuable results. Benjamin is "worried about
his future," but these worries are completely unspecified,
for no apparent reason. What would be lost if we were told
a little something about these worries, which don't really
seem meant to be a joke? But when later we're told nothing
about his reasons for beginning the affair with Mrs. Robinson, the effect of this silence is to me decidedly unpleasant.
Mrs. Robinson at first treats Benjamin with a smoothly
insolent obliviousness to his feelings and his privacy that
completely justifies the rage that he in fact can barely control. Later her sexual advances seem nastily calculated to
make him feel young and inexperienced, and they completely succeed in doing so. She is a thoroughly repellent
woman, whose behavior involves Benjamin in embarrass-
ments far stickier and more unnecessary than anything he
experiences at his parents' parties, from which he repeat-
edly retreats in depression. Then suddenly, out of the blue,
he calls her up and initiates the affair. As I read this, we
are meant to be surprised and shocked at first, and then,
knowingly, to "get it." The meaning we are meant to get is
of course a very crude one, as it is bound to be in this short-
hand style: it is in fact a cliché stood on its head. Benjamin
gets involved with Mrs. Robinson not in spite of her nastiness but because of it. This ten-cent-store paradox isn't
insight; it's a kind of password, admitting us into a flattering
complicity of sophisticated candor about human motivation
and human hehavior. Such passwords, such instant-insights,
are a betrayal of the intelligently adult tone that the beginning of *The Graduate* seemed to promise. They are in
fact notoriously adolescent.

This adolescent toughness and frankness about sex gov-
erns the entire conception of the character of Mrs. Robinson, with Anne Bancroft's performance in the role com-
pounding the effect almost intolerably. Stanley Kauffmann
(whose high praise for the whole movie leaves me baffled)
has praised in particular Nichols' direction of Miss Bancroft,
and I would agree that he has kept her ordinarily raw and
strenuous passions under some control. But this too seems
a negative choice. For Miss Bancroft's undeniably powerful,

even brutal, temperament comes strongly through the one-note actressy toughness and bitchiness that Nichols has held her down to, but it comes through in a flat and dry tone that makes this characterization one of the most actively distasteful I have ever encountered. And the characterization of Elaine, the daughter, doesn't offer a meaningfully different conception of love relations, since it is merely the implausible opposite of the conception represented by Mrs. Robinson. Katharine Ross is a remarkably charming actress who brings out the warmth, compassion, and honesty of the characterization as well as anybody could; but she was given as little to work with as anybody else in the movie, and she therefore can't finally disguise the brutal polarization in the adolescent dream world of *The Graduate*. Benjamin's choice is between the nightmare woman and the dream girl.

There is however one image in the movie that gives us a different slant on Benjamin's relation to Mrs. Robinson. Usually we see her treating Benjamin contemptuously, sometimes actually reviling him. But something far more interesting shows up in a rather badly edited montage sequence intended to represent the quality of Benjamin's depression during the summer and during the period of the affair in particular. Most of the shots of the boy floating on a rubber raft in his swimming pool are insufficiently expressive in themselves and organized without any sensitive rhythm. But one little episode is a sudden revelation: we see the boy leaving the swimming pool and putting a shirt on; then we see him indoors, and Mrs. Robinson slowly unbuttons the shirt and begins to make love to him, while his face registers a curious blank inexpressivity, a kind of willful, heavy, almost sullen passivity. It is as if Nichols suddenly got a clue to the whole affair and the whole movie. We begin to understand Benjamin's anger and depression about "performing" well and being "rewarded" well for the performance, though neither the acts performed nor the rewards engage him, because he has not chosen them himself. The affair with Mrs. Robinson is a grotesque repudiation of this pattern: it represents a cold and sullen interest in receiving pleasure without any performance at all, without activity, without communication, without courtesy, without love. The point, then, is that Mrs. Robinson makes love to him, not that he makes love to her. This is the only form of rebellion against his parents, his culture, and his future that his genuine decency will allow. His rebellion yields self-knowledge and an awakened will; when he meets Mrs. Robinson's daughter he experiences love for the first time and wants someone for his own reasons and on his own terms.

In extrapolating this scenario out of one brief image, I am of course making up my own movie, not describing *The Graduate*, which contradicts this meaning more often than it supports it. There is no evidence that the image is more than an inadvertent suggestion on Nichols' or Hoffman's part. In any case, my scenario is not the sort of thing that Nichols could have brought to anything if he were to develop it, or rather refuse to develop it, by the methods he uses in *The Graduate*. But then these methods don't seem to me to have any positive purpose or to yield any interesting meanings. Nor do I see that the ordinary methods of dramatic realism are as boring, or as inappropriate to our new sensibility as Nichols' rejection of them suggests. Tough refusals to explain, instant-insights, calculated frustrations of sympathetic understanding—these give a movie a smart look these days; but fashions change very fast.

I have taken *The Graduate* "seriously," which will be a baffling procedure to people who thought it was "funny." *The Graduate* is funny, now and then. Of several good jokes, the best is the one about plastics. Elaine May and a man named Mike Nichols might have gotten some real mileage out of it a few years ago.

Ground Glass

A SHORT STORY

John Malone

On the second Tuesday in March, Harold went to an expensive Italian restaurant in midtown Manhattan and had ground glass for lunch. It came in a bowl of *pasta e fagioli* soup—as a kind of garnish, perhaps. As he bit down on a mouthful of the soft, succulent beans, the tender pasta, Harold's teeth crunched against something that was hard and rough-edged, but which he could feel breaking into smaller pieces as his teeth came together. A small pebble of some sort, he surmised: Harold did a good deal of cooking himself, of a fairly elaborate sort, and he knew the problems that dried beans could present in the way of gravel.

His expertise, however, proved inaccurate—which happened to Harold sometimes. Managing with considerable grace to spit out the offending particles into his spoon, he was stunned to discover that he had been chewing on a piece of glass; indeed, he had plainly bit it in two.

"There's glass in my soup," he said in bemusement.

The lady on his right, Mrs. Charlotte Green, looked up from her *antipasto* in alarm. "Glass?" she said.

"Yes. Look." Harold held out his spoon. There among the half-chewed beans lay two unmistakable pieces of glass, each about a quarter of an inch in length, approximately the size of the little green and black tranquilizers nestling in the antique silver pillbox in Harold's vest pocket. Two unmistakable pieces of glass. They appeared to be rough all around, as though they might have come from the shattered stem of a wine glass. A perfectly feasible explanation, Harold thought, but however satisfying to the intellect, not really very good for the nerves.

Charlotte Green had paused with her fork in midair, precariously balancing a chunk of tuna fish. "Did you swallow any?"

Harold's stomach questioned itself, uneasily.

"I don't think so," he said.

"You should eat some bread, I think," Charlotte suggested as she guided her fork the rest of the way to her mouth.

"Yes, I suppose I should," said Harold. He reached out and tore off a piece of crusty Italian bread from the half loaf in the bread basket. Biting off a hunk, he began to chew, and was appalled to find himself grinding more glass against his right wisdom teeth. Then Harold did an exceptionally stupid thing, by his own judgment. Instead of rinsing his mouth with water and spitting out the entire mess, ground glass and all, into his soup bowl, he merely pushed an additional lump of bread between his teeth, chewed, and gulped it down.

"Now I have swallowed some," he said.

"Oh, dear," said Charlotte. "I do hope you're going to complain."

"Waiter," called Harold. The waiter was passing quite near, but in the manner of his profession was staring straight ahead, his hairy ears tucked in against themselves, well insulated against anything less than a shout—a shout which most customers could be expected to withhold for fear of attracting the censorious attention of the diners at the next table, and the next. He would come only when convinced that he had demonstrated his complete equality with any and all capitalist pigs and fellow democrats. Harold had been a waiter for two long summers as a young man and understood the mentality completely.

But Harold did shout. As if on cue the participants at the three nearest tables craned and stared.

The waiter swiveled, smiling. Smiling? Harold, taken aback, neglected to press his advantage and said in a much more subdued voice, "There seems to be some glass in my soup."

"Glass?" The waiter's tone could not have achieved a tone of more total disbelief.

Harold retrieved the two shiny pieces of evidence from

his bread and butter plate, where he had deposited them. He displayed them in the palm of his hand.

Like a nervous fence, the waiter appraised them. Then he smiled again, but only with his teeth. He held out his hand, glancing around toward the front of the restaurant. "If you please, sir."

Harold dropped the two bits of glass into the waiter's extended palm. The love line was short and crooked but the life line was long. The waiter's fat fingers closed over the evidence.

"I should have kept a piece," Harold muttered.

"Exhibit A," said Charlotte Green.

But the waiter proceeded directly to the maître d', who looked sharply around toward Harold's table. Harold raised an eyebrow. The maître d' hurried across the room. He was short, but handsome, in a flashy middle-aged way. "Where did you find this?" he asked in an unnaturally floured voice.

"In my soup."

The maître d' stammered slightly. "Really? I can't understand it."

"I didn't bring it with me," said Harold, striving for hauteur but achieving only sarcasm.

The maître d' had swarthy skin, well-tanned from a recent winter vacation. How long had it been since Harold had had a winter vacation? Harold didn't even own a sunlamp, which was probably the more likely explanation of that dark, healthy glow. At any rate, Harold was pleased to see the maître d' flush an even darker color. "No, no, of course not, I, well, it just isn't the kind of thing that happens here, you understand."

"It looks like a broken wine glass to me," said Charlotte in her most gravelly voice. "Perhaps you have a Russian in your kitchen. I'd check on it if I were you."

The maître d' gave a strangulated giggle. "Yes, quite, I, sir, I hope there was no damage?"

"I think I swallowed a bit of it," said Harold.

The maître d' looked terribly distressed. His Adam's apple worked. "You did?"

"Yes, I'm quite sure I did." Harold was quite proud of the calm with which he spoke. He even felt quite calm. Harold was usually quite calm in emergencies, actually; it was only afterward that he became hysterical. Already he had miscalculated, though. The maître d' seemed to be taking this exceptional calm as a sign that Harold, all forgiveness, was letting him (to say nothing of the restaurant) off the hook. "Well, I hope there are no further consequences, sir," he said, beginning to sidestep. "Let me know if there are any, uh, medical problems."

"I certainly will," said Harold, with dignity.

"Well, then, very good, sir. I'm terribly sorry about this." And he wheeled away, knocking against an unfortunately empty table, and racing toward the kitchen. Harold didn't think he'd ever seen a maître d' move so fast.

"Did you really swallow some?" asked Charlotte Green.

"A bit," said Harold, bravely.

"Well, I shouldn't worry. The human body is a remarkable thing."

"I hope so," said Harold.

"Just keep yourself filled up. It will pass right through."

"I hope so," said Harold.

"I thought you were extremely calm about it. Most men would have been yelling their heads off."

"I'm just a coward," said Harold. "That's what I should have done—made everyone nervous, upset the whole place, threatened suit."

"I'm glad you didn't. Hysterical men are so tiresome." Charlotte Green speared her remaining anchovy and popped it in her mouth.

Harold ate another piece of bread. "They might at least have offered me a free drink," he said, without much conviction.

IT WAS IRONIC, really, Harold thought. There you were, making a nice gentlemanly gesture, taking a secretary to lunch because she'd been a big help to you. Not a young, sexy blond thing, either, but dear old Charlotte Green, a widow in her fifties, a pleasant gray-haired lady with a mind like a Univac; one of those indispensable women who knew more about certain practical aspects of the firm's business than the men who earned twenty-five thousand a year for making decisions. Dear old Charlotte Green. She'd saved you a lot of time. She had been entirely gracious and always accurate. You appreciated both the accuracy and the graciousness. So you take the nice old thing to lunch. And what do you get for it? A plateful of glass.

"Don't exaggerate, Harold," said Ron Bigelow, who shared Harold's office.

"It only takes a very little bit to seem like a plateful, when it's glass," Harold said.

"Listen, Harold," said Ron, tilting back in his fancy aluminum and leather desk chair, a Christmas present from his rich wife, "the human body is a pretty remarkable thing."

Why don't I have a rich wife, Harold thought. Hell, he'd settle for an aluminum and leather desk chair.

"Stop brooding," said Ron.

"I'm not brooding," said Harold. "I wasn't even thinking about ground glass. Maybe I should have my stomach pumped out."

"Oh, for Christ's sake."

"Actually," said Harold, "I think I'd rather die than have my stomach pumped out."

"Stop worrying about it, Harold. What's a little ground glass? My sister's kids have swallowed pounds of it."

"They have?"

"Sure."

"And nothing happened?"

"Of course not."

"None of them had his appendix out?"

"Yeah, two of them, I guess."

"Probably caused by the glass," said Harold. "They say grape seeds can cause appendicitis, why not ground glass?"

"Harold."

"Yes."

"Do you even have an appendix?"

"No." Harold sighed.

"Let's get some work done, shall we, Harold?" Ron Bigelow tilted and swiveled impressively in his expensive chair. Harold got up and went to the water cooler to take another tranquilizer.

AT THE LOCAL liquor store that evening the clerk extended his sympathies and recommended taking a laxative. The glass would just slide right out, he maintained. He smiled as he asked Harold to hand over the tax on his bottle of Scotch. Harold invariably put down merely the advertised price of the bottle, in exact change, as though the tax simply didn't exist. It was a kind of standing joke between himself and the liquor dealer. Harold liked having a friendly relationship with the neighborhood storekeepers; it made him feel as though there might be trees on the street when he went outside again, like the trees on the street in some mythical town where he hadn't been born. He looked forward to gathering in the sympathy of the drugstore clerk, as well, but when he got there he found that the man behind the counter was someone he'd never seen before. It seemed a bad omen to Harold. And, indeed, the clerk looked aghast when Harold related his saga. He wrapped up the package without looking at what he was doing, his eyes fixed on Harold as though on a ghost. He didn't say anything, really, but his eyes brimmed with horror.

"Harold, I don't care," said Marge, her voice sounding very thin and far away.

"The man at the drugstore looked at me as though he knew the posse was waiting for me at the end of the street."

"Harold, I have the flu," said Marge. "Asian flu, maybe even Siamese. I told you not to call. I feel horrible and I need all my sympathy for myself. I'll phone you at the end of the week."

"I may not be alive at the end of the week," said Harold.

"I'll send a dozen daisies," said Marge, and hung up. Marge had super mammary glands, a snap-crackle-and-pop mind, and Harold sometimes thought he loved her. At other times he thought she was a terrible bitch.

ON THE SIX o'clock news Dr. Frank Field gave a special report on the latest advances in artificial kidneys. So what if Harold didn't have an appendix? He still had two kidneys, a bladder, and a urinary tract. The glass could lodge anywhere, causing who knew what varieties of pain and infection, necessitating operations, convalescence . . .

Harold decided to get a grip on himself. He had another Scotch and managed to become sufficiently exercised about the latest reports on the war in Vietnam so that he practically forgot about what he himself was busy digesting, or trying to digest, in the way of foreign matter. For dinner he ate both halves of an avocado, a small steak, creamed onions, and what must have been almost a pound of mashed potatoes.

After dinner Harold went to a W. C. Fields revival and forgot all about his insides. Harold enjoyed W. C. Fields immensely. He even felt that they had something in common, though he couldn't have said exactly what. It was as though deep within Harold's thin soul a fat man with a bulbous nose was clamoring to get out. Harold laughed a great deal and nearly lost his scarf. A middle-aged lady from the same row caught up with him in the lobby and gave it back to him. "Thank you," said Harold. "Just like my son," said the lady. "He got married, though." Harold grinned uneasily and escaped into the winds of March.

It was on the subway going home that he began to think about ground glass again. Curious, Harold observed to himself, how the subways stimulate the anxiety syndrome. Or not so curious, rather. Harold had been to Paris once, some time ago now, and he remembered that a number of the subways there ran on rubber wheels, very silently, with only a pleasant whoosh to record their passage. If only all his days might pass in a pleasant whoosh, Harold thought. He should have checked his horoscope for today before venturing to reward Charlotte Green for her existence; perhaps it would have warned him off. But Harold had become disillusioned with his horoscope; indeed, he'd begun to wonder if perhaps his parents were mistaken about the month of his birth. Perhaps he'd been conceived before his parents' marriage, and they'd tried to conceal the fact from the world. That might explain a lot of things. Forced into kindergarten before his time—God, it could leave a scar on anyone.

The subway screeched and jerked to a stop at Harold's station. He retrieved himself from the all-too-willing lap of the young man next to him and ascended out of the caverns into the cold. As soon as he got home he looked up his horoscope.

Tuesday, March 14: Difficult. You may feel entirely too expansive and can easily bite off more than you can chew. Your judgment may be faulty, and you should avoid unusual expenses. Work may be delayed through health problems or the affairs of older people.

"God," said Harold, aloud, and quickly checked Wednesday the 15th:

Good. Daily affairs and routine matters will probably run easily, without opposition. Correspondence can be handled with imagination. Friends will be less contrary than of late. It is a somewhat dull day but one that is free from pressure.

That was reassuring, at least. Free from pressure and no mention of health problems. But, good lord, if he'd read his horoscope for today he would never have scheduled that luncheon. Except, how was anyone to guess that biting off more than one could chew referred to pieces of glass?
Nonsense.
It didn't have anything to do with pieces of glass. Thousands of other people, even hundreds of thousands probably, had this same paperback horoscope of the year. And whoever it might be that had concocted it, he (or she, more likely) surely hadn't considered ground glass as being one of the many things one could bite off too much of. All the same, it was disturbing. And tomorrow's forecast wasn't that encouraging. The internal ravages effected by today's lunch might not make themselves known for weeks, months even. Would you believe years? Harold grinned and went to the kitchen to fix himself a nightcap. What a lot of foolishness. He would have to remember to say no more about it to Marge. Let her bring it up, and then pass it off as nothing at all. Once she was recovered from her oriental sniffles she'd be unmerciful about such hysteria on his part. It was ridiculous, anyway. The glass would simply slide right out. Harold reminded himself to take some of that laxative before he went to bed.

Half an hour later he pulled back the covers, feeling pleasantly tired and sleepy. Harold was something of a chronic insomniac, and he'd been worried that he would have difficulty in getting to sleep. But as soon as he had stretched out in bed, sprawled on his stomach, he decided that ground glass or no he would have no trouble this night. He drifted slowly, deliciously downward, slowly deliciously downward . . .

Ground glass. The thought flew upward, like an escaping air bubble.

Ground glass.

Harold wiggled his head deeper into his pillow, as though to block his ears.

Ground glass.

Harold resisted. Harold thought about Marge. Harold thought about Marge's super breasts. But that was no good, that was just another way not to get to sleep. Harold knew from experience.

Harold turned onto his left side.

Ground glass.

Harold began to take a series of deep breaths, emptying his mind. You are very sleepy, he said to himself. You are very tired. You haven't a thought in your head. You are very sleepy and you haven't a thought in your head.

Ground glass.

Harold recalled that in some concentration camps the Nazis (or was it the Japanese?) used to feed the prisoners only once a day to insure their stomachs would be empty, and then fill their evening mush with finely powdered glass. The glass was too fine to be filtered out of their systems, and it passed through their intestines into the rest of their bodies, into the blood stream, destroying them slowly, torturously from the inside; and not knowing why they were in pain, why they were dying, they went on eating their evening mush, their powdered glass. Harold had read about it. It came back to him now.

Ground glass.

How fine was the glass that Harold had swallowed? After all, he'd ground it between his teeth (Harold's jaw worked in reflex, and he felt a cringe run through himself), had ground it finer; he himself had ground it down.

Why hadn't he spit it out, the whole mess, into his soup bowl? He was too well brought up, that was why, inhibited, socially self-conscious, afraid to make a spectacle of himself—die like a gentleman rather than live like a boor. Poor constipated idiot.

Ground glass.

Harold resisted. He called upon logic: you would have to feed someone an awful lot of ground glass before it could really do much damage. Besides, if he was to go by the Nazis, it was important for the stomach to be empty. Harold's stomach certainly wasn't empty. He'd even finished his lunch—a large portion of *saltimbocca alla romana*. And there were all those potatoes he'd consumed at dinner. Creamed onions. A whole avocado.

Ground glass.

Harold sat up in bed, furious with himself. This was absurd. Harold got out of his bed and went to the kitchen, scuffing along in his broken-backed slippers. He heated some milk in a saucepan, watching as it began to bubble and steam at the edges. Harold poured it out into a mug, added a huge shot of Scotch, and sprinkled the whole thing with nutmeg. *Ground glass.*

He couldn't take another tranquilizer, he'd just taken one. And he didn't have any sleeping pills. He couldn't take barbiturates, they left him feeling muddleheaded for half the next day; and the over-the-counter brands never worked. Harold swallowed his hot milk. Barbarous thing to do to Scotch, really. Not that it tasted bad. Harold rather liked it, in fact. Marge was the one who thought it was barbarous. She was probably right. Marge was usually right. Unsympathetic bitch.

Harold padded back down the hall to his bedroom. Must get some new slippers. Couldn't afford new slippers. Not this month. Taxes coming up. You should sue, Harold told himself. Why were you so calm, letting the restaurant off the hook that way? At least he had a witness. Charlotte Green would testify. Fifty thousand dollars for mental strain. I can't sleep, judge, I keep wondering when one of those little pieces of glass is going to lodge someplace, work its way through into a vital organ, obstruct my urinary tract, eat a hole in my liver, cause a cancerous growth.

Harold could feel the unnatural cells forming around the sharp little particle, malignant and spreading. Dead at forty from ground-glass cancer.

God damn it, he would sue. Just to cover himself. Why not? Who could say how or when one of those nasty little bits of shattered wine glass stem would make itself known in sudden excruciating pain. Couldn't even see it with X rays. They'd have to cut him open and feel around. Knives, blood, pain, daisies from Marge.

Harold slumped on the edge of his bed. Harold beat his fists against his thighs. "Stop it, Harold, just forget it," he said aloud. Wiggle your toes, feel them relax, feel the Scotch warming you, feel the muscles relax. Feel yourself calming down, Harold, feel yourself getting sleepy.

It was cold sitting on the edge of the bed. Harold didn't feel himself relaxing, not very much. Harold got under the covers and thought about Marge. Harold lay on his back and thought about Marge's breasts. It was the only way.

Harold's body relaxed. Harold felt his body relaxing. His legs tingled as the tension drained away. Harold turned on his side again, curled in upon himself. Harold let his mind float away.

Ground glass.

Harold let his mind float away. The night was dark, the sea lapped the rocks, he sat on a high parapet and the water broke below, there was a moon, the earth looked flat, the water glimmered, the sky was a bowl on the flat water. The night grew darker. The sea lapped more quietly at the rocks below him. The rocks below him.

And then, abruptly, brutally, like falling onto those rocks below, Harold was wide-awake.

Harold was terrified. There was no one thought in his mind, no one particularized thought. Just an apprehension of terror, absolute terror. *Ground glass.*

It was as though he were imploding upon himself, becoming smaller and smaller, gathering into himself with greater and greater force until, he knew, there would be only one infinitesimal dot of pure terror that must then explode outward again into—nothing.

Never before had Harold known. *Ground glass.*

Oh, everyone knew, of course. With their minds. But

Harold had never known like this before. Really known, with all of his being, with the whole of his thin soul. Never truly comprehended that it would, must, happen someday, and that he was not prepared to face it.

Harold heaved himself up in his bed, sitting very still in the enclosing blackness. Gradually his eyes adjusted to the dark and his ears opened themselves to the sound of the midnight city. "Now I know," said Harold, and lay back down and went to sleep.

People Trying to Love

Stephen Berg

STEP INTO my room tonight
their hands float ahead of them
their legs move apart
in answer to the many

For thirty-two years I have lived
and known the black iron
railings of houses
instead of you

Now even that part of me
I will never know knows
I have stayed between my own fingers
too long
believing I did not need you there

It is dark between our bodies
as we open ourselves
to the one shame
and feel what we lose
the wire stems of poppies

Trying so hard to remain
now even hatred is a false petal
shaking under the rain
sacrificed
to the many

For thirty-two years my hands
have wanted to be other things
cups pliers hammers hooks
wings belonging to a child
they touch you.

A Late Night Conversation

Stephen Berg

On the hot wall above my desk they flash.
The bare light under them is much too strong
and floods the glossy surfaces. Today
when firestorms bake the plaster where they hang,

eating my brothers' faces, I will look
for those bright figures on the edge of space.
As yet I don't know how, but sinking down
in the fine ash that nothing can escape

my boiled hands may begin to reconstruct
this cheek, that blistered nose, a T-shirt, hair,
and somehow dig until they find the rest.
Right now they hold each other. It is dawn.

Without the light on, the Sierras fade
in one, where Bob scowls, and a green backyard
thins like a winter sky. Phil squats there, drunk,
and Charlie, smoking in his room, looks hard,

and I, well, I just lie back, miles away,
pulling my wire, like all of us, afraid,
because sometimes, in the dark, you and I
laugh at each other like the smiling dead.

The Survivor

Stephen Berg

Rising without names today
I want to be a fat man in America
and carry a gun,
I want to sit for the rest of my life
looking at the walls, collecting,
thinking about those terrible images
of dissection I burst
out of my mother with, dreaming.
If my face melts off like wax,
if I am beaten across the thighs
until they stick together,
if I find myself drunk in a strange town
looking for a stranger to be my friend,
if I wake with the sea in my mouth
and the wrong father,
if they take one piece of me each year—
the lobe, the glans, the lid, the cap,
the pit—
I would still want to be as fat
as an elephant, and rule, and demand
all others fall to their knees
and serve me.
Rising without names
or wonder in this country,
my fists hardened many days
in the last ovens.

"Obscenity" and the "Public Interest"

Frank Kermode

THE LONDON TRIAL of the publishers of *Last Exit to Brooklyn* by the American writer Hubert Selby, Jr., crystalized some of the issues arising from the extreme variety of attitudes that may be held within one society about the matter of obscenity. In the United States, I am told, the literate now feel that virtually total permissiveness rules; except in special instances such as the Ginzberg case, the enemies of candor are running out of legal resources. I should not like to say that this belief in a liberal victory is premature, though it might be held to underestimate the forces of reaction. But even if it is true that a book such as Selby's can no longer be tested in the courts with any reasonable chance of success for the prosecution, it is unlikely that opposition of other kinds has permanently ended. It may therefore be of interest to American readers to consider for a moment whether there is anything to be learned from the conviction of John Calder and Marion Boyars, the English publishers of Selby's collection of stories. Their trial lasted ten days, one of which was almost wholly devoted to my testimony, so I have naturally given a good deal of thought to what the court was supposed to be doing, and what I was supposed to be doing; and I conclude that although the whole thing was in many ways bewildering to the point of incomprehensibility, it did provide a kind of allegory of the situation in which authors and publishers find themselves when they must take account of the opinions of the general, rather than of the literary, public.

FIRST A NECESSARY word on the local legal position. Until 1959 any book could be prosecuted at any time in a British court for obscene libel. Under this law, well within living memory, a country magistrate condemned Boccaccio. Under a similar law, in 1944 an Australian court condemned a book which contained the word "incest," certified to be obscene by a police inspector who confessed in cross-examination that he did not know what it meant. In 1954 there was a series of prosecutions, which worried the Society of Authors. They set up a committee to draft a parliamentary Bill. Thanks in large part to the determination of Roy Jenkins, who was to become Home Secretary and is now Chancellor of the Exchequer in the present Government, the administration was forced to take notice of this private measure, which it did by substituting its own much less liberal draft. Contested with great pertinacity through committee, this Government measure underwent a good many liberalizing amendments, and by the time it became law as the Obscene Publications Act of 1959 it was much less reactionary than had at times been feared, though it was not quite the Act its sponsors had originally hoped for.

The Act of 1959 provided, among other things, that in any proceedings a book must be considered as a whole—it would not be enough to establish the obscenity of isolated passages. The prosecution would have to show that the whole book was obscene. But even if it were found to be so, it could still be held that its publication was "for the public good on the ground that it is in the interests of science, literature, art or learning, or other objects of general concern." In other words, the prosecution has to prove obscenity; if the jury thinks it has done so it passes to the second question, the question of "literary merit." There, of course, the onus is on the defense, which will depend upon its expert witnesses. Since obscenity is defined by the Act as, and only as, that which has the power to deprave or corrupt, and since the expert witnesses are expressly forbidden to comment on that aspect of the proceedings, it will be evident already that "literary merit" under the law is abstracted from the affective qualities of the work, and the handicaps this places upon the "expert witnesses" are, I am sure, relevant to the outcome of the 1967 trial. There have been two trials under the Act, and in neither of them would the Judge allow evidence to be called as to the tendency of the book to deprave or corrupt; this, it was said, the jury must decide for themselves without such help, presumably by examining themselves spiritually for stains incurred during their reading of the book. The witnesses on either side had to deal with one question only, that of literary merit so abstracted. They were of course unable to do so.

One other provision of the Act is relevant. It provided for more summary proceedings, intended to be used against "pulp" pornography. For such, any member of the public could seek a "destruction order"—ask a magistrate to have a publication destroyed. But it allowed that publishers and authors might appear in the magistrate's court to defend their property, which had not formerly been the case.

To the great surprise of its drafters, the Act first came into use at the trial of a book which they thought to be of the kind to which it would afford protection. The famous case of the Crown *vs.* Penguin Books (the *Lady Chatterley* trial) occupied six days in the fall of 1960. The Act got its first workout, and precedents were established; but it was in many ways a somewhat misleading case. The defense insisted that the jury read the whole book before having their attention drawn to particular passages. It also insisted that, in terms of the Act, a book was not obscene unless it led the reader "to do something wrong that he would not otherwise have done." The Judge explained clearly to the jury what they must do. First they must make up their minds as to whether the book was obscene, and if they decided it was, they were then to proceed to the next question: was the book nevertheless of such merit that its publication was in the public interest? On this second question, if they got to it, they should consider the evidence of the thirty-odd expert witnesses; but they should not be overly impressed by the large number of them, and they should remember that the witnesses were specialists and that the book might present a different picture to "a person with no literary background, or little knowledge of Lawrence." The possible implication, that the expertness of the defense witnesses made it possible for the jury to disregard them if they chose, was to be of importance at the *Last Exit* trial; the defense can defend only by means of these witnesses, who must be "expert"; yet their professional quali-

fications make their testimony only ambiguously relevant
to the deliberations of the nonexpert jury.

What tended to make the *Lady Chatterley* case a dubi-
ous precedent were the following considerations. First, the
book was in various ways already famous, and by a famous
writer. Second, so far as the court was informed, the sexual
behavior described in it was not perverse.* Third, the
prosecution called no witness as to literary merit. Fourth,
a great part of the trial was taken up in the discussion not
of situations but of words, the famous four-letter words
which were really all that distinguished *Lady Chatterley's
Lover*, so far as the charge of obscenity goes, from a great
many other books dealing with adultery; and it was possible for the defense to argue that these words were used
with extremely serious and even puritanical intent. As C. H.
Rolph remarks at the end of his invaluable book on the
trial, "It was the words which caused all the trouble, putting her Ladyship on trial as an adulteress where a more
conventionally spoken gamekeeper might have lent her the
impunity of Emma Bovary or Anna Karenina."

IN THE YEARS between the trials of *Lady Chatterley* and
Last Exit there was some evidence that the intention of the
drafters of the 1959 Act could be further frustrated. Most
significantly *Fanny Hill* was in 1964 prosecuted under the
forfeiture procedure described above, which bypasses jury
trial altogether. This reestablished the right of the police,
and indeed members of the public, to seek in the magis-
trates' court an order for the destruction of books which the
drafters of the 1959 Act had intended to reserve for trial
by jury. In 1967 Mr. Jenkins, true to the intention of the
1959 Act, inserted a clause in a Criminal Justice act to
prevent proceedings of the kind taken against *Fanny Hill*,
but this became law too late to save *Last Exit*. Sir Cyril
Black, M.P., a man quite certain of his own judgment in
matters of public morality, had asked in the House of Com-
mons whether the Crown would proceed against *Last Exit*.

* It was after the trial that critics, especially Mr. John
Sparrow, maintained that the seventh act of intercourse between
Connie and Mellors was an act of buggery.

On being assured by the Director of Public Prosecutions that no such proceedings were contemplated, he took copies of the book to a magistrate and asked for their destruction. After a long trial the magistrate ordered them destroyed. This prevented the further sale of the book, which had, as a matter of fact, greatly increased while these proceedings were pending. The Director of Public Prosecutions thereupon changed his mind and announced that Calder and Boyars must stand trial in the Central Criminal Court under the 1959 Act. Thus it was possible for a watchdog of public morality to cause the law officers of the Crown to change their minds in a matter which involved publishers in a criminal trial, and, at worst, in imprisonment and an unlimited fine. Because of the recent change in the law this can no longer be done in quite the same way, but that it can still be done nobody doubts. And even if he is acquitted, the publisher may face enormous legal costs. Such is the price of disagreement between the literary public and the general public as to what measure of literary merit excuses the publication of any book of unusual sexual candor.

Literary people probably overestimate their ability to judge the state of the public mind on this, as on other questions, but if the *Last Exit* trial is an indication of any value, the English mood is at present one of a certain revulsion against "dirty books." In this, as in other matters, a marked tendency to repressiveness on the part of police and judiciary meets with surprisingly little disinterested public comment. Thus the fans, but so far as I could see only a few of their elders, were disturbed by the Rolling Stones' drug trials. A couple of days ago someone got eighteen months for possessing LSD. One of my own students is serving a prison sentence of *twelve months* for participating in a peaceful demonstration at the Greek Embassy; admittedly there was some public and newspaper comment on the severity of the sentence, which was upheld by the Appeal Court, but it seems to be taken as a reflection of the tough mood we have got into during the Home Secretaryship of the very Roy Jenkins whose name was so strongly associated with liberalizing measures. Of course these symptoms are difficult to read, being very mixed, as they are in the United States. Thus 1967, the year of these drug and demonstration cases, the year of the *Last Exit* case, was also the year in which the British Parliament reformed the law on homosexuality and abortion, and a Bill further liberalizing the divorce law made good progress in Parliament.

LADY CHATTERLEY WAS ACQUITTED; *Last Exit* was not. Yet the rules of the game had changed very little between the two cases. These rules have a most curious effect upon what may be said in defense of a book; when you take literary criticism into a law court strange things happen to it. For obvious reasons I shall describe my own experience, rather than that of the twenty-nine other defense witnesses. Having read the sixty-five pages of the transcript which record my performance, I can swear that I am not motivated by vanity.

Defense witnesses were instructed that testimony as to the literary merit of the work (we were required to have ready definitions of "literary merit") could, under the rules of evidence, make reference to "honesty of purpose, moral tone, and the extent to which the book increases its readers' understanding of society," but must not include the expression of any opinion as to whether the book had "a tendency to corrupt and deprave, evidence on this last point being for expert psychiatric witnesses (if this is allowed at all)"; (it was not). I got an inkling of what I was in for during a three-hour discussion with defense counsel a few days before the trial; we went through the book commenting on one passage after another, obviously with the purpose of finding some common ground between what could be said critically and what should be said legally. The relevant differences between the criticism game and the law game began to reveal themselves.

The trial began on November 13 with brief opening submissions, after which the jury was sent out to read the book. The *Lady Chatterley* jury took two and a half days to read that book; this jury returned after about one hour and a half and announced that they were ready. This was surprising, since *Last Exit*, as American readers are free to discover, is not an easy work, even for them; it dispenses with typographical conventions helpful to the ordinary reader and cannot be read fast. For Englishmen there is the additional difficulty that much of it is written in an unfamiliar slang. After protest from the defense they were sent out to read it more fully, and on the third day witnesses were called, defense witnesses first. There were to be thirty of them, against six for the prosecution. The strange critico-legal seminar began.

Much the greater part of my testimony related to particular passages, but near the beginning I was asked for an overall impression and said that I was greatly moved by the book, especially by its originality and "moral power." What did I mean by "moral power"? I answered as follows:

> It seems to me that one of the purposes of serious novelists has always been to deal with what some of the earliest proposers of realism called "contemporary moral reality," and it seems to me that this book does therefore stand, with all its differences of manner and language, in a tradition which is a very honorable one—the tradition which uses novels not as forms of entertainment so much as ways of examining—not for propaganda purposes—but simply examining and laying before the reader a picture of contemporary moral reality. I thought that this book, dealing as it does with the lower depths of a great city, was very much in the tradition of Dickens, who spoke of the shame, misery and desertion of a great capital.

This isn't very well put, though literary people will take the point easily enough; what became very evident when one read the newspapers next day was that only the comparison with Dickens, a very limited one, made any impact. *The Guardian* headlined its story "As From the Pen of Dickens"; a satirical journal ran a piece on the trial of *Pickwick Papers*. Nobody went into the question of what might be meant by "contemporary moral reality." This kind of misunderstanding is absolutely unavoidable, I now see, when literary "experts" are used for such purposes.

When we moved on to individual passages it was soon evident that what the "expert" felt like saying and what the defense lawyer wanted him to say were by no means the same thing. There was a note of impatience in the questioning: I was told not to say so much, or to say more;

not to go forward so quickly, or to move on. Here and there I missed the point of some line of questioning. It was the lawyer's reading of the book—undertaken with the 1959 Act open before him—that mattered, not mine, except insofar as mine corroborated his. We spent a good deal of time on the biblical epigraphs to each story, touched on the four-letter words, the absence of quotes. We were trying to show that the violence of Vinnie's gang—inhuman, motiveless in the stories—is necessary to the fulfillment of the author's honorable intention. We quoted from the text: words like *shiteatinbastards,* pronounced in English accents, quietly, hung in the air of the court. Counsel introduced *King Lear* and asked me if there are passages in it that some people might find distasteful. After forty-five minutes we reached page 12 of the novel.

The second section of the book, which is mostly about an orgy in the apartment of the homosexual boy "Georgette" and his queer friends, required us to deal at some length with the cultural aspirations of the central figure. We elucidated, with the help of the judge, his references to well-known Italian operas. The judge also made some jokes, at which everybody laughed. We agreed that Georgette's mother was fond of him, so that it would be untrue to state that there was no affection in the book. We explained that to register characters like these you have to use their kind of language and use it a lot. We maintained that in his account of the way the homosexuals treat the pregnant girl the author was condemning rather than endorsing their behavior. We identified *The Raven* as a poem by Edgar Allan Poe, characterized the fine writing that occurs in that passage as falsely glamorous, noted that the subway was what we call the underground, and conjectured that Georgette, at the end of the story, was distressed by the fact that he tastes feces on Vinnie's penis. This, and other disagreeable experiences, we averred, were not recommendations from Mr. Selby. He did not appear to be proposing Tralala's horrible career as a model for other girls, or suggesting, in "Strike," that men who feel sick when they make love to their wives should make free with union funds and consort with male prostitutes.

We talked of violence, lovelessness, disorder. We said that Satan finds work for idle hands to do. We explained to the court what is meant by a *dragball,* and what is meant by a *fruit.* We admired the construction of the last section of the book, commented on the history of stream-of-consciousness techniques, claimed originality for Selby—"I don't know that these lower social depths have ever been recorded in such concrete detail"—denied that Selby has to date shown the intellectual grasp and power of Bellow and Mailer, but concluded that he presents "a hard clear image, with all the implications we might ourselves attach to it, of a society in desperate danger." We attributed to Selby "great integrity of purpose, and above all . . . a passion and sympathy for these . . . deprived and depraved people which communicates itself very strongly to the reader."

In cross-examination I was asked about "contemporary modern reality." "Moral reality was the expression I used." "Moral reality," the prosecution counsel patiently amended. What does it matter? Everybody admits you have the *highest* qualifications, but why, with the greatest respect, does it require someone like you to come along and explain to us what the book is about and how it shows contemporary moral reality? In short, the object of the prosecution was to show that the need for "expert witnesses" is in itself an indication that there's something wrong with the book. Against this, one struggled as he could. "If you mean that one has to be a professor of literature in order to do it, I don't say that. I think . . . any person whom I would regard as a literate person could do as well as I've done." But would I say "the normal average reader" would be able to analyze the book in this way? "Possibly he would lack the same degree of explicitness, which has been forced on me by the situation in which I find myself . . . . a good deal of the skill which people who read novels develop almost without knowing it is to take points without actually spelling them out." In saying that this book in no way invites imitation or participation on the part of its readers, I am speaking only for myself, surely? No, as a member of a literate public. Would I claim that every normal person would see the *literary* purpose of the violent beating described in the first story? But this question I was not allowed to answer; it was against the rules. It was exactly what the jury had to decide; my business was with literary merit only, and my answer to this important question was of no relevance.

This was much the most entertaining part of my testimony, since it involved the attempt to sail in the right direction, with the legal wind, as it were, against me. The following will do as an instance: counsel asks whether the feelings of homosexuals, under the influence of huge doses of benzedrine, are not described as pleasurable.

> KERMODE: I think you must distinguish between a passage which says that homosexuals are sometimes happy and a passage which says: come and be a homosexual. There seems to me to be no implication here whatsoever that this is a good idea. . . .
> PROSEC: . . . You're answering the question now which I'm not allowed to ask you . . . I'm sorry—it's not your fault—but those are the rules.
> KERMODE: May I ask a question, my lord? I'm not clear what I did wrong there—
> JUDGE: You didn't do anything wrong.

Counsel ignored this exchange with the judge, and proceeded to "Tralala." I said the story asked you to attend to a situation in which people can become so dehumanized. "But what am I meant to do about it?" asked counsel. "Works of art aren't meant to make you *do* something," replied the expert witness. "They're meant to make you contemplate something." "I'm not quite following you," said counsel. Nor did he follow when I said that Tralala— a girl totally degraded—aroused one's pity. At whatever level of sophistication, the expert witness is apparently hard to follow. In his reexamination defense counsel made much of the point that works of art did not make you want to go and do something.

So ended the third day. There were seven more, but in a sense the issue—or so it seems by hindsight—was already settled. The jury took five and a half hours to decide, and what they decided was that the book was obscene and that its literary merit was not such that its publication was in the public interest. They followed the advice of the prosecuting counsel, who had insisted that since anybody with thirty shillings could buy the book, it was hardly sensible to apply to it the sophisticated distinctions between art and propaganda, action and contemplation, proposed by the expert witnesses. They believed instead Mr. Robert Pitman, of the Beaverbrook Press, who said that "young people at universities who might read about orgies in this book are precisely those who would feel the printed word gives them almost a kind of authority for imitating them." They believed the one witness they would certainly have heard of, the Reverend David Sheppard, who was an international cricket hero before he took over a slum settlement in East London: he testified that although he had come across behavior of the kind described, a reading of Selby's book had *marked* him. Similarly, when Sir Basil Blackwell, the eminent book dealer, said that a reading of *Last Exit* had darkened his life, the jury may have supposed that these other expert witnesses were claiming to have experienced something like the corruption or perversion which, legally, makes a book obscene. And then, presumably, they decided they had felt it themselves.

SO THE JURY, representing one public, took the advice of the Judge and refused to be impressed by the great mass of testimony offered by members of that other, the literary public. Almost certainly they had in the back of their minds the memory of the Moors murders, which were committed by people who read the Marquis de Sade and then tortured children to death, recording their cries. Here highbrow literature had been used in a spirit of action rather than contemplation: no complex stasis of patterned responses in the murderers, Brady and Hindley, but an unspeakable devotion to do-it-yourself. This would foster the plain man's easy contempt for the highfalutin' "expert," who emerges blinking from his library to tell the world to have complicated thoughts about simple matters. Who doesn't know a dirty book when he sees one? The prosecution encouraged the jury to have the confidence of their commonsense, plain-man reactions.

It must henceforth be recognized that "literary merit" is, under the Act, a very unreliable defense, and that it must always be so, and not only in Britain, as long as the general public is made the judge of it. I suppose it was a sort of triumph to have made the Act so sophisticated as to allow such a defense—certainly our earlier censors and licensers would not have dreamed of admitting it—but no one foresaw that the law's interpreters would tell the jury to pay attention to expert witnesses only if they chose to. "You must be the judges," not only of obscenity but of literary merit. Yet one can qualify for jury service without ever having read through a book in one's life, and certainly without the slightest inkling of the place of passion, and of perversity, in the literature of the world.

The trial was, therefore, a sad parable. Imagine having to persuade such a jury of the merit of *any* book, let alone one charged with obscenity; imagine trying to persuade it that literature itself is in the public interest. And of course the difficulty is much intensified in cases of obscenity. Either you believe that literature, by means of invented forms, deepens your apprehension of human problems, subverts your moral stupidity, and, by intensifying your sense of what it means to be alive, justifies its destruction of your easier comforts; or you don't. When Horatio told Hamlet, as he speculated on our posthumous state, that he was considering too curiously, he was saying what men who content themselves with the stale fictions of an unconsidering society will always say about men who won't—men who examine death, for instance, in tragedies. And if you accept the comfortable myths of whatever decency rules at the moment, you will certainly have little patience with those who believe that to disturb this decency, to let reality break in on it, is not merely good in itself but indispensable to a proper humanity. In what W. H. Auden called "the expansive moments of constricted lives / In the lighted inn" the enemies of the comfortable myth are allowed to make a sterile appearance in jokes; the four-letter words are for the bar, not the bedroom. A man who uses prostitutes can still think *Bubu of Montparnasse* a dirty book; a man who buys hardcore pornography may nonetheless, in his most impressive civic moment, as a juror in an important trial, put away these childish things and take what seems an adult view of the matter. The important game in which he finds himself seems to require it.

For the law, which is not an ass, is a game, and calls for ritualized behavior. English lawyers justify the formalities of their proceedings, their wigs and robes and ritual cries, by saying that these things may have survived their historical causes but continue to serve, by a providential arrangement, as a kind of cooling system. The heat of litigation is reduced by ceremony. In fact an obscenity trial, which is, as I have maintained, a struggle between the culture and one of its subcultures, is transformed by the rules of law into something that resembles the real social issue about as much as chess resembles war. There is one difference, which is that the expert witness is not strictly comparable with a chess knight; to get the idea of how he is compelled to behave you would have to imagine a knight whose first step must always be sideways. He cannot, faced with such a jury, behave according to the rules of his own game. He cannot speak his own language. His task is to prevent the jury from saying, on its retirement, that it knows a dirty book when it sees one; and this is not his métier. Also he has to defend his evaluations, and the jury does not. Theirs, not his, is the public interest. The criteria by which lawyers decide what is and what is not relevant are in the public interest and not his.

POSSIBLY THE DEMOCRAT should find some grim consolation here. The form taken by the 1959 Act, hammered out in a contest between a popularly elected government and a progressive lobby, reflects an authentic democratic process. The legal interpretation of the Act—the discrediting of the progressive witnesses by the prosecution and by the judges' summing up in both trials—enacts the inertia of a genuine majority. No doubt many books owe their unpersecuted existence to this inertia—they have escaped the notice of what is after all a nonreading public. But when its attention is called to a particular work it is likely to confound literary merit with a concept of purity which excludes sexual candor, and to proceed on the assumption that sex ought not to achieve verbal expression at all, except perhaps in the ritualized and licensed media of instruction manuals and oral jokes. It will be of small use to tell this public that *Last Exit* was no more intended to make people experiment in perversion than is a joke about little Alphonse; that the tensions which are released by the laughter at the end of a joke are a little model of the tensions, equally without immediate practical issue, induced by a literary work of art.

The difference is simply between a public which reads and a much larger one which does not. Whether you think *Last Exit* will influence conduct for good or ill depends entirely upon that. The literary public is a large club, held together by adherence to certain rules. These rules evolve slowly. We have not always believed that poems, plays, and novels should carry the label "no road through to action," but we have believed it for a long time. Of course they may deal with matters upon which action is necessary; but one reason why we think *Middlemarch* a better novel than, say, *Uncle Tom's Cabin* is precisely that although *Middlemarch* deals with a great historical crisis it never says: we shall get over this only if we improve the condition of women, or whatever. So it is easy for readers who have joined the club to see that *Last Exit* is neither a plea for drugs and homosexual behavior nor a warning that we must improve our low-cost housing projects. Rather, it says: this is your kind of hell; in the city where you live this is what becomes of natural instinct; this is what you leave out of view when you benevolently contemplate your society. Even that makes it sound too much like a pamphlet, too little like an image; but it is already as far beyond the scope of the nonliterary as it would be if one spoke of "patterns of sentience" or "organization of stimuli."

A case of this kind ought to make the literary public consider how far it has detached itself from the culture as a whole. The evidence suggests that the lack of any common language in matters of aesthetics is a measure also of enormous ethical differences. In the eyes of the literate, the world of the jury will seem as obsolete as the conventional structure of some dead novel—the world, say, of an average Gothic novel before *Northanger Abbey*. The sexual reticence of the average person, except in privileged situations, is as meaningless as the design of a well-made play. Of course the conventions of nonliterate behavior change too, but they change at a different rate, and certainly not fast enough for us to expect that a man who is summoned to the Old Bailey will not put on his Sunday best and vote down highbrow dirt. After all, in swinging London we still groan under eighteenth-century Sunday Observance laws which only a few people actively endorse, but which remain unaltered because the people who don't like them would continue, in their role as serious citizens, to withhold their votes from politicians who tried to abolish them. All liberalizing legislation would come to an end if tested by plebiscite; reforms relating to capital punishment, homosexuality, and abortion are brought about in part by the skill and persistence of their supporters, in part by that same inattentiveness on the part of the general public which has allowed certain books to be published which would never have survived the ordeal of the courts.

In a period of inattentiveness, such as American letters is at present enjoying, the gap between the publics widens very rapidly. Unrestrained sexual explicitness is easy enough, and has no necessary relation to aesthetic merit. Occasionally this gives rise to concern on the part of the literate; not long ago George Steiner was saying that he thought the flood of such writing invades our erotic privacy and devalues our sexuality; that it is no real gain to the reader to have his sexual imagining done for him. This implies that the taboos of the nonliterate have their value. The argument is cogent, but neglects, I think, to consider that the literary subculture has its own taboos. The ordinary man protects himself against dangerous or unwelcome stimuli by laughter; that is why his jokes are often about such serious subjects as adultery, homosexuality, disease. The literate protect their privacy by criticism. Detailed and repetitive accounts of sex and sexual fantasy tend to comply with certain conventions. These conventions, like all others, are bound to grow rigid and be seen as intolerable insults to truth, as fossilized as Gothic; and some *nouvelle vague* will consign them to the past. Thus do the literate keep a balance between imagination and reality; they have always known how to cope with the exploitation, by inferior talents, of the imaginative values established by better ones.

Their recourse will not, of course, be a puritan counterrevolution, though it may resemble that in some ways. Nor will it solve the general problem of whether sexual explicitness, in truly imaginative works, can be shown to be to the general good. The literate, who change rapidly under the pressure of an observed discrepancy between art and reality, will already have turned their attention and their sophisticated procedures to new problems.

In short, little can be expected from a dialogue between the two publics on the subject of "the public interest." The trial of *Last Exit* has shown that, if it has shown nothing else. The literary public is, in such a situation, always the defendant, and it must defend itself not in its own tongue but in a language improvised for the occasion and unequal to it. Such a trial is acutely representative of a communications problem that is by no means merely a matter of what is or is not obscene; but obscenity is, more than other literary deviationism, a source of interest to the larger public. It is hard to see how this conflict of interest could be resolved. The present American truce may be temporary. In Germany, I am told, one can get disputed books by signing a sort of literary poison-register at the bookseller's. In Ireland there is a state censorship. In these or other ways the general public will, at times, intervene to disturb the dialectic of saturation and rejection which is characteristic of literary history. We, the literate or literary, would no doubt prefer to be without this clumsy intervention, and the unfortunate publisher whose livelihood may be at stake is unlikely to feel philosophical about it. We should prefer to work out our own salvation; but *they* insist, at irregular intervals, on our behaving as if we belonged to a larger society which includes them. If our privacy is in danger, we should prefer our own way of safeguarding it; but from time to time we must consider theirs. In this larger social context we can only be as liberal as we are allowed to be (just as we can only be as socialist as we are allowed to be) and this will sometimes seem to be not liberal (or socialist) at all. But we may find some consolation (I do not find much) in reflecting that it is only when we quarrel with it that we are conscious at all of our inescapable involvement with the other and larger society.

One Morning We Brought
Them Order

Al Lee

> "With our considerable military power but limited
> political appeal, how do we contain an adversary of
> enormous political power but modest military
> means?"
>
> —*An American military strategist quoted
> by Jean Lacouture in* Le Monde *(Sept.
> 18, 1964).*

WHEN WE rolled up the three armored vehicles
and they wouldn't budge, the sergeant said to kick
         in somebody's kidneys,
         and a corporal did.
It was a bald-headed man with a shiny
soft face. He sat tight but we could hear him whine.

Our captain was somewhere else admiring
and photographing a church's stone spire.
         It was famous or ancient.
         By the time he got back, rain
was drenching them, and us, so he ordered
us to hurry up and clobber some more.

They still sat there, some not so pretty,
when the colonel came. He had a fit.
         "Have it their way. Shoot a dozen
         in the head and see what that does."
Then, pissed off that they kept on stalling,
he had us open up on them all.

         Someone must have wanted to run
         when we set to it. I wonder

why in all those thousands not one man
used his head and started the panic.
        He would have saved everyone's neck.
        Was what we did unexpected?

        We took chow thinking of them
        that night until the women
who had kept indoors at first came out too
to harass us by moonlight. The shooting
        lasted for hours. They fought back
        with knives and died attacking.

            After looting the town,
                we poured oil around it
and lit a fire to roast anybody's ass.
Today a young girl with a covered basket
                walked up smiling: she then
                exploded, killing ten.

The Empty Theater

Lionel Abel

THE THEATERS I WENT TO this season were full—it's true I went mainly on opening nights. But from what I have been told, the crowds continued to be faithful, audiences remained enthusiastic, and curtain calls were nightly, if not rightly heard, up and down, off- and off-off-Broadway.

So the theaters are full. Yet the theater is empty. I have two reasons for saying so. First, the plays I saw, with or without merit, were empty of content; and second, the content of the one really good play of the lot was precisely emptiness. I am speaking here of course of this season's contemporary works, and not of the revival *Iphigenia in Aulis.*

Revivals or emptiness—is that what we have to face in the theater? Audiences sat down with relaxed good will before the void of *Rosencrantz and Guildenstern Are Dead.* I think on the night I went—a Saturday night—standing room was sold. Two rather carcassy figures—one thin—appeared on the stage and flitted about, egged on by the audience—though not by me—to expose to the full their desultoriness, shabbiness, stupidity, and futility: Rosencrantz and Guildenstern, minor characters from major Shakespeare, made into major characters for us. Shakespeare did not have Rosencrantz and Guildenstern on the scene for long; in his judgment they could not hold the interest of an audience. Was the Bard mistaken? He certainly would have thought so had he sat next to me on the Saturday night during which I watched a crowded house give itself over to an obedient search for zest in the witless

remarks of the two characters Shakespeare thought too dull
to differentiate other than by their names: no doubt this is
why the names Rosencrantz and Guildenstern sound so full
—so full, that is, of nothings. I could not help thinking of
how we have reached a dead end: at one time it was revolutionary to put socially insignificant people on the stage;
and then it was advanced, if not exactly revolutionary, to
put on the stage people lacking in social position, also in
moral stature. How much advance is still to be made by
further and further limiting the positive qualities of stage
characters? At the extreme limit, of course, there will be
the character for whom nothing can be said; but who wants
to hear such a character say anything? I will tell you who
wants to. The audience I watched, waiting avidly for
another jewel of nothingness from either of Shakespeare's
two nonbeings. How could anyone human find such a work
interesting? Maybe the whole audience was composed of
Rosencrantzes and Guildensterns—of people whose names
must sound exactly the same despite the different spellings.
From the stage, after all, one face is as like another as
Guildenstern to Rosencrantz.

My myth about this production is that in it a really perfect equivalence was achieved between art and life. The
characters sat in the audience—the audience preempted the
stage. I remembered the essay of Rudolf Kassner on Rosencrantz and Guildenstern in an old issue of T. S. Eliot's
Criterion; the German essayist showed that the reason
Rosencrantz could not distinguish himself from Guildenstern, Guildenstern from Rosencrantz, was that they were
both so vain: and their vanity, it seemed to me, gaped at
itself with satisfaction, in the Eugene O'Neill Theater, as
the audience was mirrored in Tom Stoppard's play.

There was a time when the gigantic individual, chieftain
or king, was considered the main cause of historical events.
And then the single protagonist was put aside by the collective giant made up of many: against the wisdom of the
single individual, against his courage or moral strength,
there was the ineluctable push of the human herd, the
cause, finally, in history. From this view, though, the many
did not exclude the one; they were many as cause but one
in effect. Moreover, the interest of the many was in something positive: the actual exertion of power. With Rosen-

crantz and Guildenstern as protagonists, we have come a long way from this rather nineteenth-century exaltation of mass action. Stoppard's Rosencrantz and Guildenstern cause nothing. They are pure effects, utterly powerless. Are they interesting to audiences, for all their uninterestingness, because the many now feel powerless, incapable of acting as one? Is this what has happened? Does no one cause events now, neither the outstanding figure nor the mass? But how can there even be effects if there is no cause? Have we reached just this bewildering point in our understanding of our place in history? This might explain the lack of restiveness of audiences, unbored by boredom, at *Rosencrantz and Guildenstern Are Dead.*

IT HAS BEEN said that Edward Albee's *Everything in the Garden* is wrongly called his since so much of it was taken from the English play by Giles Cooper. There may be something in the allegation, but I cannot credit it as significant—I strongly doubt there was anything in Cooper's play which could effectively have resisted lifting by Edward Albee, or been refused admission by his *Garden*. It did not seem to me, at Albee's play, that there was any element in it resisted by the other elements, as alien transplants seem to be by the host tissue. I think the metaphor, which is an organic one, is particularly apt: for what is peculiar about *Everything in the Garden* is its utter mechanicalness; a mechanism from someone else's machine can be fitted to one's own mechanism without any of the drama or disaster that accompanies the transplanting of a true organ. Albee's play is a skillful TV commercial, not unlike—as my colleague Al Cook noted—the TV horrors of Alfred Hitchcock; so much so, that in the theater I thought I was at home before a TV screen. And who cares, confronting a TV screen, which is the more, which the less real author, everything on TV being more or less unreal? Albee's (I shall call it his) new play is about the emptiness of middle-class virtue: all the suburban middle-class wives in it are whores, and all their husbands pimps. I must say that there is something amusing in the idea, and an amount of comedy in the development and dialogue. There is some fun in the show. But what, after all, is Albee saying about middle-class moral emptiness? What beyond that the middle class is empty of morals? He may have it in mind, too, that it is empty of life. Is Edward Albee therefore displeased, indignant, frightened? He is amused, to a degree, but hardly more so than any of us would be reading of such facts in the press. The author pretends to be a revealer, but, in fact, the revelation made in *Everything in the Garden* can only be called empty. For to point at nothing is not to point, as Whitehead once noted.

MICHEL DE GHELDERODE's *Pantagleize*, to my mind well, even excellently, presented by the APA Repertory, is neither a profound nor an original play, neither especially funny nor piercingly sad, not macabre, not grotesque, and not in the author's sometimes accomplished style. Why it was chosen for presentation by the APA I do not know. Possibly the part of the amiable ninny Pantagleize, who says of himself that he may be an imbecile and he may be a poet—to be sure there are people like that, something our critics of poetry might remember—appealed to the actor and director Ellis Rabb. I myself choose to think the play was selected because of its emptiness, which makes it fit in with the rest of the season's offerings. The play is about a revolution directed against one does not know whom, motivated one does not know how, projecting one does not know what future for society. This is a play about revolution by a man who is unable to take any attitude toward it, and thus is unable to energize his players or give them character. Such other plays of Ghelderode's as *Escurial, Hop Signor!, Splendors of Hell*, and *School for Clowns* have a definitiveness like that in Breughel's paintings. But the Flemish dramatist had little interest in society, and no grasp whatever of politics. The amateurishness of *Pantagleize* would be evident if people were looking for a play with content; as it happens, they are not.

NO DOUBT this too explains why Harold Pinter's *The Birthday Party*, written over ten years ago, was brought out as his contribution to this season. It is impossible to say with any degree of assurance what Mr. Pinter's play is about; some believe it deals with an unsuccessful effort to drop out of society. The hopeful dropout hides away in a rooming house but is finally caught up with by representatives of the Establishment, who give him the regular ritual treatment prescribed for all such cases, depriving him finally even of his capacity for speech. They then escort him back to his former function, whatever it may be, for whatever it is that wants him. Can this be the play's meaning? Not self-evidently: there is something which speaks against it. The young man presented as a dropout from society seems on our first contact with him so bilious, unpleasant, and unhappy in his isolation that we can feel no real changes occurring in his life when he is forcibly restored to his fellows. It may be said that, when restored, he is minus the power of speech which he possessed when we first met him. On the other hand, when we first met him, he seemed to have little interest in that power. What did he want to say? Practically nothing. So the change we witness in him is from practically to almost nothing, for he does make some sounds as he's escorted offstage. Our choice is between thinking the play has some marginal meaning, or almost none; but of course it would be a real feat to produce a play that would be totally meaningless. I must add that there are one or two quite brilliant scenes, whatever their meanings, and a remarkable performance by Edward Flanders, who plays the part of Mr. Goldberg.

PETER WEISS'S *Song of the Lusitanian Bogey*, put on by the new Negro Ensemble Company, did not give this attractive group an opportunity to display the gifts we assume them to have. The only contribution Weiss's exceptionally boring work may be said to make is that it provides yet another, and unexpected, instance of this season's emptiness. We generally think of empty works as lacking in content; and if we are interested in politics and society, we may mean by emptiness the lack of social content. Form we may think consistent with emptiness; content, social content, we may think its opposite. Peter Weiss's latest work—I shall not call it a play—has the virtue at least of indicating the error in this whole way of thinking. There is nothing in Weiss's work but content—social content, at that. Yet it evokes in us the very same boredom most often produced by works of pure form. Content without form is not fullness; in fact, we cannot feel the presence of content when there is an absence of art. Fullness of content has nothing to learn about absence from works of pure form.

BRUCE JAY FRIEDMAN came to the theater having gained by his novels some reputation as a humorist. Now if one goes to his play *Scuba Duba* expecting nothing but humor, one is not going to be disappointed. Jokes there are, plenty of them, and jokes that really make one laugh; Walter Kerr, who has told us about his passion for comedy, loved it. Mr. Kerr, in his approval of the play, though, is mistaken on one point: jokes are not the same as comedy. Comedy is what the jokes are in, and for us not finally to be bored, they have to be in something. In *Scuba Duba*, the jokes are in nothing. There is nothing we believe before we laugh, and nothing we believe after having laughed. A comedy is not a succession of gags, and I do not think the proper way of judging a comedy is the quantitative one —that is, the counting of laughs from the beginning to the end. I believe there are many more laughs in Shaw's comedies than in Molière's—yet Molière is by far the greater dramatist. Why? Because a comedy is good to the degree that the characters in it interest us when we are not laughing at them. When we do laugh, our laughter has more vigor, more violence. We laugh without thinking that this is what we are in the theater for. But Mr. Friedman, having thoroughly emptied his play of believable characters and situations, has given us no alternative except to laugh at his marionettes or get up and leave the theater, which is, finally, what I did. After all, it was impossible to watch the stage with the slightest interest when something funny was not happening on it. Yes, there is humor in the play. But in a way the whole thing is an attack on humor, exposing the fact that we cannot enjoy it pure and unalloyed. Art for art's sake is a possibility—humor for humor's sake is just a bore.

IONESCO'S PLAY *Exit the King* is about nothing, which we must take seriously, but also must not erroneously mistake for something. It is about a man's death, his simultaneous going into, and intake of, nothing: or, rather, of nothingness. Death is not seen here as ashes to ashes or dust to dust. Flesh is not as grass, neither is it as dung. It is revealed to be nothing going on into nothingness. How could we die if we were truly real? This is the powerful thought, no doubt suggested by Heidegger, who is cited at one point in the play, that emerges from the action as we watch King Berenger I, over four hundred years old, told by one of his wives and also by his physician that he is going to die in an hour and a half, at the play's end. The king responds first with disbelief and then by growing older right in front of us; we watch him pass from vigor to infirmity to decrepitude to sightlessness, to idiocy, muteness, and death, sans eyes, sans taste, sans touch, sans everything. Remaining life is unwound before us like a spool of thread, a pull here, another pull there, some more jerks; there is less and less of it, and then it is gone. And the whole thing, though not without moments of shock, especially at the close, is delightful and engaging.

Let me stress about this wonderful little work that it is both modern in feeling and makes modernism meaningful. We all have to die, and at some point before our dying the reality of all our notions of life is going to be put in question. The question may never be expressed in words, but it will be there. Do we believe in God, in the immortality of the soul, the immortality of the race, the eternity of ideas? Or do we, in fact, believe in nothing but that we should persist as long as possible? This last is King Berenger's belief, as the play's action reveals. Can one die while believing in nothing except that one should not die? Such is the king's conviction, his last one. He asks others to die for him and, when no one offers himself, reproaches the "egotists."

Ivan Ilyitch, in Tolstoi's tale, screams for three days before dying. Ionesco's King Berenger audibly sucks in a draught of nothing, and then loses his power to speak. He yields up what he wants to keep, his mountains, his plains, his kingdom, even the color blue. He gets nothing for each thing he gives up, and what he gives up he gives up for the sake of nothing. He does not consent to die, as Ivan Ilyitch did after his period of rebellion. There is no salvation for King Berenger, no appeasement of agony, I almost said, no reconciliation. Except for this bit of theatricality: at the very last, he ascends his throne and is dead.

IN CONTRAST TO these contemporary shows is the Cacoyannis production of *Iphigenia in Aulis*. There has been
much criticism of Euripides, but not one critic ever called
the dramatist empty. His plays are even overfull—of politics, patriotism, pacifism, religion, metaphysics, psychology,
normal and abnormal. *Iphigenia in Aulis* is no exception.
Just look at the number of conflicts in this one drama, and
the range of action it suggests. Here is the Greek army becalmed and unable to sail for Troy; here is Agamemnon
at odds with his brother Menelaus; Achilles against the
two of them; Ulysses behind the scenes stirring up the army
against all three; here is Clytemnestra, entering on the path
that will lead to her horrid murder of her husband; and
here is the infant Orestes, who some day will avenge his
father. The gods are both believed in and disbelieved in;
Artemis is responsible for the fact that the fleet is becalmed,
but Menelaus, however, thinks she can be dealt with by
murdering Calchas, her spokesman. There is a rather un-
patriotic debunking of Agamemnon, which we must forget
when we listen to Iphigenia on Greece and on freedom. The
army is intent on murdering a girl—and this is the army
defending Greek honor! We are offered an analysis of
Agamemnon by his brother, a psychoanalysis of him by his
wife, and a turn to metaphysics by Iphigenia when there is
nothing else to turn to. If the play is weak in character, it
is certainly strong in plot. Is the play then a tragedy? I do
not think so. Here I should like to cite H. D. F. Kitto's
judgment that if the play has its merits, "Greek tragedy
has its standards."

What is the play about? The fleet is unable to sail, and
the oracle has advised that only if Iphigenia is sacrificed
can the army leave for Troy. This the army has been told,
so it demands the girl's life. Does the king have no choice
but to kill his daughter? Those who admire the play will
say that he does not, for can he stand against his whole
army? They may add that in this work the social takes on
a tragic force, like that the gods once had, and they may
say this is the very reason they find Euripides modern.
To my mind this view is all wrong; the social cannot equal
the divine. If a god asks a man to kill his daughter, can
the god's motive be questioned? But men's motives may

always be questioned; they are not entitled to be treated as unambiguous. We can admire Abraham, ready to kill his son even though no one told him to: he thought God wanted it. But let every soldier of the king's army demand that he kill his daughter, and we cannot excuse him if he yields.

Having diminished Agamemnon, Euripides had no choice but to exalt Iphigenia, and he does so with the paean in which she declares her readiness to die for Greece. Kitto has called this paean nonsense, and here again I must agree. I must note here that the whole structure of Greek tragedy, including this attempt at it, rested on the fundamental conflict of Greek life, that between the family and the state; it was grotesque of Euripides to have made the most noble representative of the state the young girl who would like to be married to Achilles, while the male characters—Menelaus, Achilles, Agamemnon—represent either just their personal interest or, if the state, that cravenly. Antigone, in Sophocles' play, is heroic in the name of the family—her heroism befits a woman. And in the *Electra* of Sophocles, the city is vindicated by Orestes, not by his sick sister, whose concern is exclusively and morbidly with vengeance on her mother for her father, with no thought whatever for Argos.

At *Iphigenia in Aulis* I felt some pity for Clytemnestra, a little for Iphigenia, and nothing whatever for her father. Terror I felt not at all. So for me there was no catharsis. Is this not sufficient to show the work is not a tragedy? A modern scholar, Professor Gerald Else, holds, however, that catharsis describes not the feelings of one in the audience but the action as unfolded at the play's end. A tragedy is a play whose action is purified—that, he says, is the meaning of catharsis. Now this very interesting but, I think, wrong view will not apply at all to such authentic tragedies as *Antigone, Electra,* or *Oedipus at Colonus*. It does apply perfectly, I concede, to *Iphigenia in Aulis,* not indeed as terminated by Euripides but as amended by Cacoyannis for his Circle in the Square production. We can indeed make a clear sense of the play if we regard the sacrifice of Iphigenia as an advance atonement for, and a purification of, the Greek action against Troy led by her father. But the fact that Professor Else's theory does seem to work for a second-rate play of Euripides, and even better with the play's ending altered, is hardly an argument for his view.

I began by contrasting the revival *Iphigenia* with the season's contemporary plays, empty or about emptiness. But now I have to say that even the Euripides drama, when one reflects on it, is not so different from the others. It is full of content, yes, but as Kitto indicates, the story could not have been taken very seriously by its author; Kitto suggests, too, that it was shrewd of Euripides' contemporary, Agathon, to treat the same story much more lightly, thus avoiding what the British classicist, in a fine phrase, has called the "disconcerting ghost of tragedy." But it is to this old ghost we owe what must pass for the fullness of this theater season.

The Rationing of Love

R. V. Cassill

FOR MORE THAN TWENTY YEARS I was sure my father made too much of the coffee episode. Really, I told him whenever he mentioned the matter, it was nothing, nothing, nothing. I wished he would put it out of his mind. I hadn't taken it seriously to begin with and would long ago have forgotten it if he had.

"But it was only one darn little cup of coffee and you were going *over there*," he always insisted, blaming himself. "I told myself so many times, why, it was only a nickel's worth, but there was all that wartime rationing, you know."

Of course I knew. Had I ever, even for the blink of an eye, refused to accept his first explanation?

THE DAY I went to be drafted in 1942 he refused me a second cup of coffee with my breakfast. He was working as a counterman at the Bolton & Hay Restaurant in Des Moines, having come up from Gath to attend the summer session at Drake University. He was after the master's degree required for his job as superintendent of the consolidated school in Gath.

I had not seen him since my wedding day. For more than a year I had been serious—giving up my college notions of being a painter so I could support a wife by selling farm implements in her hometown of Waterloo. I mean my first wife, and how odd it seems to think of her as "first wife" in the context of these memories, how odd not to think simply of her name. Ora McGilvery. "Ora means gold," my father told me solemnly at the wedding, implying that I should treat her accordingly.

I had come down alone by bus from Waterloo the evening before I was to be inducted at Camp Dodge. I'd stayed the night in the old Victoria Hotel, a rearing and raffish building whose corridors held some scent of illicit arrivals and departures, some stirring premonition of the worldwide turbulence into which I was being drawn. In my little room I had wakened intermittently at three and four in the morning to hear prowling footsteps outside my door, and when I woke I wondered if my wife was crying in the newness of our first separation. Before daybreak I had made myself think that she was all right, and from that it seemed to follow that everything about to happen to me was going to be all right.

So I felt really good as I walked down from the hotel to meet my father at the Bolton & Hay Restaurant. The hot morning seemed as snappy as the ruffle of drums. The capitol dome gleamed in the radiance of my self-confidence, and the shafts of the Civil War monuments there across the river on the capitol grounds held up their testimony to the bravery of us Midwestern heroes.

A cinder-skinned news butcher was shouting, "Tommies can't stop Rommel!" Maybe the Tommies couldn't, but I was on my way that morning, in the nick of time. Look out, Hitler, here comes Ioway! I guess I really felt a little impatient that I had to stop to see my father at all before I took a bus out to Camp Dodge.

Fortunately my father was ready to share my mood. He wasn't taking the fall of Tobruk very hard. Most of the news he had to tell me was about my mother, brothers, and sister, and the folks in Gath. He wasn't bothered that I'd never "got back to painting" since I left college. He was glad Ora could stay with her parents while I was away. But mostly he was eager to tell me about himself.

There was a countryman's twinkle in his eyes and a conspiratorial lowering of his voice as he told how he had euchred his fellow waiters into letting him have the earliest shift at the lunch counter. "You take a lot of these city people aren't used to getting up till maybe six or seven in the morning. So I told them I'd just as soon come down and open the place up and get the coffee urns going and bring in the bakery stuff and milk. And, shoot, there's hardly anything doing here until after seven. So I have time to read the papers and go over my lessons. . . ."

For his job he wore a white dickey and jacket and a

limp little bow tie, innocent as the rags that children wrap around their puppies. He was still deeply tanned from working in his garden at home before the summer-school session had started.

He said, "You take these other fellows who don't come on duty before seven-thirty, why they miss the best part of the day. By the time they have their four hours in, why, I'm back up on the campus and I've had a shower at the field house and a swim if I want to, and I'm out under a shade tree with my books." Four hours of work each day earned him his meals and a dollar in cash that went to help pay his room rent.

While he was watching me eat eggs, bacon, and toast and drink my coffee, he said, "Now you just keep your money in your pocket, son. You may not get civilian food like this for a while, and it's my treat."

Of course I made no argument about that, and since I didn't want any sentimentality to edge in, I kept us talking about his summer. "You've got a pretty soft deal, Dad."

I hadn't meant at all to criticize, but my remark shifted him ever so slightly onto the defensive. "Your mother thinks I just come up to the University to loaf." Well, yes, it was true that my mother kept enforcing a family attitude that he was always too soft to take advantage of his opportunities. "Why," he said, "I'm taking nine hours credit this summer, and with what I've accumulated at Ames and Cedar Falls these last few years I'll get my degree . . ."

"This summer?"

He didn't even bother to shake his head. ". . . with a little more extension work and making up my education credits, in nineteen forty-five. I'll bet the war will last at least that long, and the school board won't be likely to push me too hard for my degree as long as all those fellows are in the service and teachers hard to find."

"It won't take us till forty-five, Dad," I said, with the first queasy tremor of doubt I'd felt all morning.

"Who knows? You know, Buddy, your mother even said it didn't seem very dignified for a man my age to be working a board job like you boys did when you went to college. But shoot, I don't know what dignified is if it isn't being willing to do what has to be done."

I was glad then and later that he had said this to me before I left. For too many years while I was a kid at home I'd sided with the other children and my mother in a disrespectful tolerance of his weakness in the face of the school boards who sent us packing every three or four years from town to town, of his kid-glove treatment of the schoolmate bullies who used to knock my brothers and me around for no better reason than that we were the "superintendent's kids." We had blamed him—not too harshly, but persistently—when he let himself be cheated by the small-town garagemen and merchants who took advantage of him because he was a public employee dependent on their good will. We were used to resenting him—a little—because he didn't "stand up to people" and show off his dignity.

I liked him awfully much for telling me his side of all that old misery, but I only said, "I've got to run, Dad. Can I have another cup of coffee before I go to camp?" In a sort of embarrassment I waved my empty cup at him. It's funny how I remember that cup—a big awkward piece of restaurant crockery with two thin green bands painted around it.

He hesitated a minute, thinking. "Well, I'd like to son. . . ." He tried to grin when he shook his head and his grin began to hurt us both.

"I don't really want any," I said quickly.

"You know we're trying to do our bit with coffee rationing."

"I *know*."

"It's only that the boss says . . ."

"It was an awfully good breakfast, Dad."

"Now, you keep that money in your pocket. No sir, I'm paying for this. Do you need anything? You're going?" He was out from behind the counter quicker than I ever saw him move. As he walked to the door he put his arm over my shoulder, and as we stepped into the explosive sunlight of the street he kissed me quickly on the forehead. He hadn't kissed me since I was five.

He had unbuckled his wristwatch and was trying to fasten the old, sweated band around my arm. "Noticed you weren't wearing one," he said. I let him fasten it, looked at the time, said I'd have to run now to catch the right bus to Camp Dodge.

"Come on back," he said, "Please, come on now, you've got time for one more cup of coffee with me."

But I said I hadn't and that I really, really had drunk all the coffee I needed for a while.

II

IN A BAD WAR, in my own worst phases of it, I lucked out with a consistency just short of miraculous. I mean, the miracles were there to be remembered when I had the heart to poke under the garbage for them.

For one thing, on a rain-drenched island as far from combat as it was from any place fit for human habitation, I started painting again while I was convalescing from a rare Asiatic type of diphtheria. It wasn't the throat kind of diphtheria. It spread big colonies of ulcers all over my skin and poisoned me internally so that I was weeks in getting my strength back after the sores cleared up.

Two cultivated ladies named Fitch and Helspur ran the Red Cross hut at the hospital. When they found out I'd had "art training" they not only rummaged out a fine set of oil paints and canvas, they even wanted me to start classes for the other patients. I was too tired for that. Mostly I sat on the back steps of the New Zealand hut they occupied and painted a banana tree on which the bananas were ripening as my abused cell structure mended.

"You're a regular Van Gogh with those yellows," Miss Fitch told me. It was her profession to be flattering.

I put the lovely, creamy brushful of yellow paint back down on the palette, lit a cigarette, and grinned at her through the rising goblin shapes of smoke. I had learned how important it was in my condition and at that juncture of the war in the Pacific to take things easy and slow when you could. She sat down with me and compared the painted yellows with the real bananas.

I said, "You know the first time I ever saw a banana tree? Understand, I always lived in small towns, but my father was a teacher, and he was always going to some college to summer school. . . ."

I'd set her off now. Her father and her uncle and her two great uncles had all been teachers. At Amherst, Smith, and Duke. She herself had been working on her doctorate at Columbia before she joined the Red Cross. She understood *exactly* what it meant to come from "a family of educators."

While she was running on enthusiastically I shook my head slow and steady. "No, no, no. It wasn't like that for us. My father only went into teaching to raise enough money to buy a farm. He kept on because the family kept growing, that's all. He started out a long time ago with not much more than an eighth-grade education. It took him almost twenty years of summer schools to get his B.A. *Anyhow*, depending on which college we lived nearest, he used to go off to Cedar Falls, or Ames, or Drake. From the time I was very small I remember his bringing the whole family over to see where he was going to college. Next to the stuffed zebras and whale skeletons in the natural history collections, what I remember best is the greenhouse at the college in Cedar Falls where they had a banana tree just like that one."

"Wonderful!" Miss Fitch said. I could tell she was picturing my father as some grave and stately academician teaching us kids the Latin names of the rare flora—while what my father really had said was, "Imagine that! Bananas growing right here in Iowa! Look at 'em growing upside down!"

Because she was such an enthusiastic listener, I told Miss Fitch, "Once when he was in summer school at Ames he took me to see the great, wonderful indoor swimming pool they had there. Imagine that! But it *was* great and wonderful to me. I'd never seen anything like it. The reverberations of the boards in there when the guys dived, the color of the water. . . . The color of that chlorinated water was just like the water up around Ulithi, and the mortar shells around us when we were wading in . . . I tell you I'd heard them before when Dad took me to that swimming pool and the diving boards rumbled."

I picked up my brush again from the palette and my hand was trembling. I wasn't any Van Gogh and I didn't any longer expect to be, but the painting—and the associations between one banana tree here and another back there —were making a bridge I needed to live by.

"It makes all the difference if you come from a family of educators," Miss Fitch said, far away in her dream of an Amherst girlhood. It didn't matter that I could never explain to her the petty quarrels in my "family of educators" —about how much of our homemade furniture we'd take with us when we moved from one rinky-dink town to another; whether they should sell my mother's piano after she forgot how to play it; whether the school board hadn't promised to find Dad a lot to keep our cow in when they hired him.

"I'm sure you came by your interest in art from *them*," Miss Fitch said.

"Sure. My mother was a frustrated artiste of the piano," I said lightly. "Naturally, at least one kid had to carry on the yokel dream of busting out of the small town. What does it matter? All that's in the bag now, anyway. Next week or the week after—whenever they cut my orders and there's a ship going that way—I'll go up to Okinawa to join my outfit."

Not knowing how much she'd helped with a miracle, Miss Fitch promised that when I left she and Miss Helspur would pack my new canvases and see that they got home to my wife.

I LUCKED OUT, too, when I fell off a troopship in Buckner Bay at Okinawa. The war was over then and we were loading to go home. We were loading from a small boat onto the S.S. Sherman. Tom Hartman was ahead of me on the ladder. I suppose our weird, larking gratitude for surviving the war had become a kind of hysteria. So we were horsing around and it was my own foolish fault that I lunged for the guard rope, missed it, and pitched into the bay.

It happened, too, that I was wearing a field pack full of souvenirs as I fell. That made a bad outfit for swimming. So when I went down headfirst past the small boat, I thought the surprised faces of the boatmen might be the last ones I would ever see.

I went deep before I could get the pack off my shoulders. First I couldn't understand that I had to let it go. Then, as the green of the water got darker around me, the pack clung as if it owned me—that bag full of Okinawa pottery,

Japanese pistols, a stained battle flag, and a wooden Buddha I'd looted from a house split open by shellfire. It held onto me like someone drowning who was afraid to let me live if I couldn't take him back up with me.

I don't remember shaking loose from it. All at once I was rising fast and the weight was gone. The strangling water fell away from my face. I saw the boatmen's hands reaching down for mine.

So far so good, but in the same glance I saw my father's wristwatch streaming bright droplets. My first coherent thought as the Navy men were hauling me into their boat was: I finally ruined it for him.

Then all the superstitions I'd been nourishing for three years of war began to concentrate on that ruined watch. I remember how wildly I talked about it to Tom Hartman that night as the ship wallowed east toward home. "I should have got it back to him in the condition he gave it to me."

"Does your father make a lot out of little gestures like that?" he wanted to know.

"I do, whether he does or not." Then I remembered and laughed. "He's as bad as I am. He'll want to buy me a cup of coffee the minute he sees me." I told Tom what had happened the day I was inducted.

He said, "Well, you better let him buy it for you."

All at once I went morose. I suppose the aftereffects of nearly drowning were coming up on me the way a pain in the jaw comes when the Novocain wears off. "No, that's silly," I said. "Nothing's going to put things back the way they were before we left. It's too late for some of the things we missed. Are you scared about going home?"

I wish he had said he wasn't. All too easily he knew what I was talking about. "Everybody our age, everybody who's been over as long as we have is a little bit scared. You hear it from everybody," he said. After a while he said, "That's silly. What's to be scared of? Lights, music, girls . . . ?"

We didn't say it, but we were afraid of having permanently lost the track of our lives. Mine—up to the day I'd been drafted—had been nothing but fooling around, as if I'd just been killing time until the war came and a use was found for me. "I found a job just so I could get married," I said. "I wasn't even good at it, or at anything else. So what now?"

"So you might as well have drowned this afternoon." I didn't blame him at all for saying it. He was a man with worries of his own.

I had the mental, moral shakes that night, trying to add up the score of my life in the world as I'd seen it—and coming out with a big round goose egg as of that hour. Coming out with a kind of sad contempt for what I'd grown up trusting. I remembered one time when my father gave the commencement address at Chesterfield for a graduating class of twelve. I had to go to all his public speeches when I was little. Usually I hadn't listened. This time, though, I'd listened because he was talking about Grandpa, whom I'd loved more than anybody. Grandpa, he said, had got in some land dispute with a neighbor. There had been talk among the farmers about how the quarrel could come to a knifing. This neighbor—who must have been a wild man in a generally peaceable community—actually got to carrying a pig sticker with him and showing it at the country store and saying what he meant to do with it.

One day he came by on the road in a spring wagon while my father and Grandpa were raking hay. My father told how Grandpa climbed the fence, went to the middle of the road, and stopped this wild guy, then walked up to him and put out his hand to shake.

That's all there was to the story, and there was my dad up in front of that squirming audience that couldn't care less, him with his bow tie and his soft little grin, holding out his hand to show how it was done. That was his idea of how all problems, domestic and foreign, could probably be handled.

Ah, but behind our ship as I recalled this were the dead cities of Okinawa and Japan. By now the first snow had fallen on the flat cinders of Hiroshima, Nagoya, and the rest. There was Naha blasted into rubble and Shuri Castle where the artillery had blown away everything but the foundations of the ancient walls. With things like that right behind us, who could take seriously a little quarrel so easily mended on a dirt road in southern Iowa?

There was no connection anymore. Before I slept that night I took my father's watch topside and threw it into the froth of our wake. I could be as superstitious as any man in the Army—and believe that watch was the charm that had seen me through. The same superstitions, and a lot more besides, told me it was useless from here on out.

III

THE REAL MIRACLE of those years was what had happened to Ora. She had grown up while I was away. Without any such melodramatic gesture as tossing a watch into the ocean, she had loosened the ties with her parents. She made it instantly clear to me that I wasn't going back to a futureless job in Waterloo. She had moved to Chicago before I shipped up to Okinawa, and the first thing that faced me when I walked into her apartment on Dearborn Street were some of the banana-tree paintings Miss Fitch and Miss Helspur had sent home. She had also hung up some older things I had done in college.

There was only a sundown light in the room when we came in from the taxi, a poor light that made the paintings look better than they were. The yellow bananas glowed like candle flames against a green background more mysterious than the jungle around the Red Cross hut on the island I'd never see again.

"They're not exactly works of genius," I said when I had switched on the apartment lights.

Ora shook her dark head stubbornly. "All right. Not yet. They're going to be."

I said, "Sure. Turn out the lights again. That improves them."

"We're going to New York," she said. "You're going to study at the Art Students League. Of course you are. You've got the GI bill and you've got me. I'm an economic asset. I've got a job there already. I mean I'm almost sure I have. We might, we just might even have a place to live, though that's tougher in New York than here, even."

"A decent job?" I asked.

She made a face at me, a good-natured grimace, but she was disappointed by my caution. "Oh, don't talk like your father or my father or we'll never get anywhere. If New York won't have us, we'll keep going. We'll go on to Paris. Why not?"

"Now you're talking worse than my mother," I said. "There's no use in that."

"I'm not talking like anybody. I'm talking about *us*."

Let it be understood that our conversation was taking place almost the instant I had returned from twenty-eight months overseas. We had not even kissed yet since we came into the apartment, though we had kissed hard and well when she met me at the station and in the taxi that brought us to the North Side. All the anxiety and hope of my return had avalanched into this moment of decision.

And though we had much more to figure out before we left, I knew from then on that we would go. She had challenged me to put up or shut up about all I knew had fallen short in my parents' lives. I said, "O.K."

Then Ora was kneeling beside me in the wide easy chair, kissing me and rubbing her tears all over my face. "You're going to have your chance. You'll be a great painter," she said. Beyond the fringe of her hair I saw the charcoal velvet silhouette of buildings beyond our little window, a sky the color of a wonderful slice of melon. I had a painter's eye, all right. But it took Ora to show me that even Chicago was not a big enough town to hold us.

PARIS WAS our city. New York didn't seem to have room for us that year. We went past it with a lordly air and borrowed boat fare. Paris was home for several years, and I keep thinking we should have been happy there, since we both loved it so much. But we weren't. Our years there provided "the foundation of my career," as it says in the brochure printed just last year by the gallery in Chicago that handles my painting, now that I've come back to work and teach in the Midwest. There never was a young couple in Paris who got more excitement and pleasure in discovering the fine parks, the old splendors of cathedrals and chateaux, places to eat and buy things, the displays of weather over the Seine, and the way the trees would darken secretly in the Luxembourg Gardens after the steel gates were closed for the night across the street from our apartment.

Too rich for our blood? There was a fault somewhere.

Ora worked first for an American oil company and later for the American Embassy. In the first years I walked alongside the Luxembourg Gardens every morning on my way to the Grande Chaumière where I was painting with

Léger. Paris was very poor in those years just after the war, and we weren't. We had a sports car pretty soon for summer trips into the Loire valley and the Dordogne. When Ora went to the embassy we had PX privileges, American goodies for ourselves and for the black market. Happy or not, we lived the big life, and we stayed long enough to see Paris change again into the prospering capital of the world. Among the Fulbright students and other new waves of young Americans we were accepted as old settlers. I was painting pretty well. I was making contacts with people who could do me some good.

Letters from my parents in those years came like drafts from a window one has forgotten to close before lying down for a warm nap. My mother's indicated she thought we were living an idealistic missionary life—presumably weaning the French away from their bad habits of drinking wine, making love indiscriminately, and abusing their colonial peoples. She hoped we would not have children until we got back to the shelter of American sanitation.

My father, who only wrote short notes at Christmas or for our birthdays, seemed to make no distinction between my being "over there" among the Bohemians and my having been "over there" with the Army. I used to read his letters in my favorite café on the square at St. Sulpice and parody them for my friends. I would remember them with a kind of terrible nostalgia while I was getting stewed in the *caves* around St. Germain—or at the Select, in the winter of Eleanor. One night when the police picked me up for riotous behavior in Montparnasse I went into a yelling fit in the back of the *salade panier*, the police van. The next day I could remember only that I had been trying to tell my father I was a long time out of the Army and the damned South Pacific and nobody was giving me orders anymore.

IF THERE EVER WAS a chance to clear up such truths for him, I had it when I came back to Iowa in 1954 to tell my parents why Ora divorced me. They hadn't known her well, but they cared about her and knew that I had, too.

So my efforts to be scrupulous in my explanations only confused them further. They wouldn't believe me. They

wouldn't comprehend that it had been all my fault instead
of the fault of the corrupt French environment. They
couldn't quite see why, just because I took some initial interest in the paintings of a Fulbright student named
Eleanor Marshall, I should have run off to Africa with her.
Or why, when the intoxications of novelty wore off with the
drugs we got from the Algerians, Eleanor and I had begun
a hesitant, slow circling back toward Paris. I could recall the
nastiness and despair of those weeks in Alexandria and days
in Naples, but I just lacked the language to tell the old
folks our great sin excursion collapsed because we had used
up the money I stole from Ora and saved from black-
marketing PX goods.

I heard my own voice tell them these things. I doubt if
they heard much. They were living now in another small
Iowa town where again my father was teaching. The house
to which I had come was excruciatingly like the other
houses I remembered living in while I was growing up.
The same dark, small living room, the same softwood floors
varnished dark, the same high school graduation pictures
of my brothers, sister, and me on the piano that had been
moved so often and played so little.

It was early summer and the kitchen windows were open
as we sat at supper. A light rain was falling on the potted
flowers my mother had set on a shelf outside the windows
to get some fresh air. My mother said, "I suppose that
Eleanor will be coming back soon to join you."

I shook my head carefully, as if I might spatter filth over
her clean kitchen if I shook too hard. "She's not going to
join me, Mama. She came to New York before I did. I'm
not going to see her, didn't I make that clear?"

It was lucky my fingernails were chewed short or I might
have drawn blood from the clenching of my hands. The
last thing I'd wanted from this visit was the kind of dull
sympathy I was getting. Maybe in some dream I had expected I was going to be punished here, like the time I
was punished for shooting at the Alleman girl with my air
rifle when we lived in Chesterfield.

"I don't understand much about divorces," my mother
said, still resisting, still sure things could be arranged for
the best, "but it seems to me there's no reason you and she

can't be married if you wanted to as bad as all that."

I remembered Eleanor and me lying side by side on a bed in a bad hotel in Rome. It was raining outside that room, too, but it was very cold there so the chill came right through the walls. We'd lain fully dressed with nothing to say to each other, merely passing a rare cigarette back and forth, waiting for the day to be over. The moisture of our lips on the cigarette paper was the only intimacy between us by then.

"At least we'll be spared marriage, whatever other payment we still have to make."

I'm not sure my mother caught the full savagery of what I'd said. My father did. He'd never been stretched past the point of endurance by the untouchable loveliness of my Paris, never seen with a painter's hopeless eye the high white clouds over Oran in the inexpressible Mediterranean light. How could he imagine Eleanor's strange mouth ready to be kissed? He only thought my paintings were "all right if there's people want to buy such things." But he knew what counted.

While I had been talking to my mother he had risen from the supper table. He stood at the window and his hands reached outside, fumbling with or caressing the wet geranium leaves.

After a while he said, "Darn it, I've thought so many times, why didn't I give you that second cup of coffee when you were going away?"

As if that one thing alone might have saved me from all my delinquencies! As if without this one default of courage he might have kept me true!

IV

MY MOTHER NEARLY DIED last fall. She dwindled and grew dull through the spring and summer. Each time I drove over from Illinois with my wife and three young children she seemed progressively less interested in finding toys from the attic for the little ones, even less sure of their names. Getting old, we said.

Then she fell down the basement stairs while she was bringing in flower bulbs from the garden about to freeze.

She may have hit her head in the fall. She was very confused and dazed afterward. But when she was taken to the hospital in Des Moines the main source of her trouble was diagnosed as a tumor of the spleen, which had been seriously affecting her blood-sugar level. This had been going on long enough to suggest there might have been brain damage before her tumble.

Occasionally, when we visited her in the hospital, she would seem like her old self. These were times when she had been given medicine to counter the insulin surplus and had taken a lot of extra sugar in her orange juice. When my father, brothers, and sister hovered around her bed she could still beam and chatter and press our hands and thank us for "coming all that way" to be with her at such a time. "All that way. . . ." Perhaps she still thought I was living in Paris. At any rate, her quaint manner of putting it made me remember all my travels as if they were a single journey toward this time of anguish.

With extraordinary effort she could remember each of her grandchildren. When I prompted her, she asked about my children individually and by name. Were they anxious for snow? Did they like kindergarten and school?

But she was frightened, too. Sometimes, even at her most lucid moments and even when all of us were with her, she would ignore her children and speak only to my father. She questioned him about insurance, about the burial plot they had arranged for in the yard of the church where they were married, and about whether someone was taking care of her plants while she was away.

We saw that she always scared him with such talk. "You're not going to die, Mother," he told her over and over again—while the rest of us resolutely avoided any mention of death in her presence.

Often we found her out of her head—when the level of her blood sugar was not being artificially maintained—and she raved her distrust of the doctors who came several times a day to "bother her" and "wasted so much time" in getting it over with.

Her operation, when it took place, was mercifully briefer and luckier than we had been led to expect by the doctors. Her tumor was benign. Very little exploratory surgery was needed to locate it, though it had not showed in the X rays.

Nonetheless, some ultimate transformation had been wrought on her in those hours when she was under anaesthetic. I was alone with her in the recovery room—we were permitted to go in to her only one at a time—when the fog of ether was leaving her. She was discovering that her right arm was bound to a board to keep the intravenous tube in place, and she fought the bondage piteously, trying to tear the tube out of the vein. Another tube was taped over her forehead and into her right nostril. I restrained her as gently as I could. She hated me for siding with all her other persecutors.

"They have no right to an old lady," she said. "Cut her all open. Bring her in here and cut her body." There was a horrifying strength in the free hand that wrestled against mine to get at the IV tube. Then she became aware of the other tube in her nose. "What's that for, too?" she said, and clawed for it.

I had to call a nurse, and we tied both hands down to make her leave the tubes alone.

She hadn't the strength to raise her head, of course. The hatred in her eyes was like the blow of a fist. She glared at me as if I were her murderer. "You have no right," she said.

"It won't be long now, Mama," I said. "I know you're very uncomfortable right now. They'll give you something for the pain and to make you sleep."

"Oh, the pain," she said. "Untie me. Let me loose."

"No. I won't."

"*Let me loose!*" Her voice was like a man's, compelling and brutal. Perhaps if the nurses had not been working nearby I might have done what she demanded.

"I can't let you loose," I said. "You'll be all right. You'll sleep. You'll rest. You'll sleep."

She turned her head to the side. Her crepey cheek was almost as crimson as blood from the great effort she was making. The tears on her cheek were tears of anger. "Why didn't they get it over with?"

"It's not going to be over," I said. "Don't you understand? You didn't have cancer. You'll be all right. It will take a while to get your strength back, but you're going to be fine."

"Why?"

I'm not certain she meant anything by this syllable. Surely I shouldn't have tried to answer then. But I said, "Why, because we need you. We all need you. My children, too. They've been wanting to come and see Grandma and go up into the attic with her again. Play the piano with her. . . ."

Now she knew exactly what she had to say. It was as if she had always been trying to clarify it. She said it now with a last, hoarded emphasis of deliberation. "No one has any right to bring children into the world." She meant me. She meant my sons. Our wickedness and our suffering had been from her, and she repented us. "Where's Ora? Where's your wife?" she asked with awful scorn. "Ora had no children. What have you done with her?"

I said nothing.

She smiled a little, a smile of terrible cruelty. "We have no right," she said tiredly. Then—perhaps she was sinking back into the vision or dream that had deviled her while she was on the operating table.

"The children are burning everywhere," she said vaguely.

It was less than an hour after that when my father and I walked down the hill from the hospital in the November sun. I saw that my shadow was longer than his on the concrete slope ahead of us, but his step was jauntier than mine. As if he didn't know yet—as if he was never going to find out—the truth my mother had just told me.

"The doctor said it was no bigger than a fingertip," he said of the tumor that had been removed from her. "Boy, the doctor said it was certainly good luck they found it so quick when the X ray couldn't find it."

"We've been very lucky."

"Well, we sure have." He took a long trembling breath. It sounded like my youngest boy when he has been crying hard and is trying to reestablish a normal rhythm of breathing. "And you know, lucky with the Blue Cross and all. Just couldn't have been luckier."

He had a right to his relief, but I was suspicious of its excess and warned him, "She's not going to be the same, Dad."

"Why," he said, "why, I know that. Why, *of course not.* We're getting older, and all."

"She's in her seventies. It isn't going to be easy for her to make a comeback."

"Of course it won't. And I don't know what's the best thing to plan. The doctor said that, well, maybe the best thing for me to count on is to put her in a nursing home awhile because her convalescence might be months, and he thought I wouldn't be much of a hand for taking care of her."

It might well be more than a matter of months. The doctors to whom I had spoken avoided the word *convalescence.* She was too old. There was no return from the descent she had begun. "We ought to consider a nursing home," I said cautiously.

"Why, why, I told him *no!* Why I'd crawl on my hands and knees to take care of her before I'd let them take her away."

He tossed that off as a matter of fact. So jauntily. I doubted if he had even weighed the realities of what might be still to come. He just knew what he had to do—and I envied him for that as I never expected to envy another human being. All his life with us we had thought him too soft, gentle but a little foolish—and he had nursed his courage in the shade of soft foolishness until the time to use it well had come. I knew that, and the wonderful thing is that I think he knew it too.

"Well," I said, "well. We better turn and go back to the hospital."

"Just down that next block. All right?"

I had supposed we were merely getting a breath of fresh air before we rejoined the rest of the family in the vigil at the hospital.

No. He had known exactly where he was leading me. In the next block was the Bolton & Hay Restaurant where I'd said good-bye to him when I went in the Army. Suddenly there we were, in front of it.

"You know, son," he said with his old easy, floppy smile, "you know there's something that's bothered me. . . ."

Of course I knew what was coming, and I wanted no part of it. He had no trick to play except a sentimental one, and that was not nearly enough. The things we had done wrong with our lives were signed, sealed, and irretrievable. Ora was gone; I had my new wife and children. My mother was going to live, but her faith in life had not lasted quite as long as her outraged body. I had paid more than a man should choose to pay for my small share of success. My mother had not touched her piano for thirty years. We had been lucky to come this far with a divided verdict.

We had been lucky. My father said so and I believed him. But I saw now that the reckless old fool wanted still to gamble for more. I caught my breath as if watching a clownish acrobat preparing to challenge the trim, athletic professionals on the high wire. He was going to insist you *could* go back, in spite of time, and make the past all right.

"Now," he said, rather formally, "I could just as well have given you that cup of coffee you asked for that morning. Just as well as not."

His trick depended on just one thing—on my willingness to believe in it, at the price of all I'd paid so much to learn. I guessed I could if I wanted to. Nothing was stopping me.

I said, "Well, since we're here, why don't you get it for me now?" The worst had been ahead of us. Now it was behind us. Both of us could claim that much victory.

He said that to give me the coffee I had asked for was just exactly what he intended to do.

Like a boy, I followed him into the restaurant.

CONTRIBUTORS

Lionel Abel recently edited the anthology *Moderns on Tragedy* (Fawcett). He is the author of *Metatheatre* (Hill and Wang), a study of modern drama, as well as four plays that have been produced off-Broadway, one of which, *Absalom*, has been published by Grove Press.

Donald Barthelme's fiction appears frequently in *The New Yorker*. He has published a collection of stories, *Come Back, Dr. Caligari* (1964), and a novel, *Snow White* (1967). "Robert Kennedy Saved From Drowning" will appear in his new collection, *Unspeakable Practices, Unnatural Acts*, which Farrar, Straus and Giroux is bringing out in May.

M. F. Beal graduated from Barnard College in 1960. Miss Beal lives on a ranch in Oregon where she is raising three daughters and completing her first novel.

Stephen Berg is on the faculty of the Philadelphia College of Art. A translator of Spanish and Hungarian poetry, Mr. Berg has contributed his own work to a variety of magazines. His first collection of poems, *Bearing Weapons*, was published in 1963 by the Cummington Press (Iowa City, Iowa).

John Berryman recently received the Academy of American Poets award for "distinguished poetic achievement." His collections include *Homage to Mistress Bradstreet* (1956), *77 Dream Songs* (1965), and *Sonnets* (1967). "Three Dream Songs" are a part of John Berryman's forthcoming book, *His Toy, His Dream, His Rest*, to be published by Farrar, Straus and Giroux in the fall of 1968, and by Faber & Faber in England.

Hayden Carruth lives in Johnson, Vermont and describes himself as a "free-lance poet." He is the author of six volumes of poetry, a novel, and a collection of criticism.

R. V. Cassill, who teaches at Brown, has recently organized an association of college writing programs. Mr. Cassill's novels include *Clem Anderson, Pretty Leslie, The President*, and the forthcoming *La Vie Passionée of Rodney Buckthorne* (Bernard Geis).

J. V. Cunningham's poetry has been appearing for the past thirty years in such journals as *Hound and Horn,* the *Bookman, Partisan Review,* and *Southern Review.* Mr. Cunningham, a professor of English at Brandeis, is currently a Guggenheim Fellow.

Bob Dawson's poems have been published in *Transatlantic Review* as well as in his collection, *Six Mile Corner* (Houghton Mifflin). He is also the author of a manual on sculpture.

George Dennison's essay on Jean Genet appeared in *NAR* #1. "The First Street School" is from a book on libertarian education that he is writing for Random House.

Robert Garis has written on fiction, drama, ballet, and film for *Commentary, Hudson Review,* and other journals. A professor of English at Wellesley, Mr. Garis is the author of *The Dickens Theatre,* a study of Dickens' novels, and is presently writing a book on Ibsen.

Albert Goldman teaches English and comparative literature at Columbia. Along with a book on De Quincey, *The Mine and the Mint,* Mr. Goldman has published many essays and reviews on literature, music, and popular culture. He is now at work on a study of contemporary American humor.

Josephine Herbst was among the finer stylists who came to the fore in American writing during the 1920's. Miss Herbst has written seven novels, including the trilogy *Pity is not Enough;* a biographical study of eighteenth century naturalists, *New Green World;* and, more recently, a novella, "Hunter of Doves," which appeared in *Botteghe Oscure.* Miss Herbst's *The Starched Blue Sky,* "a personal and literary account of three decades," is nearing completion.

Allan Kaplan's poems have appeared in *The Nation, Chelsea Review,* and the *Paris Review.* Mr. Kaplan is a graduate student at New York University.

Frank Kermode is Lord Northcliffe Professor of Modern English Literature at the University of London. His study of contemporary fiction, *The Sense of an Ending,* appeared in 1967, and a new collection of his essays will be published this year by Random House.

John Knoepfle is a member of the faculty of St. Louis University.